The Fundamental Units of Physics and
The Logic of Theoretical Physics

BY

EIGIL RASMUSSEN

DORRANCE & COMPANY
Philadelphia

Book One

The Fundamental Units of Physics

BY

EIGIL RASMUSSEN

DORRANCE & COMPANY
Philadelphia

CONTENTS

(Kepler). 315, Laws of Motion (Newton). 316, Idealized Orbital Elements. 317, Earth and Sun Gravities on Km. Spheres. 318, Earth Orbits. 10,000 Km. and Surface. 319, Observed Earth Satellites. 320, Lofting and Escape Velocities. Energy. 321, Eccentric Orbits. Earth and Moon. 322, Mass Ratio Reductions. Earth-Moon Orbit. 323, Solar Surface Orbit from Earth's Orbit. 324, Lofting and Escape Velocities. Energy. 326, Idealized Planetary Orbits. 327, Conversions to True Planetary Periods.

816, Neutron's Mass. 817, Energy Equivalent of Mass. 818, Mass Defect. Packing Fraction. 819, Atomic Number. 820, Isotopes. 821, Radioactivity. 822, Atomic Weights. 823, Atomic Radii. 824, Nuclear Radii. 825, Atom's Quantized Orbits. 826, Hydrogen to Helium Quantas. 827, Electron Orbits and Wavemechanics. 828, Quantized Energies and Orientations. 829, Sub Quantum States. 830, Electron Spin. 831, Magnetic Moment. 832, Zeeman Effect (Magnetic). 833, Stark Effect (Electrostatic). 834, Pauli's Exclusion Principle. 835, The Elements. 836, The Inert Gases. 837, Composition and States of 32 Elements. 838, Ions. 839, Valency. 840, Molecules. 841, Diatomic Molecules.

PREFACE

The accepted values of all physical constants were, until recently, approximations obtained by experiments using the results of other experiments and a web of algebraic idealizations for reference. I noted that the formal relations in this algebraic web do not change, even though its definitive figures are changed by experiments and selective changes of the units of action, and that the figures defining the atomic constants can therefore be reduced to simple proportions. By assuming that proportions in nature are ideally simple, I discovered its unit of length and simplified its formal relations within the web. My principal objective with this book is to define these idealizations, convert them to known values, and prove that they are in full accord with the atomic constants obtained by experiment, observation and measurement.

My second objective is to provide the student of science with an introduction to theoretical physics which anyone with an elementary knowledge of mathematics and science can understand. The chapters are, therefore, a blending of general background information and new discoveries in special-purpose sections. Important algebraic formulas are followed by seven-digit figures, since large figures giving the expected results prove my postulates by showing that the margin of probable error is less than "one-in-a-million." The formulas are accompanied by references to the origin of their figures.

The limitations of this special-purpose book makes it supplementary to others on physics. My discoveries are proved by text and figures, thus making it possible for the reader to follow my reasonings and my conclusions. They make this book of vital importance to students of theoretical atomic physics.

Los Angeles, January 1970.

INTRODUCTION

Atomic physics is the foundation science. Its natural laws, relations and proportions, discovered by physicists through countless experiments and observations of natural phenomena, form an integrated whole—a solid foundation upon which the physical aspects of all other sciences rest. Practical physics, chemistry, astronomy, optics, electricity and other sciences apply the principles of atomic physics to their problems, and their researches and discoveries contribute in turn to the advancement of atomic physics.

Laws and principles of atomic physics which, at the time of their discovery, appeared to be without useful purpose, have since then been utilized by practical scientists. A combination of theoretical and practical science is the foundation upon which the numerous devices of modern technology have been and are being developed. A reasonable knowledge of atomic science is, therefore, an essential part of education in a world of electronics, atomic bombs, artificial satellites and exploration of the planets.

Logic tells us that the causes (the elements) of phenomena are simpler than their products, and that the first cause, or causes, must be the simplest possible. Experience tells us that some of the aspects of the first cause can be deduced from observations, and that there are others, such as its origin and nature, which must forever remain beyond understanding.

No responsible physicist, therefore, pretends to know the "true" nature of the first cause. No one knows whether it is rational or irrational, natural or supernatural, physically real or a product of mind; but in practice, however, we act in accordance with the former alternatives, since it is a clear rule of science that useful postulates are limited to useable deductions from observable facts of nature. Assumptions which go beyond proof by experiments, mathematics and logic cease to be science and must be treated as science fiction. These include the supernatural, the irrational and the products of mind: their actions, which are incomprehensible without a knowledge of purpose, are barriers to logical explorations in depth by their inherent suggestion that the limit of understanding has been reached. They can be used by careless scientists to shield ignorance and prejudice.

The fundamental particles of physics are so small that it is impossible to know what goes on within an atom by direct visual inspection. The information we have about these particles was obtained indirectly through their radiations, absorptions, and reactions to experimental changes in the environment. A first conclusion is that atoms and their particles are physically real bodies, reacting to forces and phenomena like visible masses. This conclusion is qualified by the observed quantizing of states and energies within atoms and molecules.

Atomic physics is possible because a combination of experiments, measurements, and comprehensible logical interrelations based on the principles of simple mechanics provide algebraic formulas and specific mathematical information which can be verified and extended by new experiments and different formal relations. While logic is essential to understanding, mathematical proof can be obtained without knowing how or why its formal factors are related. The need for mathematical verification increases as theoretical physics approaches the essentially incomprehensible first cause and as relations are discovered for which no logical explanations appear possible.

In scientific research the mathematical proportions obtained by experiments are nuggets of information of little intrinsic significance, but potentially of great importance when integrated by their logical implications into a unified whole. Note that mathematical exactness is vital to proof by experiment; logic is essential to comprehension, and philosophy assigns probable values to facts and beliefs within an accepted frame of reference. Mathematical proportions are the bricks of physical science, logic is the cement that binds them together, and philosophy provides the blueprint that transforms them into a useful edifice.

In ancient times the facts of physics were few, and science was of necessity limited to philosophical speculations. With time, the growth of knowledge made logic and measurements increasingly useful to science. Through the centuries, with the growth of specific knowledge, physicists showed an increasing preference for the specific and provable—for the exactness of mathematics—and a distrust of logic and philosophy. By neglecting or refusing to explore the logical implications of new discoveries, their theories became rigid and stale and in obvious conflict with facts. At the turn of the century the difference had reached a point where it became necessary to revise or abandon the theories of classical science.

The growth of mathematical preference in science has taken the form of a momentum whose force and direction is building up to a climax. It is approached by modern science in its efforts to remain viable in the face of increasing contradictions between facts and theory. Its basic premise, that we ignore comprehension by making logical explanation incidental to mathematical proof was first suggested by Einstein. He noted that classical science postulates a universal stationary ether through which physical bodies move; however, no experiment has ever been devised that shows the earth's motions through this ether. Since we cannot accept the alternative postulate that the earth is carrying the ether with it, it is to be assumed that all motions in space are relative. (In Book Two, I solve this problem by postulating a contracting ether whose momenta contains the waves of matter; thus producing a force gradient (a fourth dimension), relative to which their masses are always stationary in local space.)

Since there can be no logical explanation of Einstein's relativity postulate in terms of classical science and commonsense experience, its acceptance is also a rejection of the logic of experience and the assumption that natural phenomena are potentially comprehensible. Modern science must, therefore, confine the development of its theories to the relations and proportions obtained by experiments, and the potentialities of mathematics. These limitations are defined by the positivist philosophy. Proof, in the writings of physicists, appears as abstract mathematical formulas without logical, causal or mechanical associations beyond their immediate subjects.

Experience tells us that without understanding all physical theories will founder on contradictions and uncertainties. The theories of modern physics derive this essential base from the postulates, laws and axioms of classical physics. These are valid for the phenomena of everyday experience because relativity effects are marginal at low velocities, but become significant at speeds approaching that of light. It follows that the logical association of phenomena with everyday experience at the base of classical science is also the foundation which makes the excursions of modern science into the incomprehensible possible. It is a bond with rationality and experience which is lost when proof by mathematics is extended beyond its proper province; as when its limitations and possibilities are treated as a philosophy which rejects the logical implications of phenomena.

It is my contention that understanding is as essential as proof in theoretical science, and that we must, therefore, apply the principles of classical physics to our problems as far as possible. We can prove that the phenomena of our physical world are comprehensibly logical, but we cannot prove the opposite without the use of postulates which are questionable because they are usually unprovable negations. By confining my mathematical and logical proof within the limits of classical science, as far as possible, I shall attempt to make the mechanics of physical relations and proportions more comprehensible, bringing out implications that are usually ignored by scientists.

Practical experience tells us that proof by mathematics alone is not always synonymous with understanding. It is also necessary to show that the relations it defines are based on scientifically acceptable deductions from facts and probabilities—that these relations are comprehensibly logical and do not violate the accepted laws and axioms of physics and their implications within the Grand Design. We must not confuse mathematical proof with understanding, or remain satisfied with mere proof where comprehension is attainable. Every physical phenomenon has logical implications that should be explored to their limits for that elementary understanding of origin and evolution defining the phenomenon's potentialities in various relations. This kind of information, comparable to the clues gathered by a detective in his search for truth, is available to everybody, but is often ignored by scientists for superficial reasons. Their restrictions on theoretical explorations are based on the foibles and follies of human nature and the limitations of the positivist philosophy; although reason tells us these restrictions should be confined to those imposed by nature, as defined by the implications of its phenomena.

This book is for those interested in theoretical and practical physics and their related sciences. Because my explorations of the implications of physical phenomena go beyond their usual limits, they increase the amount of useful information and make it more comprehensible. Starting out with simple background information for those who are new to the subject of theoretical physics, it is built up into an increasing complexity of formal relations and mathematical proportions in the subsequent chapters. Each chapter contains one or two principal subjects, subdivided into sections.

To make these sections more comprehensible I show the logic of their mathematical relations in terms of ordinary mechanics wherever possible, and refer their various factors to other sections and the Table of Constants on page 152, Chapter 11. No mention is made of those marginal refinements of relativity physics that have no practical effects on observed atomic constants; however, the relativity effects on high velocity electrons are defined. It is my belief that relativity is not a product of mind, but must be physically real, and my re-definition of relativity effects within the classical frame appears in Book Two, Section 4-5.

The most important constants of physics are defined and related to phenomena, and their interrelations are outlined, defined and analyzed in detail. The text gives essential information without irrelevant comments. Significant formulas are in algebraic terms, followed by the corresponding seven-digit figures. The algebraic symbols are usually defined above the formulas in which they appear, and the origin and relations of the figures they represent are referred to their definitive sections and the Table of Constants, page 152. The validity of my figures and formal proof is, therefore, easily checked, and the reader is not asked to accept any figure on faith alone. My use of seven-digit figures for the atomic constants points up the fact that my formal results are usually accurate to one part in a million. This accuracy made my discovery of the natural unit of length and the ultimate system of units possible.

The ideal proportions which made this discovery possible originated, some years ago, in my decision to work out the table of 882 integrated physical constants and their equivalents appearing in chapter 11, page 152. My search for the most reliable physical constants in physics texts was frustrated by a lack of agreement among the physicists. Different values were given for such key constants as: the speed of light; the fine-structure constant; the unit of electrostatic charge, and an electron's rest mass energy and wavenumber. Furthermore, when the figures of each group were treated as a system, their formal reductions rarely agreed beyond three or four digits. The agreements obtained by a rationalization of figures in tables of atomic constants were equally questionable.

In my search for the most reliable seven-figure constants, I took note of the fact that it is in the nature of algebra to idealize proportions, and that the use of algebra by physicists is based on their acceptance of the proposition that many constants in nature are in ideal proportions. These are constants which can be reduced to other constants by formal reductions within an integrated web of numerous factors without the addition of compensating figures. For such idealizations to exist in nature, however, they must have originated as geometrical proportions with one to two or four ratios as their base, because ideal ratios must be abstractions from simple proportions.

My theory of ideal proportions also led to the conclusion that it should be possible to work out a simple sequence of atomic constants. I did so by analyzing the relations between factors in various formal reductions to atomic constants. (See Sections 217 and 1005-6.) This sequence has been highly useful for the purpose of obtaining the constants of atomic physics for any system of units I choose.

The postulate that nature's mathematics is, of necessity, the simplest possible, leads to the conclusion that atomic proportions within the web must be in ideal roots and powers and geometrical ratios, and that observed deviations from ideal proportions are due to the use of arbitrary units of action in the definitions of the physical constants. These units, the centimeter, gram and second, were replaced by the natural unit of length, an electron's mass, and the time it takes a light wave to move one natural length, respectively.

Since the unit of length defines wavelengths and wavenumbers, a change of their observed values to the natural proportions mentioned above led to my discovery of the natural unit of length, as defined in Section 221. By logical extension, it became possible to assign specific values to the key constants mentioned in the preceding paragraph. (See Sections 222, 614 and 709.) The simple one-to-two ratios in nature at the base of all ideal proportions, when raised to higher powers by geometrical transformation, retain proportion values that can be brought out by their logarithms in powers of two, as described in Chapter 10. This relationship is particularly prominent in the ultimate system of units, Sections 1020 and 1023, where the electronic constant and geometrical pi are the only factors in formulas defining fifteen atomic constants.

Since the figure values of these two basic factors are known to as many digits as we can use, we can obtain the exact values of the remaining constants and their proportions. Because my figure sequence and the conventional reduction formulas using them give proper results for all systems of units, their ratios must be the same where deviations due to different basic constants are absent or removed. The ideal proportions of the ultimate system, therefore, appear as specific quantities in the gaussian system of units. It can be confirmed by using the figures thus obtained in the accepted reduction formulas, because the results must always be those anticipated to as many digits as we choose to use. The idealizations are also confirmed by the four systems defining a transition from the observed conventional values of the gaussian system to those of the ultimate system in Section 1023. My idealizations of the gaussian cgs (centimeter-gram-second) constants are all within the margins of their experimental probable errors, as defined in physics texts.

Although logic is essential to understanding, it is a tool which is easily misused. A theory of physics which is, as far as possible, without bias and error can be developed by concentrating upon the mathematics of experiments and by limiting their logical implications to essentials. My acceptance of this postulate of modern physics does not mean that we agree on its application, because, to me, the mechanical implications of a physical fact range far beyond the limits imposed by modern science. Obviously, we are not solving the problems of physics by ignoring those implications of facts and theory for which we have no facile explanation. We must accept nature on its own terms, and not try to force it into the mould of our own preferences.

We cannot integrate the facts of physics without a theory of causes and consequences, and a philosophy of their meaning and purpose which makes it possible to evaluate implied relations; we can, however, reduce their most controversial implications to a minimum. We can exclude all theoretical explorations beyond those essential to the interrelations of phenomena, as defined by mathematical reduction formulas. This was done in the proof sections, Chapter 10, in full agreement with the practices of modern science. But proof is not comprehension. It leaves a void because understanding, an essential ingredient of scientific realism, can only be attained by logical exploration beyond the facts—by treating all implications as real until the contrary can be proved. Such explorations in depth are outlined in Book Two.

Los Angeles, California.   Eigil Rasmussen
January, 1970.

Chapter 1

MATHEMATICS   ALGEBRA

The mathematics in this chapter is intended to serve both as an informative background and a source of reference. Symbols are limited to those most commonly used and a few which are needed for special purposes. Common and basic logarithms are described in detail; the latter because it is used extensively in the sections on proof. This is not a book on mathematics, and the subject is confined to those aspects which are essential to an understanding of relations and proportions in the sections of theoretical physics which follows. The sections on orbits, algebraic idealizations and the redefinitions of units serve as an introduction to my idealizations of the physical constants.

101 Mathematics and Algebra.

Mathematics is the science of numbers; algebra is the shorthand of this science. Mathematics define the relations between quantities and the operations by which they are demonstrated and proved. Algebra is the branch of mathematics dealing with the values, relations and properties of numbers in terms of symbols and signs.

All numbers are multiples and/or divisions of unity—one. The relationship between two or more sets of figures is a specified difference between their base units, as defined by measurement, theory or fiat. A mathematical formula specifies the operational relationship between numbers. The number values of physical phenomena are first obtained by experiments based on observed or postulated relations. Because different factors and formulas can usually be found to give the anticipated results, the existence of a relationship can be proved by showing a coincidence of number values. Mathematical proof of a relationship can therefore be obtained before a reason for its existence is known, but in most cases logical deductions from experiment and observation anticipate what mathematics prove.

The signs and symbols of algebra represent numerical values and describe the nature of their mathematical conversions. Most of these stand for universally accepted values, relations and processes; however, since they cannot cover all contingencies, it is often necessary to invent new symbols or redefine old ones for specific purposes.

Algebraic formulas are combinations of mathematical symbols; usually letters of the Greek and Roman alphabets, both capital, lower-case and italics, combined with numbers, exponents and specially designed signs and symbols. Since the same symbol is often used for various purposes, it may be necessary to specify its meaning when used in a formula.

102 Signs and Symbols.

$+$ Addition. Plus or positive. $a + b = c$

$-$ Subtraction. Minus or negative. $c - a = b$

$\pm$ Can be either plus or minus according to circumstances.

$\times$ or $\cdot$ Multiplication. $a \times b = c$, $a \cdot b = c$,   or $ab = c$

$\div$ or $:$ Division. $c \div a = b$, $c : a = b$,   or $c/a = b$, $\frac{c}{a} = b$.

$=$ or $::$ Is equal to. $\neq$ Does not equal.

$\parallel$ Parallel to. $\nparallel$ Not parallel to.

$\because$ Because. Since. $\therefore$ Therefore. Hence. Then.

$>$ Is greater than. $<$ Is less than. $b > a$, or $a < b$.

$\frown$ Uncertain difference between quantities. Sometimes for similarity.

α Varies as. $\propto$ Proportional to. $a \propto b$.

∞ Infinity. Indefinitely great.

$\ldots$ Continuity. Continue sequence as shown.

0 Zero. Infinitesimally small. (In logarithms $0 = $ unity $= 1$)

Σ Sigma. The sum. Summation of the product of.

$)$ Sum. Result within a continuing sequence. $ab = c)/d = e$.

$\odot$ Station point. Circle. Circumference equal to $360°$.

$°, ', ''$ Degrees, minutes and seconds. (Such as $5°12'34''$)

π Pi. The ratio of a circle's circumference to its diameter.

$\int$ Integral. The formula following this symbol is to be integrated.

$\int_b^a$ The integral is to be taken between the limits a and b.

$-$ Vinculum; ( ) Parenthesis; [ ] or $\left\{ \ \right\}$ Brackets; | Bar. All indicate quantities which are to be taken together.
Examples: $\overline{a^b + b}$; $a \times (b + c [e \quad d])$; $4(a + b)$; $a + x/y | z$.

103 Mathematical and Physical Terms.

```
Terminating decimals.    Examples: 500/4 = 125.    5/4 = 1.25
Repeating decimals.         "       1/3 = .333...   1/7 = .1428574'1428574'
Non repeating decimals.     "       π = 3.14159265   √2 = 1.41421356
```

Rational numbers. Terminating and repeating decimals.

Irrational numbers. Endless non-repeating decimals.

A set. Group of elements or members recognized as belonging together.

Subset. A set within a set. An identifiable subdivision within a set.

Constant. A number symbol representing a fixed numerical value.

Variable. A symbol representing an x element within a set.

Radical. The root; fundamental; original; underived.

$\sqrt[n]{A}$ A radical. n, index or order; A, radicand.

a = bc a, product; b and c are factors of the product.

a = b/c a, dividend; b, numerator; c, denominator.

$a^2 a^3$ The numbers two and three are the exponents of a.

7abc Seven is the coefficient of abc.

104 Symbols Used With the Text.
    Symbols are in capital or small letters according to their most frequent use in the text and the formulas.

A	Angstrom wavelength.	F	Faraday. Electrolytic quantity.
B	de Broglie wavelength.	F	Force of acceleration.
B	Inductance in henrys.	g	Gravity constant of mass unit.
c	Velocity of light.	G	Gravity at earth's surface.
C	Centigrade temperature.	G	Gram. Any system's mass unit.
C	Constants. Waveratio: $2\pi\phi$.	h	Planck's quantum energy unit.
C	Capacitance in farads.	ħ	Planck's quantum divided by 2π.
C	Calories heat.	H	Horsepower unit of work.
D	Dyne. Force or momentum.	H	Gauss magnetic field intensity.
e	Electrostatic charge unit.	I	Electric current in amperes.
e	Electromagnetic energy unit.	J	Joule. The mks unit of work.
E	Erg. Energy.	K	Boltzmann's molecular energy u.
E	Electromagnetic in abcoulombs.	K	Kelvin's zero mole temperature.
f	Frequency in unit time.	L	Lengths.

L	Length & time ratios; nmt/rmt.	U	Unit.
m_o	Mass of electron.	$\widetilde{v}$	Wavenumber of electron's mass.
m'	Energy of electron's mass; emu.	$\dot{v}$	Wavelength of electron's mass.
M	Mass of particle or body.	v	Volume of gram mole.
N	Newton. The mks unit of force.	V	Electron volt.
N	Avogadro's number.	V	Volt charge potential.
ȯ	Orbit. Its radius in hydrogen.	V	Velocity of a mass.
P	Period in orbit.	W	Work done in terms of energy.
Q	Quantity. Electrons and charges.	W	Watts. Current in joules.
Q	Statcoulomb. Electrostatic.	π	Pi. Circumference/diameter ratio.
r	Radius. Radius curve.	¢	Natural length in centimeters.
r	Radius wavelength of electron.	$\propto$	Fine structure constant.
R	Rydberg's wavenumber.	Φ	Electronic constant = $1/\propto$.
R	Resistance in ohms.	γ	Free photon (light) waves.
R	Ratio of orbit elements.	λ	Momentum waves of moving mass
s	Second: A unit of time.	μ	Magneton.
s	Spin. Electron's magnetic field.	I	Magnetic flux in maxwells.
t	Time unit. Duration.	$\dot{x}$	(Dot over symbol) Wavelength.
T	Temperature. Time.	$\widetilde{x}$	(Wave over symbol) Wavenumber.

Abbreviations.

cgs   Centimeter-gram-second.
emu   Electromagnetic unit in cgs.
esu   Electrostatic unit in cgs.
mks   Meter-kilogram-second.
ngs   Natural length-gram-second.
nmt   Natural length-electron's mass-natural time.
rmt   Electron's radius length-electron's mass-electron's radius time.
cm.   Centimeter length.
nl.   Natural length.
rl.   Electron's radius length.
nt.   Natural time.
el.   Electron.

105 Multiplications and Divisions.

Multiplications and divisions are performed before additions and subtractions, unless the formulas indicate otherwise by signs of inclusion. Therefore: a + bc and (a + b)c give different results. Example: $5 + 4 \times 8 = 37$, while $(5 + 4) \times 8 = 72$.

a,b,c, Known quantities.   x,y,z, Unknown quantities.

$a_1 a_2 a_3$ Several quantities of the same kind.

a^n. That is: a to its nth power. An indefinite quantity.

$a_1 a_2 a_3 ... n$, or $a_1 a_2 a_3 a_n$. Continue sequence as shown (to nth power).

a, a^2, a^3, a^4. Powers of figures symbolized by a. Note: $a^2 = aa$, $a^3 = aaa$.

$a^{1/2}$, $a^{1/3}$, $a^{1/n}$, or $\sqrt{a}$, $\sqrt[3]{a}$, $\sqrt[n]{a}$, or $(a)^{1/2}$, $(a)^{1/3}$, $(a)^{1/n}$. Define square root, cube root and nth root of figure symbolized by a.

$\sqrt{-1}$ Imaginary number.

Because $1 \times 1 = 1$, it follows that multiplications of figures smaller than unity give results whose values are less than their principals, and that they are greater in divisions.

Examples: $4 \times 4 = 16$, $4.0 \times 0.4 = 1.6$, $0.4 \times 0.4 = 0.16$, $0.04 \times 0.04 = .0016$.

$$(2 \times 10^3)^2 = 4 \times 10^6, \quad (2 \times 10^{-3})^2 = 4 \times 10^{-6},$$
$$\sqrt{9 \times 10^{-6}} = 3 \times 10^{-3}.$$

106 Four Number Systems.

The system of numbers in general use originated from finger counting; its ten digits correspond, therefore, to our ten fingers. Obviously, it is not the only system of numeration possible. Suppose our forefathers had decided to let each letter of the alphabet stand for a number, or had decided to count the fingers on one hand only. Or suppose they had only three or two fingers to count. Below, the numbers of four systems are defined up to twenty-five, with digits of ten, five, three and two respectively.

Since all number systems start with unity, the zero which appears at the end of each sequence shows that nothing is defined for it, and that there is a transition of unity to the order above, thus giving us ten as the last of the prime numbers. Note that all the numbers in a system are symbols showing how many times unity is to be taken to equal that number, and that each space to the left of unity increases the number value of its figure by the number of units in the prime sequence. In the universal system it is increased by ten.

The number systems ten and two are the most important; the first because it is the one in general use, and the latter because it is the simplest possible. The other two were included to show that any conceivable number system can be used as a rational basis of mathematics. The binary system is being used in many types of calculators because its two numbers, one and zero, can be defined mechanically by an "on-and-off" device. The four systems are numbered up to 25 in their sequences below.

No. of digits.   Number sequence of four systems.

10	1	2	3	4	5	6	7	8	9	10	11	12	13	14
5	1	2	3	4	10	11	12	13	14	20	21	22	23	24
3	1	2	10	11	12	20	21	22	100	101	102	110	111	112
2	1	10	11	100	101	110	111	1000	1001	1010	1011	1100	1101	1110

Continued.

10	15	16	17	18	19	20	21	22	23	24	25
5	30	31	32	33	34	40	41	42	43	44	100
3	120	121	122	200	201	202	210	211	212	220	221
2	1111	10000	10001	10010	10011	10100	10101	10110	10111	11000	11001

107 Binary Number Mathematics.

The binary system of numbers has only two digits, one and zero. Since the latter defines empty spaces in a sequence of units, the location of one's in the sequence defines their powers. The value of a one is doubled each time it moves one space to the left. It follows that its value in ordinary numbers increases as shown in the table below. Since this increase is also the sequence of its natural logarithm, its log values are also given.

Basic logarithm	0	1	2	3	4	5	6	7
Ordinary numbers	1	2	4	8	16	32	64	128
Binary numbers	1	10	100	1000	10000	100000	1000000	10000000

Note that the logarithms of the binary numbers are equal to their numbers of zeros. A sure way to get the binary number of any ordinary figure is by using the three sequences above. Take the largest ordinary sequence number which can be subtracted from the number chosen. Subtract it and repeat the process with the remainders until nothing is left. For example: The figure 1065 combines the log numbers 2^{10}, 2^5, 2^3, 2^0, as shown below.

Log 2	Numbers	Binary numbers
2^{10}	1024 =	10000000000
2^5	32 =	100000
2^3	8 =	1000
2^0	1 =	1
Added	1065 =	10000101001

Binary numbers can be added, subtracted, multiplied, divided and converted into fractions like ordinary figures as shown below.

Additions.

```
   10=  2        111=  7
  100=  4       1000=  8
10000= 16      10001= 17
10110= 22     100000= 32
```

Subtractions.

```
10110= 22     100000= 32
  110=  6       1111= 15
10000= 16      10001= 17
```

Multiplications.

```
      6 × 4 = 24                5 × 5 = 25
100 × 110 = 11000        101 × 101 = 11001
            000                        101
            100                        000
            100                        101
```

Divisions.

```
    24 ÷ 6 = 4                 23 ÷ 7 = 3.285714
11000 ÷ 110 = 100       10111 ÷ 111 = 11.01001
110                            111
 000                          1001
 000                           111
                              1000
                               111
                                 1
```

108 Logarithms.

The most commonly used mathematical operations in science are multiplication and division. Logarithms were invented to simplify such calculations by converting their numbers into exponents that multiply by addition and divide by subtraction. However, this conversion also makes ordinary addition and subtraction by logarithms impossible. Tables of common logarithms usually give the logarithm equivalent of any figure up to five or seven digits.

The logarithm of a number is the exponent of the power to which a constant number (its base) must be raised to equal that number. The logarithm of 1000 to the base of 10 is 3, because $10 \times 10 \times 10 = 1000 = 10^3$; while 32 to the base of 2 is 5, because $2 \times 2 \times 2 \times 2 \times 2 = 32 = 2^5$. Its binary number (see Section 106), being 100,000 equals $10 \times 10 \times 10 \times 10 \times 10 = 2^5$. Note that the power of 10 in the binary system is only 2 in ordinary numbers. The simplicity of basic (binary) logarithms suggests its use in an introduction to the subject of logarithms. The first ten numbers of its sequence are defined below.

Log$_2$ exponent	0	1	2	3	4	5	6	7	8	9	10
Number	1	2	4	8	16	32	64	128	256	512	1024

Example: Exponents $2 + 5 = 7$. **Its numbers** $4 \times 32 = 128$. **Log**$_2$ $7 = 128$.

In the example above, the addition should be a multiplication sign, with the addition implied for log numbers, in order to conform with their algebraic definitions. Since most numbers fall between those which can be expressed by a simple exponent, their logarithm numbers have decimals in their exponents. Thus, the logarithm of 1000 in powers of two is log $2^{9.96578}$, while 32 in powers of ten is $10^{1.50515}$. They can also be put down as $\log_2 9.96578$ and $\log_{10} 1.50515$. The integral part of a logarithm index number is called the characteristic and its decimal part the mantissa.

There are three systems of logarithms in general use, called common, natural and basic logarithms. They can be converted into each other by multiplying or dividing their exponents as tabulated below. Tables of common logarithms are easily obtained.

Base numbers	Logarithms	Common	Natural	Basic
2.0	Basic to	0.30103000	0.69314719	1.0
2.7182818l	Natural to	0.43429448	1.0	1.44269502
10.0	Common to	1.0	2.30258509	3.32192809

109 Common Logarithms. Base 10.

Logarithms to the base ten are in general use throughout the world, and tables of common logarithms with from three to seven digits can be found in any library. Because the characteristic of a common log number is the same as the numerator of the figure it represents, any figure can be converted into a log number by removing its exponent and consulting a conversion table. After this dimensionless number has been converted into the mantissa of its $\log_{10}$ number, it is reassigned a dimension by adding the exponent as its characteristic. The figures 3.2×10^{-3}, 3.2 and 32000 all have the mantissa .50515. After adding their exponents we have log -3.50515, 0.50515 and 4.50515, respectively.

When the sum of mantissas added is more than one, the characteristics of their results are increased, as in the figures they represent. This means that the number characteristic of a negative result is reduced, as shown below. Note that $3.77815 \times 3.77815 = 7.55630$.

Negative number squared $(6 \times 10^{-3})^2 = 36 \times 10^{-6} = 3.6 \times 10^{-5}$
Logarithm of numbers -3.77815 -5.55630

110 Natural Logarithms.   (⊖)   Base 2.71828181

Logarithms to this base are used in preference to common logarithms in a number of statistical formulas, such as electrical, thermal and engineering formulas which include variables. This system of logarithms is more difficult to use because its base is irrational. The base is obtained by multiplying a series of fractions as shown below. The result of each multiplication is converted into a decimal as shown by the second line, and all the numbers and decimals are then added for the base number.

$$1 \times \tfrac{1}{1} = 1) \times \tfrac{1}{2} = \tfrac{1}{2}) \times \tfrac{1}{3} = \tfrac{1}{6}) \times \tfrac{1}{4} = \tfrac{1}{24}) \times \tfrac{1}{5} = \tfrac{1}{120}) \times \tfrac{1}{6} = \tfrac{1}{720}) \times \tfrac{1}{7} = \tfrac{1}{5040}, \text{ and so on.}$$

$1 + 1 + .5 + .166667 + .041667 + .008333 + .001388 + .000198\ldots n = 2.71828$

111 Basic Logarithms. Base 2.

This logarithm of binary numbers, being the simplest possible, is frequently used by teachers as an introduction to the subject. It is used extensively in this book to bring out the natural proportions of physical phenomena on the assumption that it is the mathematics of nature. To get maximum benefit from its use for this purpose, all reciprocal numbers have the same numerical values, with their negative numbers preceded by a negative sign.

Binary logarithms are also called "basic logarithms" and "powers of two" in this book. Years ago I worked out three tables of basic logarithms that are reliable, but time-consuming in use. For this reason they are not included, although I have used them extensively in my research. I recommend the conversion of numbers into common logarithms by the use of seven-digit tables, and then into powers of two by using the ratios defined in Section 108.

The sequence of negative log numbers below, defined as fractions and decimals, adds up to two at infinity.

Log 2   0   -1   -2   -3   -4   -5   -6   -7   -8
Fractions $1 + 1/2 + 1/4 + 1/8 + 1/16 + 1/32 + 1/64 + 1/128 + 1/256 \ldots$
Decimals $1 + .5 + .25 + .125 + .0625 + .03125 + .015625 + .0078125 \ldots n = 2.$

The sequence in binary numbers is unity followed by an infinite number of one's: 1.111111 ... n. Anticipating my theory, we will postulate a natural phenomenon in which unity is its expansion force at unit distance, and the decimals a force containing it along a descending gradient to zero at infinity. Note that the opposite forces are equal, that the gradient is a natural transition, and that a cut-off distance of effective power makes infinity finite. It may be an inch, a mile or a light-year.

112   Tables of Basic and Common Logarithms.

Logarithms in number sequence.			Numbers in basic log sequence.		
Number sequ.	Basic. Log 2	Common. Log 10	Numbers.	Basic. Log 2	Common. Log 10
1	0.0	0.0	1	0	0.0
2	1.0	0.30103	2	1	0.30103
3	1.584963	0.47712	4	2	0.60206
4	2.0	0.60206	8	3	0.90309
5	2.321928	0.69897	16	4	1.20412
6	2.584963	0.77815	32	5	1.50515
7	2.807355	0.84509	64	6	1.80618
8	3.0	0.90309	128	7	2.10721
9	3.169924	0.95424	256	8	2.40824
10	3.321928	1.0	512	9	2.70927
11	3.459432	1.04139	1024	10	3.01030
12	3.584963	1.07918	2048	11	3.31133
13	3.700440	1.11394	4098	12	3.61236
14	3.807355	1.14613	8192	13	3.91339
15	3.906891	1.17609	16384	14	4.21442
16	4.0	1.20412	32768	15	4.51545
17	4.087463	1.23045	65536	16	4.81648
18	4.169924	1.25527	131072	17	5.11751
19	4.247928	1.27875	262144	18	5.41854
20	4.321928	1.30103	524288	19	5.71957
21	4.392317	1.32222	1048576	20	6.02060

113   Negative Logarithms.

In mathematics the sequences of increasing numerical values are always from one to nine regardless of whether its figure is more or less than unity, but the negative exponent of a figure increases with reduction of its numerical value. The common and natural logarithms of numbers follow the same rules. Their mantissas are always positive, and their characteristics are positive or negative like the figures they represent. However, in basic logarithms, as used in this book, characteristics and mantissas are positive or negative together. It follows that wavelengths and wavenumbers, being reciprocals, are defined by the same figures, with the one less than unity preceded by a negative sign.

It is my contention this method of mathematical analysis brings out proportions that are hidden by negative log values in common logarithms. Let us assume there is a unit of action in nature whose elements, force-distance-time, are also unity; and that their action potentials decrease with distance and increase with time. In order to make their deviations from unity observationally meaningful by idealizations, it is necessary to show them in true proportions. The mantissas of ordinary logarithms do not do so for negative values, but those of basic logarithms do. It is also simpler in use, because all its figures are added or subtracted in the usual way, as shown below. Note that the reciprocal of a negative log number is used to obtain its basic log number. The figure used is the same as that in the example, Section 109.

```
Negative figure squared    (6×10⁻³)²   = 3.6×10⁻⁵
Its reciprocal number sq.   (166.66...)² = 27777.77...
Basic log of numbers       -7.380822    -14.761644
```

The difference between common and basic logarithms for negative numbers is brought out by the table below. Note that the mantissas of the two reciprocal log 10 columns add up to one, while those of the log 2 columns are identical.

Prime numbers	Log 10	Log 2	Reciprocal numbers	Log 10	Log 2
0.09	-2.95424	-3.47393	11.111...	1.04575	3.47393
0.1	-1.0	-3.32193	10.0	1.0	3.32193
0.2	-1.30103	-2.32193	5.0	0.69897	2.32193
0.3	-1.47712	-1.73697	3.333...	0.52288	1.73697
0.4	-1.60206	-1.32193	2.5	0.39794	1.32193
0.5	-1.69897	-1.0	2.0	0.30103	1.0
0.6	-1.77815	-0.73697	1.666...	0.22185	0.73697
0.7	-1.84509	-0.51457	1.42857	0.15491	0.51457
0.8	-1.90309	-0.32193	1.25	0.09691	0.32193
0.9	-1.95424	-0.15200	1.111...	0.04575	0.15200
1.0	0.0	0.0	1.0	0.0	0.0

114 Convergence on One or Zero.

In mathematics all figures are multiples and fractions of the unit one, the convergence point of all changes of value. It follows that mathematical formulas deal with different concepts of unity and the relations between them. Because mathematical units can be subdivided indefinitely, the number of values which can exist between one and zero are theoretically as abundant as those between one and infinity.

The physicist's need for mathematical units of action to define relations between natural phenomena must also be needed by nature to produce those relations and their observed invariable proportions. Logic tells us specific relations and proportions in physics evolved from specific first causes. Since all actions in nature are the products of forces acting through time across a distance, it is to be assumed these three factors (force, time, distance) have specific unit values in nature, and that they produce the observed phenomena through the simplest possible interactions and geometrical relations. This postulate made it possible for me to discover the fundamental units of length and time in nature. (See Section 221.)

We must further assume these units originated from opposite forces of different origins whose interactions, in terms of forces, time-rates and distances, converge on zero. In experiments there is, however, a clear distinction between factors which are quantized and cannot be reduced below the quantizing dimension, and factors which can be reduced to zero. Because the former converge on unity and the latter on zero, there is a natural difference of one between them in mathematical formulas. In some formulas it may be necessary to halve or double the result to bring it into accord with observation. Note that a velocity is not quantized, but may have a specific value in the atoms because the momentum of a moving body is in a natural quantum state.

115 Ratio: Circle's Circumference to Diameter. $\pi = 3.14159265359$

Pi, the ratio obtained by dividing a circle's circumference with its diameter, is a factor which appears frequently in physical formulas. Some of those appear in the table below. Note that the reciprocal of a log 2 number is that number preceded by a negative sign, and that the reciprocal of a log 10 number, when their mantissas are added, give unity as the result. Since the common log number of pi is 0.4971499, its reciprocal must be $\log_{10} -1.5028501$. (See Section 109.)

useful formulas.

Terms	Numbers	Log 10	Log 2	Terms	Reciprocals
$\sqrt{\pi}$	1.12837917	0.052455	0.174252	$-\sqrt{\pi}/2$	0.88622693
$\sqrt{\pi}$	2.25675833	0.353485	1.174252	$-\sqrt{\pi}/4$	0.44311346
π	1.27323954	0.104910	0.348504	$\pi/4$	0.78539816
π	1.90985930	0.281001	0.933466	$\pi/6$	0.52359878
π	1.33133536	0.124288	0.412874	$1/\sqrt[4]{\pi}$	0.75112555
π	1.46458567	0.165717	0.550499	$1/\sqrt[3]{\pi}$	0.68278696
$\sqrt{\pi}$	1.77245385	0.248575	0.825748	$1/-\sqrt{\pi}$	0.56418958
$\sqrt{\pi/2}$	1.25331414	0.098060	0.325748	$1/-\sqrt{\pi/2}$	0.79788456
2	1.57079633	0.196120	0.6514961	$2/\pi$	0.63661977
$\sqrt{2\pi}$	2.50662828	0.399090	1.325748	$1/-\sqrt{2\pi}$	0.39894228
$\sqrt{4\pi}$	3.54490770	0.549605	1.825748	$1/-\sqrt{4\pi}$	0.28209479
$(\pi)^4$	6.08806824	0.784479	2.6059845	$1/(\tfrac{1}{2}\pi)^4$	0.16425572
	3.14159265	0.497150	1.6514961	$1/\pi$	0.31830989
	4.18879020	0.622089	2.066534	$1/\tfrac{4}{3}\pi$	0.23873241
	6.28318531	0.798180	2.6514961	$1/2\pi$	0.15915494
	9.42477796	0.974271	3.236458	$1/3\pi$	0.10610330
	12.56637061	1.099210	3.6514961	$1/4\pi$	0.07957747
	18.84955592	1.275301	4.236458	$1/6\pi$	0.05305165
	9.86960440	0.994300	3.302992	$1/\pi^2$	0.10132118
	31.00627664	1.491450	4.954488	$1/\pi^3$	0.03225153
	97.40909067	1.988600	6.6059845	$1/\pi^4$	0.01026598

116 Mathematics of Circles and Spheres.

The circumference of a circle is equal to $2\pi = 6.28318531$ times its radius. This figure is used repeatedly in the mathematical formulas of physics. The area bound by a circle is related to its diameter and radius by these formulas:

$a = \tfrac{1}{4}\pi d$	Diameter to area	$a = \pi r$ Radius to area
$d = \sqrt{4a/\pi}$	Area to diameter	$r = \sqrt{a/\pi}$ Area to radius

The line of a circle is normally divided into 360° (degrees). Each degree equals 60' (minutes), and each minute equals 60" (seconds). A circle is, therefore, equal to 21600 minutes or 1296000 seconds. All three are used to define the angle of two lines diverging from its center as a fraction of the circle. For example: The radian $\Phi = 57°\ 17'\ 44.8''$.

A radian is the angle formed by two lines joining at the center of a circle when the distance between them along its circumference is equal to its radius. A radian is therefore $1/2\pi$ of its circle, or 0.159154943 of its circumference. It is equal to 57.2957795°, or 206264.8''. One degree equals 0.01745329 radian.

The area of a circle is two-dimensional, while that of a sphere is the surface of a three-dimensional shape. A sphere's surface area is exactly four times larger than the area enclosed by a circle with the same radius. Formulas relating the elements of a sphere appear below.

$a = \pi d$	Diameter to area	$a = 4\pi r^2$	Radius to area
$d = \sqrt{a/\pi}$	Area to diameter	$r = \sqrt{a/4\pi}$	Area to radius
$v = \frac{1}{6}\pi d^3$	Diameter to volume	$v = \frac{4}{3}\pi r$	Radius to volume
$v = \frac{1}{6}ad$	Area-diameter to volume	$v = \frac{1}{3}ar$	Area-radius to volume
$d = \sqrt[3]{6v/\pi}$	Volume to diameter	$r = \sqrt[3]{v/\frac{4}{3}\pi}$	Volume to radius

Assuming the radius of a sphere is equal to unity, its volume multiplied by three gives its area. For other radii it is equal to the difference between radius squared and cubed times three. The four elements of a sphere with unit radius are:

Term	Number		Log 2	Log 10
Radius		1.0	0.0	0.0
Diameter		2.0	1.0	0.301030
Volume	$\frac{4}{3}\pi =$	4.18879020	2.0665336	0.622089
Ratio	$a/v =$	3.0	1.5849625	0.477121
Area	$4\pi =$	12.56637061	3.6514961	1.099210

Note that $4/3 = 1.333..n) \times 3.0 = 4.0$.

117 Different Kinds of Averages.

Formal reductions to averages in physics depends upon what we are defining; is it mass, velocity, momentum, energy, or a group of probabilities? Since a momentum is defined as mass times velocity, and energy as one half of that mass times velocity squared, their averages are obtained in different ways. The average energy of a group of air molecules is further complicated by their different masses, with velocities and energies per unit mass increasing with a reduction of mass, and different velocities for equal masses. It ranges from near zero to an undeterminable maximum, with the greatest number moving with speeds near that anticipated for the temperature.

Four different kinds of averages appear below, with examples showing their different results.

Geometric root mean.

$$-\sqrt{a_1\,a_2\,a_3\ldots n/n}\qquad\qquad \sqrt{5\times 8\times 11/3}\qquad = 6.992$$

Geometric mean.

$$\sqrt[n]{a_1\,a_2\,a_3\ldots n}\qquad\qquad \sqrt[3]{5\times 8\times 11}\qquad = 7.6059$$

Arithmetic mean.

$$a_1+a_2+a_3+\ldots n/n\qquad\qquad 5+8+11/3\qquad = 8.0$$

Root mean square.

$$-\sqrt{a_1{}^2\;a_2{}^2\;a_3{}^2\ldots n/n}\qquad\qquad \sqrt{5^2+8^2+11^2/3}\;= 8.3666..n$$

118 Mathematical Idealization of Orbits.

The discovery of mathematically ideal proportions is of vital importance to theoretical physics because they make it possible to change the figures and formal relations of its constants without violating the facts of physics. We can simplify them toward the simplicity by which they are implemented by nature. The subject is introduced by noting the idealized elements of periodic orbits.

The circular motion of a mass around a theoretically unmovable center is defined by four factors: Velocity, radius, period and attractive force. For a specific radius the attracting force at orbit distance determines its velocity and period, because it must equal the orbiting body's centrifugal force. Let us assume its four elements of motion have been determined, and that we want to obtain their values for other distances. It has been proved that the new orbit values are always in the ratio R: $v = -R^1$, $r = R^2$, $p = R^3$, $a = -R^4$, to those of the first orbit for increased distances. Note that the period of the primary orbit includes the factor 2π, and that its presence is implied but not defined for the abstracted periods. This ratio is true for both gravitational and electrostatic orbits—for planetary motions and for electrons circling atomic nuclei.

The convergence of these four ratios on unity leads to the conclusion that, in nature, there is a fundamental reference orbit in which velocity, radius and attractive force have unit values. A mathematical analysis of the changes which occur in the constants of atomic physics when the accepted units of action—the centimeter, gram and second—are changed, leads to the conclusion that the elements of a hydrogen electron's orbit converge on such a unit. The unit velocity is the speed of light, the unit of distance is an electron's radius, and the unit of force is the proton's electrostatic charge at that distance. An electron's smallest possible orbit in hydrogen is defined by the ratio $c\propto$ or c/ϕ, the speed of light times the fine structure constant or divided by the electronic constant, as follows: $-\phi,\ \phi^2,\ 2\pi\phi^3,\ -\phi^4$, (See Sections 215, 1020-23.)

119 Algebra Idealizes Relations.

The acceptance of a mathematical formula by science is based on the assumption that its algebraic symbols transcend the specific values they represent at that moment. It specifies relations and proportions, but not the values of its symbols. These can be changed by experimental reevaluations and the use of different units of reference, without changes of the algebraic formulas to which they are related. Our system of physical constants is based on a unit of action experimentally defined by the centimeter, gram and second. If we were to double or halve one of these units, the formulas from which their values are obtained do not change, even though the figures defining the physical constants are profoundly changed.

It follows that the accepted units of length, mass and time can be changed to any values we choose, if we can justify the change by showing that the new constants are closer to the simple proportions anticipated for nature. We expect nature's true figures and formulas to be simpler than those used to define its observed constants in arbitrarily selected units of action. It is assumed that the basic constants of nature are either unity, geometrical deviations from unity or values whose deviations from unity are related to each others through simple roots and powers, and combinations of such values with geometrical constants. Nature's quantum states give us its unit of mass, their wave relations give us its unit of length, and the speed of light defines its unit of time as the time it takes a light wave to move one unit of length. These relations and proportions provide a broad base for the conversion of accepted to natural units and constants. (See Sections 215 and the algebraic web in 222.)

120 Redefinitions of Reference Units.

The reduction of a mathematical unit increases the ratio relations it defines in inverse proportion. A reference unit is essential to mathematics for the purpose of obtaining related values, such as the unchanging proportions of geometry. However, when it is used to define the relations of observable physical proportions, its assigned value apparently can be anything we choose to make it, provided that it remains in proportion to other observed values as defined by formal reductions.

Below is a diagram showing what happens when a mathematical unit is increased or reduced by sixteen. The fractions divide the large unit by a sequence of halvings for simplicity of reductions. We know that a fraction can have any value between one and zero. The fractions are in decimals above, and in the new units below.

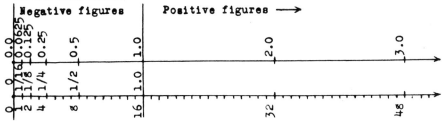

A change of unit value by sixteen produces significant changes in the results when the same formulas are used, and in the formulas when the results are to be identical. Let us multiply $2 \times 3 = 6$, on the large scale. This result is $6 \times 16 = 96$, on the small scale; but $32 \times 48 = 1536 = 6 \times 16^2$, on the small scale. The equivalent of six is obtained by $32 \times 48/16 = 96$. Suppose we multiply the small unit 0.0625 on the large scale by any figure, the result on the small scale will be identical with that figure. It follows that if the small unit is a true unit in nature, the identity above take the form of a coincidence of figures for related phenomena with known values. Other relations are brought out by these figures:

Large scale,	$0.5 \times 0.125 = 0.0625$	$0.5 \div 0.125 = 4.0$	$0.5^3 = 0.125$
Small scale,	$8.0 \times 2.0 = 16.0$	$8.0 \div 2.0 = 4.0$	$\sqrt[3]{8} = 2.0$

The base units of the first and last sets of figures determine their directions and results; the second set give identical results because we are dealing with proportions, and the power and root of the third set give identical results on the small scale. In practice, the conversion ratios between two systems of units is not so obvious.

The difference between a natural and artificial unit of physics is complicated by fractions and the different gradients of its phenomena. The simplest changes are those related to the unit of length, such as wavelengths, radii and distances. Energies and momenta change with changes of the units of length, mass and time, because all three are included in their definitions. The gradients of electrostatic and gravitational forces produce further complications when the units of action are changed.

The arbitrary nature of the accepted units of action make it necessary to include factors in their reduction formulas which cancel out potential deviations from the results of experiment. It is evident that a system of units based on natural proportions eliminates these factors, and thus simplifies the often complex formulas of physics. We can prove the physical reality of these idealizations by checking their results against those obtained by conventional formulas, because their final figures must be the same.

121 Relations of Units and Systems.

Physical phenomena are the products of interacting forces; the nature and power of those forces are defined by the changes which occur when a specific force is imposed upon a particular phenomenon against the opposition (inertia) of its natural configuration in experiments. Force is the common denominator in all physical phenomena. Energy consists of contained forces with potential resolutions into directed forces.

Force is defined by the rate at which it causes a specific mass to accelerate. Momentum is the force potential of that mass at a specific moment of time. The unit of force is the momentum of a unit mass accelerated to unit velocity in one unit of time (see Section 207). The momentum of any mass at any velocity is equal to mass times velocity: $F = MV$.

The unit of energy is the action potential of a two-unit mass at the velocity defining a unit of force (see Section 208). The energy of any mass at any velocity is one half of that mass times velocity squared: $E = \frac{1}{2}MV^2$. The energy of a unit rest mass is the speed of light squared: $E = Mc^2$.

Suppose we compare two systems of units both having the same mass and time units but with their length units differing by 16. The force acting on the smaller unit, and its velocity, is 1/16th of that defined for the larger unit, and their energy difference is the reciprocal of one half of sixteen squared, or 1/128th unit.

If a system's time unit alone was reduced to 1/16th, then the force and velocity of the new system increases by 16, and its energy by 128. The mass must move faster to cover the same distance in less time. A reduction of mass reduces the force in direct proportion.

122 Scalars and Vectors.

A scalar quantity can be fully described by a magnitude; a vector requires both magnitude and direction. Quantities which can be specified by an unchanging number, such as distance, time, volume, mass and etc, are scalar quantities. A directed force is a vector, since its action upon a mass produces directed changes of speed and direction. Two forces acting on a mass at an angle to each other define its consequent acceleration in an intermediate direction by a vector parallelogram.

123 Dimensional Formulas.

Dimensional formulas give essential information only. They are used to check equations, because the two members of an equation must have the same dimensions. The basic units of physics, mass, length and time, are expressed by M, L, T, and their conversion ratios, by m, l, t. A negative exponent means that the symbol is inversely related—that it appears in a formula as a divisor.

The area of a surface is expressed as: $S = CL^2$. C stands for unity when L is the side of a square, and it symbolizes $\pi/4$ when L is the diameter of a circle. Its dimensional formula is L^2. Length cubed gives us the formula L^3 for volume. This essential information is expanded into algebraic symbols giving additional details, such as the addition of C above and its conversion into the symbols of a specific mathematical relationship. These, in turn, are converted into figures. For those who want more detailed information I recommend, SMITHSONIAN PHYSICAL TABLES, publication 3171.

124 Physical Definitions and Formulas.

L^2 Area of a square. L^3 Volume of a cube. M/V or ML^{-3} Its density.

L/T or LT^{-1} Velocity. Ratio of length to time.

T^{-1} Angular velocity. Angle in a given time to that time.

VT^{-1} or LT^{-2} Linear acceleration. The rate of change of velocity with time.
$a = dv/dt$.

T^{-1}/T or T^{-2} Angular acceleration. The rate of change of angular velocity.

FM^{-1} or LT^{-2} Intensity of attraction. The force of attraction per unit mass on a body placed at a specified distance from the center of its cause. It is the formula for acceleration.

MV or MLT^{-1} Momentum. The product of mass times velocity.

ML^2T^{-1} Moment of momentum. The product of a body's momentum by the distance of its line of motion from the point it is circling.

ML^2 Moment of inertia. The motion of a body around an axis as it is opposed by the inertia of its mass.

ML^2T^{-1} Angular momentum. The product of a body's moment of inertia and angular velocity.

MLT^{-2} Force. The rate of change of momentum. Its unit is one dyne.

LF or ML^2T^{-2} Torque. A twisting motive; the produce of force and length.

FL^2 or $ML^{-1}T^{-2}$ Intensity of stress. The ratio of total stress to the area over which it is distributed.

FL^2M^{-1} or L^3T^{-2} Absolute force of a center of attraction. The intensity of a force at unit distance from the center of its cause, and its force per unit mass at any distance by distance squared.

FL or ML^2T^{-2} Work. The product of a force acting on a body, defined by the displacement it produces.

ML^2T^{-2} Energy. The work done to produce a change of the velocity of a body is called kinetic energy; while a change of its shape or configuration is potential energy.

WT^{-1} or ML^2T^{-3} Power of activity. The time rate of doing work. Let W stand for work and P for power, then P = dw/dt.

FLT^{-1} Power of activity in gravity, with F standing for the force factor.

Chapter 2

METRICS UNITS OF PHYSICS

The simplicity of the metric system has made its length, mass and volume units the most widely used units of measurement in commerce and science. By adding the second as its unit of time, the metric system is used by scientists to define the units of action and, through them, they obtain numerous secondary units by mathematical abstractions and experimental measurements.

In this chapter the terms and proportions of the metric system are defined. Its units are then used to define various secondary units and ratios observed in nature. They are followed by sections on idealizing sequences and the ideal proportions which made my idealization of the international units of physics possible.

201 Metric System.   Length. Weight. Volume.
                                                          Meter. Gram. Liter.

In 1793 the National Assembly of France comissioned a group of scientists to develop a rational system of weights and measures. This system, known as the metric system, is used by all scientists and nearly all countries. Its units of length, weight and volume are the meter, gram and liter, respectively. They are related to secondary units through multiples of ten, with each unit identified by a prefix to its generic term; such as millimeter, kilogram, etc. The units are:

Milli	.001	Deca	10.
Centi	.01	Hecto	100.
Deci	.1	Kilo	1000.

202 Meter. (The unit of length.)   cm = 0.959731214 nl.

The meter was originally intended to be one ten millionth of the distance from the earth's pole to its equator, but those who measured it made a slight error. The value adopted in 1793 is now the standard unit of length of the metric system. It is the distance at zero centigrade (the melting point of ice) between two cross lines on a platinum-iridium bar in a vault at the International Bureau of Weights and Measures in France. The conversion of its length into wavelengths of light makes it possible to reproduce the meter anywhere on earth. It is the standard of length used by all nations; being also used to define the inch and other units used by the United States and England. Some of these are defined below.

```
Kilometer    1000 meters = 0.621372 mile  = 3280.83 feet
Meter       39.37 inches = 1.09361  yard  = 3.28083 feet
Centimeter    .01 meter  = 0.3937   inch  = 10⁹ angstrom
Millimeter    .001   "   = 1000  microns
Micron       10⁻⁶   "    = 10000 angstrom = Light wave range
Angstrom     10⁻¹⁰  "    = Atom's Radius = 10⁵ electron radii
```

Note: One natural unit of length (nl.) equal 1.0419584 centimeters.

203 Liter. (The unit of volume)

The volume of a cube is its length along one edge cubed. A liter is the content of a cube whose edge is one decimeter in length. It is equal to 0.1 meter, or 10 centimeters cubed. The volumes of meter and centimeter cubes are also used as reference units. The content of a cubic meter is equal to a kiloliter.

```
Cubic decimeter = 1 liter = 10³ centimetrs = 1000 cubic centimeters
Cubic meter = 1 kiloliter = 10³ decimeters = 1000 liters
Cubic centimeter = (0.1)³ liter = 1/1000 cubic liter.

Centiliter  = 0.338 fluid ounces
Liter       = 1.0567 quart      = 61.003 cubic inches
Decaliter   = 2.6418 gallons
Cubic meter = 1.308  cubic yards = 35.314 cubic feet
```

204 Gram. (The unit of mass and weight)

One gram is defined as the mass of one cubic centimeter of distilled water at its greatest density (4° centigrade) in an atmospheric pressure of 760 millimeters of mercury. One kilogram is, therefore, equal to one liter of pure water. Note that mass is the same everywhere, while weight varies slightly with the difference in gravity at different localities. In ordinary practice, however, the two terms are interchangeable. A small error appeared in the original determination of the kilogram. The standard unit of mass is a mass of platinum in a vault at the International Bureau of Weights and Measures in France.

```
Milligram = 0.01543 grains
Gram      = 0.03215 ounce, Troy = 0.64301 pennyweight
Gram      = 1000 milligram    = 15.43236 grains
Decagram  =   10 grams        = 5.64383 drams
Hectogram =  100 grams        = 3.52739 ounces
Kilogram  = 1000 grams        = 2.20462 pounds
Metric ton = 1000 kilogram = 0.9842 long ton = 1.102311 short tons
```

205 Second. (The unit of time and duration)

Time is a measure of duration, defined by observable repetitions of physical phenomena. A mean solar day is used by physicists for reference. The day is divided into 24 hours; with each hour equal to 60 minutes and each minute equal to 60 seconds. One second is therefore equal to 1/86400th of a mean solar day.

```
Day    = 86400 seconds = 1440 minutes = 24 hours
Hour   =  3600 seconds =   60 minutes = 0.041666... day
Minute=     60 seconds = 0.01666..hour = 6.9444...×10⁻⁴ day
Second= 0.01666... minute = 2.777...×10⁻⁴ hour = 1.157417×10⁻⁵ da
```

206 Principal Units of Action. (cgs, mks)

In theoretical and practical science the principal units of action are: the centimeter, the gram and the second. From their defined interrelations we obtain three fundamental experimental units of action: a unit of force called the dyne, a unit of energy called the erg, and a unit of time defined by the distance a light wave travels through empty space in one second, called the speed of light. In conjunction with the metric units and the geometry of physical relations, these units serve as a base of reference for the abstraction of additional units by observation and mathematical formulas.

207 Dyne. (The cgs unit of force)   F = 0.00101972 gram weight.

The centimeter-gram-second (cgs) unit of force and momentum: that acceleration thrust which, by acting for one second upon a mass of one gram, imparts a velocity of one centimeter per second; an acceleration thrust of one centimeter per second per second per gram mass. The momentum of a moving mass is defined in dynes by multiplying its mass in grams by its velocity in centimeters per second. A mass with the weight of one dyne is equal to the reciprocal of the earth's gravity in dynes; or about one-milligram weight.

208 Erg. (The cgs unit of energy) $(E = \frac{1}{2}mV^2)$

The centimeter-gram-second unit of energy. The kinetic energy of a moving mass is defined as one half of its mass times its velocity squared. It follows that the equivalent of the dyne as defined in the preceding section is only half an erg. To obtain one erg of energy the mass or velocity must be doubled. The erg is, therefore, the energy of a two-gram mass moving with the speed of one centimeter per second, or it is the energy of a gram mass accelerated by a force of 1.41421356 dyne (the square root of two) acting through one second. Note that this force is also the velocity of a unit mass-second.

209 MKS Units.   Unit of force. Newton = 10^5 dynes
                                                 Unit of energy. Joule = 10^7 ergs

The meter-kilogram-second unit of force and energy. Except for their larger powers, the newton and the joule are defined in the same way as the dyne and the erg. They are related as shown below:

Newton = 100 cm. × 1000 gram = 10^5 dynes.

Joule = (100 cm.)^2 × 1000 gram = 10^7 ergs.

The mks system of units is called "the practical system" because its units are within the range of ordinary physical phenomena. They are used by the international system of physical and electromagnetic units for reference and the experimental determination of its constants. It is never used as a complete system. (See Sections 408-9.)

210 Velocity of Light. $c = 2.997930 \times 10^{10}$ cm. second.

The velocity with which energy is transmitted from point to point across empty space; expressed as the distance a light wave moves through one unit of time. Also: the number of times a stationary 1-cm ether wave passes through a four-stage dynamic cycle in one unit of time. The speed of light is defined as the distance, in centimeters, a light wave moves in one second through empty space.

The speed of light was first determined by Romer, in 1676, when he noted that the periodic eclipses of Jupiter's satellites increased toward a maximum when the earth was receding from the planet, and that they decreased when it was approaching. The speed of light is obtained by dividing the diameter of the earth's orbit by the difference in time between maximum and minimum deviations from eclipse means.

Michelson and others obtained more exact values for the speed of light by causing light rays to be reflected by a revolving mirror through a long tunnel to another mirror which reflected them back to the first, and from there to the observer. Because this mirror has moved between the two reflections, the angle of the last reflection changes with the speed of the mirror, and the speed of light can, therefore, be obtained by mathematical analysis.

The earliest estimates of its speed was 2.99776×10^{10} cm. per second, but more recent estimates, based on improved methods, increased its value to 2.99793×10^{10} centimeters per second, the figure which I use in this book.

211 Light Velocity by Formula.

It is evident that formulas containing two or more measurable factors and the speed of light can be used to obtain its approximate value. In the Table of Physical Constants, page 152, the speed of light relates mass to electromagnetic energy, and that energy to electrostatic energy in columns A, B and C. The speed of light appears also in Section 213 as the difference between electrical permittivity and magnetic permeability; in the sequence formula (Section 217) with constants whose values can be determined by experiments, and is obtained by:

e   Electrostatic unit charge. 701, 19C
F   Force on K orbit electron in hy. 713
m_o Electron's rest mass in grams. 708, 21A
$\tilde{v}$ Electron's rest mass wavenumber. 709, 21U
¢   Natural length in centimeters. 221, 7T

$$c = \sqrt[4]{\frac{\frac{1}{2}\tilde{v}F¢e^{L}}{m^{L}(\frac{1}{2}\pi)^{4}}}$$

212 Energy Equivalent of Mass.   ($E = mc^2$)   Gram $= 8.987584 \times 10^{20}$ ergs

The energy which appears when a mass is resolved into its original primitive state. It is equal to its mass multiplied by the velocity of light squared; with the mass in grams and the speed in centimeters per second. The formula, $E = mc^2$, was suggested by Einstein on the basis of an electron's increase of mass at high velocities. Noting that this increase causes any mass to become infinitely great at the speed of light, he suggested that no physical mass can ever attain that velocity.

Observation shows that an electron and a positron may unite and resolve into the free waves of two photons receding in opposite directions. When their wavelengths are measured and redefined as energy, each photon's energy equals that of an electron's rest mass. Einstein's theory is also confirmed by the release of atomic energy and by the wave-energy equivalents of physical motions.

Because an electron's increase of mass is negligible at low velocities, a relationship of simple proportions appears between mass, (Section 709), motion (de Broglie), wavelength (Section 610) and velocity. When the ratio changes at different speeds are projected to the speed of light without the observed increase of mass with speed (Section 1027), the energy expended to attain that speed is equal to one half of the electron's rest mass energy. An electron's de Broglie wavelengths and its radiation wavelengths converge with an increase of velocity to coincidence at twice the speed of light; assuming as before that the observed increase of mass with an increase of velocity does not occur. (See the table in Section 1027.)

213 esu/emu Ratio: Speed of Light.

The observed difference between a stationary electrostatic force field and the electromagnetic force it brings into being when moving. In experiments the magnetic field is produced by electrons circling a center. Its unit of action is the force of one dyne, one centimeter from the center of an electrostatic charge or magnetic field. (See Sections 501 and 512, and also 34B and 32C.)

In the latter part of the nineteenth century the mathematical investigations by Clerk-Maxwell of the relationship between electrostatic and electromagnetic fields showed that their action potentials differ by a ratio equal to the speed of light. This has been interpreted as the electromagnetic origin of light waves, a postulate which was confirmed by Hertz discovery of radio waves in 1888.

Maxwell found the ratio of the dielectric constant to magnetic permeability, defined as electrical permittivity $\epsilon = 1/4\pi k$) and magnetic permeability ($\mu = 4\pi$) of space, respectively, to be equal to the speed of light as defined below.

$k = c^2 \quad = 8.987584 \times 10^{20}$ See Section 212 and 34C in the Table, page 152.
$\epsilon = 1/4\pi k = 8.854152 \times 10^{-21}$ Electrical permittivity of space.
$\mu = 4\pi \quad = 12.5663706$ Magnetic permeability of space. Section 115.

$$c = 1/\sqrt{\epsilon\mu} = 1/\sqrt{8.854152 \times 10^{-21} \times 12.5663706} = 2.99793 \times 10^{10} \text{ cm./sec.}$$

A simpler and more fundamental definition of the emu-esu ratio is obtained by noting the magnetic field produced by the motion of a single electron. This magnetic field is directly proportional to the momentum of its all-electrical mass. Since momentum is defined as mass times velocity, it follows that an electron's magnetic field increases in direct proportion to its velocity, and that its charge and magnetic field values become theoretically identical at the speed of light.

An electron's electrostatic charge is defined as its force at one centimeter, and its magnetic field as its electromagnetic force at one centimeter when moving with the speed of one centimeter per second. It follows that the difference between them is equal to the speed of light as defined by Maxwell. Let 2.99793×10^{10} electrons circle a center with a speed of one centimeter per second, and the magnetic field they produce at that center is equal to one electron's charge. A magnetic field is increased by increasing the number of electrons circling the center of a magnet and/or increasing their velocities, either through the loops of a conductor or within the magnet itself. See Sections 405 and 504 for experimental definitions of the electrostatic and electromagnetic force ratios.

214 Constants of Physics.

A constant of physics is, by definition, an unchangeable quantity within the accepted frame of reference. A fundamental constant is a natural quantity or proportion that does not change under any conceivable conditions. A fundamental unit of physics is either unity, a direct abstraction from unity, or the observed value of a unit of physics. (In this last case the term "fundamental" should probably not be used.)

The accepted constants of physics are based on the three arbitrarily selected units, length, mass and time, from which the units of force and energy are abstracted. Since most constants change value when one of the three primary units is changed, they are "constants" only within a particular frame of reference. It is evident, however, that the physical dimensions and ratios obtained by experiments do not change: they are true constants transcending the units used to define their numerical values. If, for example, we change the unit of length, then the defined values of wavelengths, wavenumbers, radii and distances change in direct proportion, but their ratio differences remain unchanged. Among these fundamental constants, the waveratio constant, the fine structure constant and its reciprocal, the electronic constant, are the most important.

A fundamental unit of physics should, by definition, be unity—one. However, our use of arbitrary units of action makes numerical deviations from unity inevitable; therefore, there are constants of physics which must be unity in nature but are not so by our definitions. Among them I note the units of length, mass and time. The natural units of length and time are related through the speed of light, with time defined as the time it takes a light wave to move one natural unit of length. The natural unit of mass is that of an electron, because the units of length and charge coincide with it when the unit of length is an electron's radius.

The classical definition of an electron's radius shows that its mass is all-electrical. Let the electron's radius be the unit of length, and its mass and charge must also be unity, if the speed of light is unity. A proton's positive charge is also unity, even though its mass is greater than unity. Although its mass is specific and unchangeable, the absence of a convergence coincidence of values or a definable geometrical ratio difference makes a proton's mass unsuitable as a foundation unit in physics.

215 Idealized Electron-Hydrogen Units.

Note that the ideal proportions defined in this section will be used to idealize the accepted constants of physics in the subsequent sections.

Even though the accepted units of science—the centimeter, gram and second—are arbitrary selections relative to those of nature, their practical usefulness is beyond question. It follows that any other properly integrated system of units is equally useful and in full accord with experiments. A search for the true units and constants of nature must be based on identity, simplicity and rational integration of constants with the unchangeable ratios of measurable dimensions, such as wavelengths, radii and distances.

The convergence of two or three factors on a common point, when a system of units is changed or for the purpose of defining a constant, means that they have identical values at that point. In nature it may also imply unity, if other values abstracted from such a system give rational results. The formula: $r = e^2/c^2 m_0$, defines the convergence of an electron's mass and its negative electrostatic charge to coincidence at its radius—the radius of its fundamental wave. It gives us three units: a unit of length equal to the electron's radius, a unit of mass equal to that of the electron, and a unit charge value. A time unit equal to the time it takes a light wave to move one electron radius is added.

Since a proton's positive charge is also unity at an electron's radius distance from its center, we can postulate an electron orbit at unit distance with unit attraction, circling the proton's center with the speed of light. Using this orbit as reference, we can define an electron's smallest true orbit in hydrogen by using the ratios: $-R, R^2, 2\pi R^3, -R^4$, as defined by Section 118. Since R in this orbit is identical to the electronic constant ϕ, the latter is used in the table below. Its value is 137.044809. (See Section 614.)

The fundamental units of physics.		Hydrogen electron's K orbit elements.		Abstracted orbital elements.	
Velocity of light	1.	Velocity in orbit	$1/\phi$	Bohr magneton	$\frac{1}{2}\phi$
Electron's mass	1.	Radius of orbit	ϕ^2	Rydberg's wl.	$4\pi\phi$
Electron's charge	1.	Orbital period	$2\pi\phi^3$	De Broglie wl.	$2\pi\phi$
Electron's radius	1.	Electrostatic force	$1/\phi^4$	Orbit frequ.	$1/2\pi\phi$

The system above is called "The Ultimate System" because its formulas include only two factors, the electronic constant and geometrical pi. It is defined in details in Sections 1020-22. In Section 1023, it is related to the international system of units through the ideal and new international systems.

When an electron's mass is resolved into the energy of a free (light) photon, its wavelength increases by $2\pi\phi$. Since the pulsation time of this energy is increased by that amount, its effectiveness is reduced in proportion. A reduction of the wavelength of a free photon to unit length anticipates an increase of energy to $2\pi\phi$, the same as the conversion increase of an electron's wavelength. It is the energy of Planck's quantum in the ultimate system of units.

216 The Algebraic Web.   (See Section 222 for web.)

The first principles of theoretical physics are that its fundamental causes are simple, that they are functionally interrelated, and that the basic factors of observed phenomena therefore converge on a common origin; an identity of values at unity, a one-to-two ratio, or a geometrical or functional difference. All these factors are present in the ultimate system of units defined in the preceding section.

Observations show that the interrelations of fundamental phenomena in physics are ideal states that can be defined by a web of mathematical factors whose values are abstracted from within the web or from pertinent geometrical ratios. The web is therefore a closed system of idealized constants and geometrical factors. The algebraic symbols within the web stand for specific values within a particular system of units which can be used in various formulas to obtain the numerical values of its other constants. The vital importance, however, of the algebraic web is that its symbols and formulas give proper results regardless of the changes made in a system's fundamental units of length, mass and time. By changing these units from the arbitrary values of the gaussian system to those of a more rational system, we can bring the constants of that system into a comprehensible accord with its unchangeable ratios.

Note that those formulas of the gaussian system of atomic units which fall within the web will give proper results when used with any other system. But the greater simplicity of a natural system anticipates a simplification of some formulas and the appearance of new ones. In defining the values of a web we are concerned with all proportions within it, and not only with those which are directly related. The web can therefore be outlined by maximizing the number of formulas defining each constant, and by reducing the algebra of each formula to the smallest number of factors possible.

217 Sequence of Atomic Units.

By taking the simplest proportions within the algebraic web, we can work out a sequence of values for any system of units which are in full accord with those obtained by conventional formulas. It gives us a quick and easy way to obtain the principal constants of a new system of units without violation of the numerical values which can be obtained by conventional formulas. It is a great time-saver when we decided to change a system's constants by changing its length, mass or time unit.

The conventional formulas, from which simple proportions and the sequence below were worked out, appear under various headings throughout this book. Note that the symbols m, c and $\dot{v}$ at the beginning of the sequence, represent the units of mass, time and length, respectively. m_o is the reciprocal of a gram mass in electrons, c is the distance a light wave moves in a unit of time, and $\dot{v}$ is the size of an electron's rest mass wavelength in a length unit. This sequence has been used to obtain the known values of the gaussian system as well as those of the ultimate system. (See Sections 407, 1005, 1020 and 1023.)

$$mc=m')\dot{v}=h)/2\pi=h)c/\phi=e^{\lambda})^{1/2}=e)/4\pi\tilde{v}=\mu.$$

m_u	Electron's mass	h	Planck's quantum, emu	ϕ	Electronic co.
c	Speed of light	2π	Circle in its radii	e	El's charge, esu
m'	El's m.energy, emu	$\hbar$	Pl. quantum to orbit	$\tilde{v}$	El's m₀ wavenumb
$\dot{v}$	El's m.wavelength c/ϕ		Hydrogen K orbit vel.	μ	Bohr magneton

218 Ratio Sequence to Tables of Constants.

The energy of an electrostatic field is defined in esu as the product of stationary electrons or protons; the energy of an electromagnetic field, in emu, is the product of moving charges. Maxwell defined the difference between their units as being equal to the speed of light, with one esu being equal to one emu times the speed of light. (See Section 213). Einstein defined the rest mass energy of a unit mass as being equal to the speed of light squared. Planck defined the energy of a unit wave in emu, and showed that energy and wavenumber values change in direct proportion. This has been confirmed by the energy-wavenumber relation of an electron's rest mass and by the known energy of observed radiation wavelengths.

The formulas, $E = mc^2$, and c = esu/emu, can be redefined as mc = emu, mc^2 = esu, emu $\times$ c = esu. Since h is Planck's energy in emu, we have the formula, esu $\times$ 1/hc = wavenumber. The sequence formula below can be used to enlarge the sequence of the preceding section into a square table as in sections 407 and 1024, and in columns A, B, C and U in the large Table of Physical Constants, page 152. (See also the location table in Section 1004.)

Mass $\times$ c = emu) $\times$ c = esu) $\times$ 1/hc = wavenumber.

219 Nature's Mathematics

Our mathematical descriptions of natural phenomena by algebra within a closed web of functional interrelations imply ideal proportions and a mathematics of nature. It is to be assumed that nature acts out the observed atomic constants and interrelations in the simplest possible manner through elementary proportions and geometrical ratios, with no irrational figures added as coefficients to make their results correspond to the values obtained by experiments.

It is to be assumed the observed atomic constants exist as one-to-one, one-to-two and one-to-four ratios, and as geometrical differences at their natural base. These simple ratios change to their experimental values through dimensional changes associated with changes of the units of action–length, mass and time. They appear in the form of roots and powers, and of such geometrical differences as radius to volume, radius to area or radius to circumference (Section 116.) The irrationality of the accepted values is caused by the arbitrary nature of the gaussian units of action, while our perception of its origin is inhibited by our use of powers of ten in figures and logarithms.

Nature's mathematics are assumed to be the simplest possible, acting through doublings and halvings, roots and powers whose values are best expressed by a logarithm of powers of two (Section 111).

220 Electronic and Waveratio Constants. ϕ = 137.044809 ratio

C = 861.077930 ratio

The waveratio C is the difference between a center-acting, spherical, stationary wave, and a plane-polarized wave moving with the speed of light, when both have the same energy. In Section 215 the former is defined as the wave-radius-energy of an electron's rest mass, and the latter as the wavelength of a free photon with the energy of an electron's rest mass. This is also the theoretical wavelength of an electron's charge-induced wave when moving in its smallest hydrogen orbit. However, the statistical distribution of this wave as it circles the electron's orbit with the velocity of light reduces its effective power by 2π, thus giving us the electronic constant ϕ as its electromagnetic field. Its Bohr magneton is this constant halved.

Another possible explanation of the electronic constant is based on the electromagnetic fields produced by moving charges. The attraction of an electron by a proton produces an acceleration and an electromagnetic field proportional to its velocity. With the conversion of its motion into the periodic orbit of a hydrogen atom, the electron's electromagnetic field has half of its energy converted into a Bohr magneton. Because the electron's electromagnetic field forces are abstracted from its electrostatic field, its charge potential relative to the proton decreases as its orbital velocity increases with a contraction of its orbit. Its smallest orbit in hydrogen appears as a natural balance between its decreasing electrostatic attraction and increasing centrifugal force. It appears when its velocity is less than light by ϕ and its electromagnetic field is equal to ϕ relative to the radiation unit $2\pi\phi$. Its Bohr magneton is ½ϕ (Sections 215 and 1023).

The waveratio C, being the difference between two measurable wavelengths, is an absolute constant—an unchangeable figure in all systems of units. Since ϕ is always less by 2π, it is also an absolute constant. Their values can be determined from numerous appearances in mathematical formulas. (Sections 215 and 813). In basic logarithms, C is equal to 9.75. The formula $C/2\pi = \phi$ is therefore $\log_2 9.75/2.651496 = 7.098504$.

221 Natural Units of Length and Time. ϕ = 1.0419584 centimeter

T = 3.475593 × 10^{-11} second

The unit of length was obtained by the idealization of the algebraic web in

Sections 216 and 222, and by a comparison of ideal proportion values with observed energies and wavelengths in the gaussian system of units. The unit of time is the time it takes a light wave to move one natural unit of length. Both units are used to define the atomic constants in the ideal system of units, Sections 1014-16 and 1023. The table in this last section also defines the new international system of units in which all wavelengths and constants are in natural length units. Its ideal proportions are converted into gaussian constants by using the length ratio above, thus idealizing the accepted international constants of physics. The validity of their theoretical proportions is indicated, first of all, by the algebra of the ultimate system, and secondly by the seven-figure values used throughout this book.

The natural unit of length can be proved by those formulas in which it is a factor; i.e., the conversion of constants from old to new international values in Section 1023, and its appearance in the last two formulas of Section 813 in conjunction with the electronic constant conversion to electron wavelengths. The natural length can also be proved by noting that its idealizations of the gaussian constants make it possible to use numerous decimals in their formulas within the algebraic web without the usual errors in the anticipated results. Its value in centimeters was obtained by averaging the difference between ideal and experimentally determined constants.

The natural unit of time is the time it takes a light wave to move one natural unit of length, or the pulsation time of a wave with that wavelength. This means that wavelengths and wavetimes can appear as interchangeable terms in ideal proportion formulas. Since Planck's quantum of energy is equal to one natural wavelength or waveperiod and changes its value in inverse proportion, its ratios may appear in formal reductions as their reciprocals. In dealing with fundamental causes we must be able to distinguish between actions across a distance and actions through time where their formal values are identical.

My theory of the evolution of matter, defined in Book Two, shows that the natural unit described in this section is fundamental. It defines an electron's radius unit by postulating a reduction of wavelength through an accumulation and concentration of its rest mass energy, and a functional extension of its forces into space. That the natural unit is slightly more than one centimeter is an irrelevant coincidence.

222 International Units Made Specific.

The simple natural proportions and identities of atomic constants defined in the preceding sections can be converted into gaussian constants through the sequence and length ratios of Sections 217, 218 and 221. The figures thus obtained are within the margins of probable errors of those accepted. We first define the constants and proportions of the algebraic web by changing the units of length, mass and time to those of nature, and prove the new figures acceptable by showing they are in ideal natural proportions. Reversing this process we reconvert their figures into accepted international constants.

It will be noticed that all figures in measurable lengths, such as wavelengths, radii, distances and the speed of light, can be converted from natural length units to centimeters through the ratio ϕ of the preceding section. The figures thus obtained can then be used to obtain the other constants of the gaussian system of units within the algebraic web. The figures below are from the ideal system of units, Section 1015. Note that the algebraic web anticipates a maximum number of formulas and a minimum number of factors in each formula.

Natural length in cm. 221	B_{H}	Hy. K orbit de Broglie wn. 610
Electronic constant. 614	δ_{H}^{*}	Radius of Hy. K orbit. 812
Waveratio constant. 613	$\tilde{v}$	Electron's mass wn. 709, 21U
Rydberg's wavenumber. 609, 17U	$\tilde{r}^{*}$	Electron's radius wn. 711

ealized proportions in natural length wavenumbers and ratio units.

Number	Log 10	Log 2	The algebraic reb.
1.04195840	0.017850	0.059298	
137.044809	2.136863	7.098504	$\phi = C/2\pi = \sqrt{\tilde{v}/2R} = \sqrt{r/\delta}$
861.077930	2.935043	9.75	$C_{,} = 2\pi\phi = r/\tilde{v} = \frac{1}{2}\delta/R$
114341.722	5.058205	16.802992	$R_{H} = \frac{1}{2}\tilde{v}/\phi^{4} = r/4\pi\phi^{3}$ $B/2\phi = (\frac{1}{2}\pi)^{4}\phi^{4}$
3.133987×10^{7}	7.496097	24.901496	$B_{H} = \tilde{v}/\phi = r/C\phi = r/2\pi\phi^{4} = 2(\frac{1}{2}\pi)^{4}\phi^{3}$
1.969142×10^{8}	8.294277	27.552992	$\delta_{H} = 2\pi B = 2CR = r/\phi^{4}$
4.294967×10^{9}	9.632960	32.00	$\tilde{v} = r/C = 2R\phi^{4} = B\phi = \frac{1}{2}(2\phi)^{4}R$
3.698301×10^{12}	12.568003	41.75	$\tilde{r} = \tilde{v}C = 2\pi\phi\tilde{v} = C\phi B = 4\pi R\phi^{3}$

Radius is reciprocal of wavenumber used.

tural length units converted to centimeter wave numbers and lengths.

Natural wns.	L/L ratios	Cm. wavenumbers	Cm. wavelengths	
114341.722	$\div 1.0419584$	$= 109737.317$	911.2670×10^{-8}	cm.
3.133987×10^{7}	$\div 1.0419584$	$= 3.007786 \times 10^{7}$	3.324705×10^{-8}	"
1.969142×10^{8}	$\div 1.0419584$	$= 1.889847 \times 10^{8}$	0.529143×10^{-10}	"
4.294967×10^{9}	$\div 1.0419584$	$= 4.122014 \times 10^{9}$	2.425998×10^{-10}	"
3.698301×10^{12}	$\div 1.0419584$	$= 3.549375 \times 10^{12}$	2.817397×10^{-13}	"

223 Active and Inactive Mass Units.

The inert masses we see all about us are composed of atoms and molecules in constant motion. Atoms are composed of electrons, protons and neutrons whose motions and action potentials produce their observed properties. But we cannot see these motions because our tools are comparatively crude. We perceive matter as inert because relatively large areas and numerous periods average zero. If matter is composed of waves, it is evident that the stationary waves of electrons and protons appear to be those of inert masses when our probes treat them as statistical means in space and time, and that they are intensely active when the length and time units used are smaller than the wavelengths and pulse times of the waves they define.

Assuming that matter acts upon space with a fourth-dimensional deformation which resolves into a static equality of opposite forces, their instantaneous equal action potentials may take the form of an electrostatic field, while the absence of these potentials appears as a timeless configuration space with gravity as a marginal effect.

224 Static and Dynamic States of Matter.

The static and dynamic states observed in natural phenomena are defined by mathematics as scalars and vectors, respectively (Section 121). Because the rest masses of fundamental particles does not appear to change with time, they are timelsss (scalar) factors in mathematics; while their electrostatic charges, being directed forces acting continuously across a distance, are time-related vectors. Since it takes time for information regarding the force and location of a charge center to be transmitted through space to another center, and to be acted upon by it with an acceleration and/or an absorption or release of energy, time is a factor in all transmissions of energy between the centers of interacting masses and between a mass and its field. It prevents the instantaneous resolutions of matter by giving it time to adjust to local changes.

The deformation of space by matter appears as static (fourth-dimension) stresses, functionally irreducible in neutral matter and potentially reducible in electrostatic charges. Positive and negative charges are the two different wave shapes possible for energy-related forces, defined by the action potentials of reducible static stresses. The tendency of opposite charges to unite and resolve into a neutral state appears as an attraction because an approach produces a mutual reduction of charge-induced stresses. Similar charges repel because their local overlapping stresses are reduced by dispersal. My theory of the nature of electrostatic charges appears in Book Two.

A functional interaction between contained neutral matter and a containing deformation of local space by matter produces a fourth-dimension effect observed as a tendency of separate masses to gravitate toward each other. Its force is proportional to mass and inversely proportional to the square of the distance between masses. Gravity is a timeless response to the local deformation of space by other masses because there is no exchange of energy or reduction of mass-related stresses by an approach; each mass simply reacts to the shape of space in its immediate vicinity.

Electrostatic forces are immensely more powerful than those of gravity because they are implemented by the forces residing within matter, while gravitation is a marginal effect which does not change their powers.

225 Experimental Units of Length.   (For meter: see Section 202)

The wide range of electromagnetic waves, from kilometer-long radio waves through light waves to cosmic rays, makes it desirable to use different units of length for their measurements. Radio waves are usually in meters, while centimeters are used for light waves. The angstrom is also used for that purpose and for the measurements of atomic radii. The length of a centimeter makes it a practical tool for the counting of spectrum lines. Because the radii of most atoms are close to one angstrom, it is often used to define their sizes.

The natural unit of length will, some time in the future, become a useful base of reference. Since it is close to one centimeter, its usefulness will be increased by calling it the "new centimeter," or by adding some other descriptive term or notation to the terms used to describe the metric units of length, thus indicating their conversion to new values.

The wavelengths of x rays and cosmic rays are too short to be diffracted by a grating spectroscope. To obtain their wavelengths the physicists makes use of the equal spacing of molecules in a crystal solid, giving us the xu unit in the table below.

m	Meter	100 centimeters	mu	Millimicron	10^{-7} cm.
nu	Natural unit	1.0419584 cm.	a	Angstrom	10^{-8} cm.
u	Micron	10^{-4} cm.	xu	X unit	10^{-11} cm.
r	Electron's half radius wavelength			$1.4086985 \times 10^{-13}$ cm.	

That x (xu) unit of length is an approximation. It is defined in practice by taking the grating space of the molecules in a crystal of NaCl at 18 degrees centigrade as 2814 x units. Recent determinations of this unit show it to be less than 10^{-11} centimeter by 1.00206. The electron radius unit is used to determine the size of atomic nucleas, as defined in Section 824. Its wavelength, being twice that figure, is the unit of length of the ultimate system in Sections 1020-24.

The spectrum of radiating cadmium contains a narrow red line whose wavelength can be measured with great accuracy. In 1907 the International Union for Solar Research defined the angstrom in terms of this wave. It is to be measured in dry air at 15 degrees centigrade temperature, an atmospheric pressure of 760 millimeters, and a gravitational acceleration of 980.67 centimeters per second. Its wavelength was defined as 6438.4696 angstroms. The corresponding centimeter wavenumber is 15531.641 waves.

Wavelengths above 2000 angstroms are usually measured in the air; those below in a vacuum. Because electromagnetic waves move faster through a vacuum, the wavelengths in the visible range of the spectrum are shorter by about one part in 3610 when measured in the air. The ratio difference of 1.000277 is proportional to the refractive index of the air and vary with wavelength. When the red cadmium line is measured in a vacuum its wavelength is therefore:

In the air.   Ratio.   In a vacuum.

6438.4696 X 1.000277 = 6440.25 angstroms.

Chapter 3

GRAVITATION   SATELLITES

The experimental value of the gravity constant is defined and compared with its formal theoretical value; with the latter defined for the first time in history. The masses of the earth and sun are obtained from the force of gravity on the earth's surface, the orbital periods of satellites, and from the motions of the planets. A ten-thousand kilometer reference orbit is defined for the earth and a million kilometer orbit for the sun. A simple sequence of powers relates their four orbital elements to the corresponding figures for satellites and planets. Lofting and escape velocities and energies are defined.

301 The Gravity Constant.   Theoretical g = 6.6665607×10^{-8} dyne
Used g = 6.67×10^{-8} dyne

The gravity constant is the gravitational attraction, in dynes, between two one-gram masses one centimeter apart. The figure is so small that even the most exacting experiments leave a large marginal error beyond four significant digits. The value in general use was obtained at The United States Bureau of Standards by noting the deflection of a small ball when a heavy ball is brought near. It is slightly larger than the theoretical value.

Although the formulas defining gravitational and electrostatic attractions are the same because their forces decrease as the inverse square of the distance, in both cases, there is a significant difference in the nature of those forces. While there are two kinds of electrostatic forces which attract and repel according to their relative signs and combine to produce a neutral state, there is only one kind of gravitational force, and that force is always an attraction between masses proportional to their mass values. Furthermore, the gravitational attraction of a mass cannot be deflected or reduced by any known form of interception.

Nothing this difference between electrostatic and gravitational forces, Einstein defined gravity as a tendency of separate masses to merge, because each mass produces a deformation of space, relative to which another mass can remain stationary only by gravitational acceleration toward it. His theory of deformation, defining a fourth dimension of space, is based on Riemannian non-Euclidean geometry. This geometry can be described by postulating a mass concentrated at the center of a sphere, with the curved surface of this sphere defining the deformation of space at that distance.

Even though I accept the deformation of space as defined by Einstein, my belief that physical phenomena must be described in physical terms led to this conclusion: Matter is composed of waves contained by a contraction of the ether, with gravity a tendency to reduce local deformations of the ether's natural dynamic progression by matter. See Book Two for details.

Newton's law of universal gravitation states: "The attraction between any two bodies is directly proportional to the product of their masses, and inversely proportional to the square of the distance between their centers." The gravitational attraction between any two masses can be determined by this formula:

$$F = g \frac{mm^1}{d^2}$$

m Mass in grams   g Gravity constant
d Distance in cm.   F Force in dynes

302 Gravity Constant by Formula.

A theoretical definition of the gravity constant must be based on the quantized energy of its mass or its electrostatic ratio relations. In both cases, formal reductions to the gravity constant are complicated by the artificial nature of the length, mass and time units now used to define its value. An obvious condition is that the formula cannot include factors obtained by experiment, and that it must be valid for all systems of units.

Let us begin our analysis by obtaining the gravity constants for the ideal and ultimate systems (Section 1023) from its experimental gaussian value, and take note of its margin of probable error. The changes of the gravity constant and the e/g (electrostatic/gravity) ratio with a change of the units of length, mass and time, are defined in Section 1012. Note that the e/g ratio does not change with a change of the length and mass units, and that it changes in direct proportion to changes of the time unit. The e/g ratio for the ideal system is, therefore, less than its gaussian value by the speed of light in natural length units, and its value for the ultimate system is less than this by the difference in their time units. Because its electrostatic charge unit is unity, the gravity constant for the ultimate system is the reciprocal of its e/g ratio. Both values can, therefore, be obtained from the gaussian constants to a first approximation. Its gravity constant can also be obtained by direct conversion, as shown by Section 1023.

Because electrostatic charges are time-related directional forces and gravitation is the time-less statistical effect of neutral states, the former is defined by relating it to an electron's radius wavelength and the latter to the square root of its rest mass energy at the distance of one natural unit of length. With this difference in mind, the theoretical gravity constant of the ultimate system of units is: $g = (\dot{v})^2 / 2 \sqrt[4]{4/\pi}$, with $\dot{v}$ being the rest mass wavelength of an electron in one natural unit of length.

$$g = \frac{(\dot{v}_o)^2}{2\sqrt[4]{4/\pi}} \qquad \frac{(2.32830643 \times 10^{10})^2}{2 \times \sqrt[4]{4/3.14159265}} = 2.5516596\dot{8} \times 10^{-20} \text{dyne, rmt}$$

Reciprocal e/g ratio of system: 3.919018×10^{19} gravity units.

The divisor used to obtain the ultimate system's gravity constant may appear as an arbitrary selection to obtain the right result. However, its factors are defined in Book Two, and, furthermore, its corresponding e/g ratio (R) gives us the e/g ratio for the gaussian system by this simple conversion: $e/g = RLc$, when L is the difference in time between the ideal and ultimate systems and c is the speed of light in natural length units, and, $e/g = RLc^1/\phi$, when it is in centimeters. The gravity constant of the gaussian system is obtained from that of the ultimate system by this formula: $g = gc\phi^2/mL^2$, and that for the new international system is: $g^1 = gc/mL^2$, when the speed of light is in the length units of the respective system.

c	Speed of light in nl. 221, 411	ϕ	Conversion from cm. to nl. 221
c'	Speed of light in cm. 210, 34B	R	e/g ratio of ultimate sy. 1020
e	Electrostatic charge unit.	L	nl. time in el. radius time. 102
g	Gravity co. of ultimate s. 1020	m	Electron's mass in grams. 708, 2
g'	Gravity co. of gaussian s. 301	$\dot{v}$	Electron's mass wavelength. 709

$$g' = \frac{gc\phi^2}{mL^2} \qquad \frac{2.5516597 \times 10^{20} \times 2.997930 \times 10^{10} \times (1.0419584)^2}{9.108325 \times 10^{23} \times (3.69830155 \times 10^{12})^2} = 6.666561 \times 10^{8}$$

$$e/g = \frac{RLc'}{\phi} \qquad \frac{3.919018 \times 10^{19} \times 3.6983015 \times 10^{12} \times 2.997930 \times 10^{10}}{1.0419584} = 4.170140 \times 10^{4}$$

303 Mass with Dyne-Cm. Gravity.

$M = 1.5000238 \times 10^7$ gram
$MM = (3873.0141)^2$ gram

The force of gravity between two bodies is equal to their masses multiplied times the gravity constant, divided by the distance between their centers squared: $F = gMM/r^2$. A theoretical sphere one centimeter in radius must, therefore, have a mass equal to the reciprocal of the gravity constant to produce a force of one dyne upon a gram mass on its surface. But two equal masses, one centimeter apart, produce an attraction of one dyne when each mass is equal to the square root of the reciprocal of the gravity constant in dynes. When the distance between their centers is increased from one to ten centimeters, the gravitational attraction between them decreases to a one-hundred part of a dyne, because gravity decreases as the inverse square of the distance.

It is evident that different parts of a mass produce a difference of attraction for another mass according to their different distances and densities. Newton proved, however, that the force of attraction on the surface of a homogenous sphere is the same as if all of its mass was located at its center. The earth's mass is not completely homogenous or spherical, but deviations of gravity on its surface due to these causes are small (see Sections 304 and 306).

304 Mass Units. Earth and Sun.

$38 A \oplus = 5.979298 \times 10^{27}$ grams
$40 A \ominus = 1.986981 \times 10^{33}$ grams

An accurate determination of the sun's mass is obtained from the orbital motions of the six inner planets. The earth's mass can be obtained from various sources; from its surface gravity, from the orbital motions of artificial satellites, from the moon's monthly period, and from the perturbations of the earth's orbit by the sun and planets. The figures below are uncompensated values from the Nautical Almanac. The sun's mass is in earth masses. The earth's mass is equal to 81.53 moons. Note that we are dealing with experimental figures with marginal errors, and that my figures may be dated by more recent experiments.

Earth's mass in grams from	Sun/Earth ratio	$\odot/\oplus + \mathbb{C}$ ratio
Satellites 5.979298 × 10²⁷	332310.03 ratio	328283.5 ratio
Moon's orbit 5.966174 × 10²⁷	333205.09 ratio	329167.6 ratio

Small differences of gravity on the earth's surface, due to rotation, oblatedness and density differences in its crust, cause a mass value from this source to have a large margin of probable error. The satellite figure was obtained from a supplement to the Nautical Almanac published in England in 1960. It defines the period of an earth satellite as 84.49032 minutes for an orbit radius of 6378.27 kilometers. It was checked against Kulikow's formula:

$$F = \sqrt{gm} \quad \sqrt{6.666561 \times 10^{-8} \times 5.979298 \times 10^{27}} = 1.996530 \times 10^{10} \text{ cgs.}$$

The figures for the moon's mass and its mass ratio are from the Nautical Almanac. Discrepancies between satellite and moon values are due to perturbations of the moon's orbit by the sun, as defined in Section 322. The earth's mass below is from artificial satellites, and that of the sun from the periods and distances of the planets. The symbols of the formula are: m Earth's mass in grams; r Its radius in centimeters; G Its surface gravity in dynes, and its acceleration in second per second; g The gravity constant.

$$\frac{Gr^2}{g} \qquad \frac{979.81983 \times (6.37827 \times 10^8)^2}{6.666561 \times 10^{-8}} = 5.979298 \times 10^{27} \text{ grams}$$

$$\text{Sun's mass} = \frac{27305.7017 \times (6.9650 \times 10^{10})^2}{6.666561 \times 10^{-8}} = 1.987959 \times 10^{33} \text{ grams}$$

305 Earth's Gravity Constant.   26C   G = 980.665 dynes per gram.

The constant above is the force of attraction by the earth's mass on each gram of matter on its surface at 45 degrees latitude at sea level, as adopted by the International Committee on Weights and Measures in 1901.

The earth's radius is 6356.909 kilometers (3949.99 miles) at its poles, and 6378.388 km. (3963.34 miles) at its equator. Its mean radius is 6.37124×10^8 cm. (3958.90 miles). When the earth's mass is multiplied by the gravity constant and divided by its mean radius squared, we obtain its surface gravity to a fair approximation. Note that the centrifugal force of its rotation causes a flattening of its poles and a slight reduction of gravity.

m	Earth's mass in grams. 38A	r	Earth's radius in centimeters.
G or F	Gravity in dynes. 207	g	The gravity constant. 302, 26K

$$F = \frac{gm}{r^2} \qquad \frac{6.666561 \times 10^{-8} \times 5.979298 \times 10^{27}}{(6.371240 \times 10^8)^2} = 981.983 \text{ dynes per gram.}$$

306 Earth's Rotation Effects.

The earth's rotation causes its shape to flatten at the poles and expand at the equator. Its causes a deviation by one part in 297 from sphericity, called the earth's oblatedness. Another effect is a reduction of the force of gravity on the equator by 3.392 dynes. Adding this to its observed force of 978.039 dynes, it is evident that its true force on an object in space is 981.431 dynes at the equator. Due to the centrifugal force of rotation and the consequent deformation of shape, the force of gravity is greatest at the poles and least at the equator, as shown by this table:

	Lat.	Cm./sec.	Foot/sec.
Equator	0°	978.039	32.0878
	30	979.329	32.1302
	45	980.621	32.1725
	60	981.918	32.2151
Poles	90	983.217	32.2577

The centrifugal effect of the earth's rotation on its equator is obtained by two formulas. Its radius is converted into a circumference which is divided by the number of seconds in one sidereal day for its orbital velocity. This velocity is squared and divided by the earth's radius for the centrifugal force at its equator in dynes. There is 86164.091 seconds in one sideral day.

r   Earth's radius at the equator.   t   Sidereal seconds in one day.
v   Rotation velocity of the equator.   m   Gram mass unit.
F   Centrifugal force on the equator. π Circumference in diameters.

$$v = \frac{2\pi r}{t} \qquad \frac{6.28318531 \times 6.378388 \times 10^{8}}{86164.091} = 46511.944 \text{ cm. per second}$$

$$F = \frac{mv^2}{r} \qquad \frac{1 \times (46511.944)^2}{6.378388 \times 10^{8}} = 3.392 \text{ dynes force on the equator}$$

307 Specific Gravity.   (Density of matter.)   Unit: Water.

The density of a substance is defined in terms of its weight per unit volume, with one cubic centimeter taken as unity. Since one cubic centimeter or pure water weighs one gram by definition, it is also the unit of density (See Section 204). The weight of one cubic centimeter of any substance is therefore also its specific gravity; the density of its mass in comparison with that of water.

Archimedes discovered the principle that a solid suspended in water lose weight in proportion to the weight of the volume of water it displaces. Its specific gravity is therefore its true weight divided by its loss of weight in water. It follows that the total weight of a floating mass is equal to that of the water it displaces.

Examples of specific gravities: aluminum, 2.7; gold, 19.3; platinum, 21.4. Woods range from cork, 0.2, to ebony, 1.3. Since one liter of air—1000 cubic centimeters—weighs 1.29 grams, its specific gravity is, therefore, 0.00129.

The earth's center is composed of heavy elements, probably nickel-iron with a specific gravity of about 10.7. About 3500 km. from its center, the density is 9.0, and decreases to 3.4, 4800 km. from the center and 1600 km. below the surface. On the surface the seas are underlaid by basalt with a mean density of about 3.0, and the continents are blocks of granite, from 10 to 30 kilometers thick, with a density of about 2.7, covered by sediments and sedimentary rocks. They float on basalt and gabbro.

308 Gram-Centimeter.   (A unit of work.) $W = 980.665$ ergs gram-cm.

   Kilogram-Meter. $W = 9.80665 \times 10^7$ ergs kg-m.

The energy expended in raising a gram mass one centimeter against gravity at the earth's surface. Its value is the same as that accepted for the earth's gravity constant, Section 305. Since this unit is too small for ordinary use, the kilogram-meter is a more practical unit. It is equal to 9.80665 joules; 7.234 foot-pounds, and 2.724×10^{-6} kilowatt-hour. (See Sections 209, 508, 26C, 29K and 29J.)

309 Gram Weight. Falling Bodies. $F = 980.665$ dynes

The standard pressure exerted by a gram mass resting on the earth's surface. Actual pressure varies slightly according to location, as defined by Section 306. Since a dyne, by definition (Section 207), acclerates a gram mass at the rate of one centimeter per second, it follows that a gravitational acceleration thrust of 980.665 dynes increases its velocity at the rate of 980.665 centimeters per second per second. This rate is the same for any mass because the inertia of a mass, its mass in grams, changes value at exactly the same rate as its gravitational force in dynes.

Starting from zero, a free-falling body will be moving at the rate of 980.665 centimeters per second after one second, but it will have fallen only one half of that distance, or 490.3325 cm. Its velocity at any subsequent time is the force of gravity multiplied by time. The distance it has fallen is equal to one half of the accelerating force multiplied by time squared. For a gram mass its velocity in centimeters is also its momentum in dynes. The energy of its motion is 1/2 of its mass times velocity squared.

a Acceleration	d Distance in cm	V Terminal velocity	
E Energy in ergs	m Mass in grams	v Average velocity	
M Momentum in dynes	t Time in seconds	W Weight in grams	

$d = vt = \tfrac{1}{2}VT = \tfrac{1}{2}at^2$ $V = at = 2v$ $v = \tfrac{1}{2}V = \tfrac{1}{2}at$ $M = mv$ $E = \tfrac{1}{2}mv^2$

Elements of a free-falling gram mass.

Time in seconds	Distance in centimeters	Mass: 1 gram	Speed in cm. (Also dynes)	Energy in ergs
1	490.3325	$1 \times 1/2 \times$ ($980.665)^2$ =	4.808519×10^5
2	1961.3300	" "	(1961.330)	1.923408×10^6
3	4412.9925	" "	(2941.995)	4.327667×10^6
4	7845.3200	" "	(3922.660)	7.693631×10^6
5	12258.3125	" "	(4903.325)	1.202130×10^7

310 Pendulum Period.

The period of a pendulum bob is independent of its weight and the length of its stroke, as long as the stroke does not exceed about 16 degrees. It is proportional to the square root of the bob's length and inversely proportional to the square root of gravitational acceleration. Calibrated pendulums are, therefore, used to determine the force of gravity at different localities. The figures below give the length of a pendulum with a period of one second. Its symbols are: G Earth's gravity; L Length of pendulum; t Time in seconds; π Pi.

$$t = 2\pi\sqrt{L/G} \qquad L = \frac{t^2 G}{4\pi^2} \qquad \frac{(1)^2 \times 930.665}{4 \times (3.14159265)^2} = 24.840535 \text{ centimeters}$$

311 Ballistics to Orbits.

The ballistic curve followed by a thrown ball is composed of a vertical and horizontal motion. Its vertical motion decelerates as it recedes and then reverses direction and accelerates to its original speed under the influence of gravity. It determines the time of flight and, therefore, the distance its uniform horizontal motion can carry the ball during that time. The motion combines two different phenomena.

Gravitational acceleration can be idealized by postulating a center of attraction so far away that its lines of force do not appear to converge. It is evident, however, that a missile following a ballistic curve which is a substantial fraction of the earth's circumference does not conform to this ideal state, because its gravitational attraction changes direction with surface curvature. Its tendency to move in a straight line is an inertial force proportional to the rate at which the changes of direction occur, acting in opposition to gravitational acceleration as a reduction of its effective power. It increases flight time, while the missile's horizontal speed (its momentum) remains unchanged.

When the horizontal velocity of a missile is so great that its opposition to gravitational acceleration, deflecting it into a curve, is equal to the rate at which the force of gravity changes direction, it will remain at the same distance from the center of attraction and, thus, move in a circular periodic orbit. Although the missile is deflected by gravity, it is not accelerated by it, since its speed and distance from the attracting center do not change. A realistic termonology anticipates our use of the word "acceleration" only where a change of speed actually occurs.

312 The Solar System.

The solar system consists of a central sun circled by nine planets, numerous comets and asteroids and countless meteors. In the table below the first column gives the planetary masses in terms of how many such masses it takes to equal that of the sun. The next column shows their distances from the sun in astronomical units, followed by their orbital periods in years, the inclinations of their orbits to that of the earth (the ecliptic), and the eccentricities of their orbits. Note that a planet's return to the same star is called its sidereal period, and its return to the same longitude as the earth (or the sun as seen from the earth) is its synodic period. The planetary orbits are ellipses of small eccentricity, moving on nearly the same plane in the same direction.

Symbol P	Planet	Mass ratio $R = \odot/P$	Orbit's radius $r = P/\oplus$	Sidereal period. Years	Synodic period. Years	Orbit's inclination	Orbit's eccentricity
☿	Mercury	6000000	0.387	0.241	0.317	7.003	0.206
♀	Venus	408000	0.723	0.615	1.599	3.393	0.007
⊕	Earth	329392	1.000	1.000	- - -	- - -	0.017
♂	Mars	3093500	1.524	1.881	2.135	1.850	0.093
♃	Jupiter	1047.35	5.203	11.862	1.092	1.308	0.048
♄	Saturn	3501.6	9.539	29.458	1.035	2.492	0.056
♅	Uranus	22869.	19.182	84.013	1.012	0.773	0.047
♆	Neptune	19700.	30.058	164.794	1.006	1.778	0.009
♇	Pluto	360000.	39.518	248.430	1.004	17.100	0.249

The sun contains about 99.86 per cent of the system's mass, and the planets contain most of its moment of momentum—the energy it would take to loft them to their orbits from the sun. The sun is a rotating mass of incandescent gases with a sidereal period of about 25.3 days at its equator and 27.3 days at its poles. Its equator is inclined 7.25 degrees to the plane of the earth's orbit and it moves in the same direction as the planets.

313 Longitudes, Latitudes and Periods.

A planet's location among the stars is defined by longitude, latitude and time. Its longitude is measured eastward along a circle of 360 degrees starting at the vernal equinox. Its latitude is measured from the plane of the earth's orbit in degrees of inclination. Time is in days, hours, minutes and seconds, with each day beginning when zero longitude on earth is opposite the sun. It is called Greenwich civil time. Tables of planetary motions appear in the nautical almanacs.

The vernal equinox is the point where the sun crosses the earth's equator from south to north about March 21 of each year. Half a year later it crosses again from north to south, about September 23. Summer and winter solstices are the times when the sun is farthest north and south, in June and December, respectively.

The earth rotates in the same direction as its orbital motion. Its equator is inclined to the plane of its orbit (the obliquity of the ecliptic) by 23.452294 degrees. The sun, therefore, moves that far north and south during each year. The moon circles the earth in the same direction as their rotations, with the moon's rotation equal to its orbital period. It takes it 27.32166089 days to circle the earth relative to the stars (one sidereal month), and 29.5305881 days relative to the sun (one synodical month). The difference is due to the earth's motion in its orbit. The moon's orbit is inclined 5.14539864 degrees to the ecliptic.

Forces are constantly acting on the earth's equator to draw it onto the plane of the ecliptic, and the earth reacts with a slow precession of its plane of rotation. This causes the longitudes of the stars on the ecliptic to increase by 50.2486 seconds of an arc (general precession) each year. One tropical (ordinary) year from equinox to equinox equals 365.242199 days; a sidereal year is 365.256360 days. There is also a slow motion of the earth's eccentric orbit which makes its period from perihelion to perihelion equal to 365.25941 days. This period is called an anomalistic year.

The earth's surface is divided up into longitudes and latitudes. Its zero longitude passes through Greenwich Observatory in England from pole to pole. It is counted east and west to 180 degrees opposite. There is a change of one day when ships cross this last longitude, called the international date line. Latitudes are zero on the equator, increasing to 90 degrees at the poles.

Because the hour hand of a 24-hour clock can be set to show the location of the earth's zero longitude relative to the sun and stars, the earth's longitudes have been divided into 24 hours. The nautical almanacs also give the locations of the stars, sun, moon and planets in hours of right ascension, relative to the vernal equinox, and latitudes relative to the earth's equator. Longitudes related to the earth's center are called geocentric, and those which uses the sun's center for reference are called helicentric.

314 Laws of Planetary Motions. Kepler.

In 1619 Kepler made public the three basic laws of planetary motions. 1. The orbit of each planet is an ellipse with the sun at one focus. 2. A line drawn from the sun to a planet sweeps out equal areas in equal intervals of time. 3. The ratio of any two planetary periods squared is equal to the ratio of the radii of their means orbits cubed. Therefore: $(p/p^1)^2 = (r/r^1)^3$.

According to law one, a planet's orbital motion is accompanied by a periodic approach and recession. Law two means that its orbital velocity increases as it approaches the sun, attaining a maximum when nearest the sun and a minimum when farthest away. Newton showed that these changes of speed are in accord with the law of gravity. Law three compares the orbital elements of two planets, because one of the factors to be equated is in time and the other in length units.

In the example below, I use the orbital elements of Mercury and the earth. In the last sequence I extend the ratios defined by Kepler to include their relative orbital velocities and gravitational forces, because velocity is the square root of their orbital radius ratio and the gravity ratio is that ratio squared. The four ratios can be defined by the sequence: $V = -R$, $r = R^2$ $p = R^3$ $G = -R^4$.

Earth's mean orbit radius divided by Mercury's, in kilometers.
$⊕/☿ = R^2)^3 = R^6$. $149.504 \times 10^6 \div 57.8726 \times 10^6 = 2.583333)^3 = \underline{17.24}$

Earth's orbital period divided by Mercury's, in days.
$⊕/☿ = R^3)^2 = R^6$. $365.25636 \div 87.9685 = 4.152127)^2 = \underline{17.24016}$

Idealized ratios of Earth-Mercury orbital elements.

Velocity ☿/⊕	Radius ⊕/☿	Period ⊕/☿	Gravity ☿/⊕
$R' = 1.607275$	$R^2 = 2.583333$	$R^3 = 4.152127$	$R^4 = 6.673610$

315 Laws of Motion. Newton.

In 1686 Newton proved that gravity is the force that causes the planets to move in periodic orbits around the sun. His law of gravity appears in Section 301. He defined the interaction between the inertia of a mass and a force acting upon it by three laws of motion: 1. Every body continues in its state of rest or of uniform motion in a straight line, except insofar as it is compelled by forces to change that state. 2. Change of motion is proportional to the force and takes place in the direction of the straight line in which the force acts. 3. To every action there is always an equal and contrary reaction; or, the mutual actions of any two bodies are always equal and oppositely directed along the same straight line.

He noted that when the third law is applied to two orbiting masses, such as a planet and the sun, they will circle a common center of inertia whose location is proportional to their relative masses and the distance between them. This means that the center of a planet's orbit is displaced slightly toward the planet, relative to the sun's center. The radius of its orbit is less than that of an infinitesimal particle circling the sun at the same distance from its center, and its period is less in proportion.

For an ideal example we will postulate two suns with equal masses circling a common center of inertia. The radius of their orbit is obviously only one half of the distance between their centers. The orbit of a relatively infinitesimal mass, such as an artificial satellite, circling one of the suns, would be twice as long at the same distance, and its orbital period would be greater in proportion. The formula is $p = 4\pi^2 r^3 /g(m+m)$ for displaced centers.

It is evident that Kepler's third law is valid only for orbiting bodies whose masses are too small in comparison with their primary to produce observable deviations from ideal proportions. In Section 327 I reduce the earth's period to less than that of an ideal orbit by 48 seconds, while Jupiter's period is reduced by two days.

316 Idealized Orbital Elements.

In Section 314 I extended Kepler's third law of relative orbital motions for distances and periods to their corresponding velocity and gravity ratios. When the ideal orbital elements of one planet are known and its velocity ratio to another planet has been obtained, the squaring, cubing and fourth power of that ratio give us their ideal distance, period and gravity ratios respectively. This relationship is true for attractions of all kinds, including the electrostatic attractions of electrons circling an atom's nucleus. It will be proved by numerous examples in the subsequent sections of this chapter. The four elements of an orbit can be obtained by various formulas from Kepler's third law, but I have never seen the sequence of ratios described as a logical extension of that law.

When the elements of a periodic orbit are worked out from observational data, the factor 2π is included in the formula defining its period. The sequence is then: $V = 1/R$, $r = R^2$ $p = 2\pi R^3$, $G = 1/R^4$. (See the original sequence in Section 215, and the reduction to a satellite's period in 318.) After the period has been defined for a reference orbit, its presence is implied for periods obtained by using this sequence: $V = 1/R$, $r = R^2$, $p = R^3$, $G = 1/R^4$.

For a simple example we will postulate a known orbit and a reduction to a larger orbit whose base ratio is two. The orbital elements of a satellite in that orbit are: Velocity $1/2$, radius 4, period 8, and gravity $1/16$th.

317 Earth and Sun Gravities on Km. Spheres. $\oplus$ = 3.986135 X 10^{10} dynes

$\odot$ = 1.324633 X 10^{16} dynes

The force of gravity one kilometer from the earth's center by assuming all of its mass is compacted within a sphere with that radius, and the corresponding attraction by the sun within such a sphere. It will be noticed that the actual attraction at that distance is near zero within their true masses. It is a theoretical postulate which makes it easier to obtain the gravitational force at any distance from their centers by dividing the constants above by distance squared.

The force of gravity on a centimeter sphere is obtained by mutiplying its mass in grams by the gravity constant, as shown below. Because one kilometer is equal to 10^5 centimeters, their forces in dynes are divided by this figure squared (10^{10}) for the corresponding attractions at one kilometer. (See Sections 302 and 304.) A 10^4 km. earth orbit reduces the attraction below by $(10^9)^2 = 10^{18}$, and a 10^6 km. solar orbit reduces its figure below by $(10^{11})^2 = 10^{22}$.

$F = gm$ = Force on a centimeter radius sphere.

Earth's constant: $6.666561 \times 10^{-8} \times 5.979298 \times 10^{27} = 3.986135 \times 10^{20}$ dynes

Solar constant: $6.666561 \times 10^{-8} \times 1.987959 \times 10^{33} = 1.324633 \times 10^{26}$ "

318 Earth Orbits. 10,000 Km. and Surface.

The two orbits below can be used to determine the four orbital elements of all earth satellites for which one element is known. The first orbit is physically impossible, since it postulates a radius equal to the earth's radius at the equator. Its force of gravity is that determined by experiments, and its other elements are obtained by formal reductions.

It is obviously desirable to postulate a reference orbit with a simple unchageable radius. At 10,000 kilometers the force of gravity is equal to the gravity constant at one kilometer divided by distance squared. Note that $(10000)^2 = 10^8$. Its velocity and period can be obtained by the formulas which follow the table, or they can be obtained by using the ratio sequence of the table below.

F	Centrifugal force in dynes.	m	Earth's mass in grams. 304, 38A
g	Gravity constant. 302, 34A	p	Orbital period in seconds.
G'	Ea. gravity at one km. 317	r	Orbit's radius in km. Ea. 305
G	Ea. gravity at orbit. 305	R	Ratios of orbit elements.
H	Height above the surface.	V	Orbital velocity in km. sec.

Ratio, symbol and term.	Earth radius orb.	Ratios of orbits.	Elements of idealized radius orbit.	Orbit in miles.
₁′ V Velocity	7.9054128	÷1.2521275 =	6.3135846 km. second	3.92308
₁ᵇ r Radius	6378.2700	×1.5678233 =	10000. kilometers	6213.72
H Height above earth's surface			3621.730 kilometers	2250.44
₁³ p Period	5069.4193	×1.9631146 =	9951.8510 seconds = $2^h45^m51.851^s$	
"	84.490322		165.86418 minutes = 0.115183 day	
₁ᵛ G Gravity	979.81980	÷2.4580697 =	398.61350 dynes force.	

The earth's gravity-radius relations are based on its theoretical gravity at one centimeter. The figure used in this book appears in Section 317 as $gm = 3.986135 \times 10^{20}$. It was obtained from a supplement to the Nautical Almanac published in England, and from the astro-physicist Kulikow's figure: $\sqrt{gm} = 1.99654 \times 10^{10}$ cgs. Using the earth's radius as given in the supplement, the force of gravity at that distance is obtained by the formula:

$G = gm/r^2$ $3.986135 \times 10^{20}/(6.378270 \times 10^8)^2 = 979.81980$ dynes force

A theoretical satellite circling the earth at that distance will have the following orbital velocity in kilometers per second. Note that the formula gives the earth's radius in kilometers.

$v = \sqrt{Gr}$ $\sqrt{979.91980 \times 6378.270} = 7.905413$ km. per second

Because the centrifugal force of a body moving in a circular orbit equals the gravitational force producing that orbit, the velocity above can be checked against its other factors by the formula below. However, because its gravitational force is in dynes per centimeter, its velocity and radius values must also be in centimeters. The satellite's centrifugal force per gram mass is:

$$F = \frac{mV^2}{r} \qquad \frac{1.0 \times (7.9054128 \times 10^5)^2}{6.378270 \times 10^8} = 979.81980 \text{ dynes force}$$

The satellite's period is obtained from its orbital velocity and the circumference of its orbit as shown below. The figures are in kilometers per second.

$$p = \frac{2\pi r}{V} \qquad \frac{2 \times 3.141592654 \times 6378.270}{7.9054128} = \begin{array}{l} 5069.41932 \text{ seconds} \\ 84.490322 \text{ minutes} \end{array}$$

319 Observed Earth Satellites.

Because the mass of an earth satellite is negligible in comparison with that of the earth, the four elements of its orbit are always in ideal proportions in free space. Near the earth its motion is inhibited by atmospheric friction. I am using the orbital elements of Sputnik II and Vanguard I for a check on the validity of my idealizations.

The Vanguard's perigee and apogee were 409 and 2453 miles above the equator, respectively, and it had a period of 134 minutes. An equatorial radius of 3963.278 miles added to its perigee and apogee gives us their distances from the earth's center as 4372 and 6416 miles. Adding these two figures and dividing them by two give us a mean orbit radius of 5394 miles and a mean distance above the Earth's surface of 1431 miles. The eccentricity of its orbit can be obtained by dividing its apogee by mean distance, with -1 subtracted: E= -1(A/M) = -1.(6416/5394) = 0.1895. The best we can expect from the figures given is a rough agreement with my theoretical values below. The figures for Sputnik II, in kilometers, are in good agreement with those published. (See Section 318 for base numbers.)

	Base numbers.	Russian Sputnik II Ratios. Satellite.	Base numbers.	United States Vanguard Ratios. Satellite.
V	7.905413	÷1.070835 = 7.38248 km-sec	4.912202	÷1.166500 = 4.21106 mi-se
r	6378.270	×1.146688 = 7313.88 km.	3963.278	×1.360722 = 5392.92 miles
H		935.61 "		1429.64 "
p	84.49032	×1.227913 = 103.747 minutes	84.49032	×1.587283 = 134.110 minut
G	979.8198	÷1.314892 = 745.171 dynes	979.8198	÷1.851565 = 529.185 dyne

320 Lofting and Escape Velocities. Energy.

Lofting velocity is defined as the initial speed a body must have in order to ascend a specific distance above the earth's surface against gravity. It is equivalent to the impact velocity of a body falling freely from satellite height as it strikes the earth. A projectile accelerated to this velocity against gravity decelerates to zero velocity at satellite height and then returns to earth. To convert it into a satellite it is necessary to produce an initial velocity equal to lofting and orbital velocities added. Its energy, defined as one half of the orbiting body's mass times velocity squared, is the theoretical minimum defined by my table. In actual practice, additional energy is needed to lift the supporting masses of rocket stages and fuel against atmospheric resistance and the pull of gravity preceding orbital speed. (Note that a rocket can remain unmovable at a height by a constant expenditure of energy equal to gravitational acceleration at that point.)

The table below defines the velocities and energies of three one-gram masses moving in circular undisturbed orbits around the earth, and the velocities and energies needed to put them there. Their energies must be multiplied by actual masses in grams to produce the corresponding velocities, but the velocities needed to put a satellite in orbit are the same for all masses. Velocities are in centimeters to preserve conversion continuity. Note that one kilometer = 10^5 cm., and that one joule = 10^7 ergs. (See Sections 207-9 for definitions and 318-19 for their four orbital elements.)

Velocities in cm. per second.	Earth radius. Basic orbit.	Sputnik II. Test orbit.	10000 km. radius. Reference orbit.
Escape velocity	11.179942 ×10^5	10.440397 ×10^5	8.928757 × 10^5 cm. se
Orbit velocity	7.905413 × 10^5	7.382475 × 10^5	6.313585 × 10^5 " "
Lofting velocity	0.0	3.998652 × 10^5	6.728180 × 10^5 "
Base vel. to orb.	7.905413 × 10^5	8.395842 × 10^5	9.226578 × 10^5 " "

ergy of a gram mass corresponding to the velocities above: $E = \frac{1}{2}mV^2$.

cape energy	6.249555 x 10"	5.450094 x 10"	3.986135 x 10"	ergs
bit energy	3.124778 x 10"	2.725047 x 10"	1.993067 x 10"	"
fting energy	0.0	0.799461 x 10"	2.263420 x 10"	"
tal L-0 energy	3.124778 x 10"	3.524508 x 10"	4.256488 x 10"	"

The velocity of escape from a stationary earth's surface, or from its gravitational attraction at orbit distance, is equal to the velocity of a satellite moving in a circular orbit at that distance times the square root of two, when all perturbations are disregarded. All the figures below are for the ten-thousand kilometer (10^9 cm.) radius orbit defined in Section 318. The velocity a body must attain to escape from that orbit is:

$V = V_0 \sqrt{2}$ $6.3135846 \times 10^5 \times 1.41421356 = 8.9287570 \times 10^5$ cm. -sec.

The corresponding energy of orbital motion is exactly one-half of its energy of escape. These energies can be checked against the velocities of the table. The energy of escape for a gram mass can also be obtained by dividing the earth's theoretical gravity at one centimeter (Section 317) by the distance from its center:

$E = Mg/D$ $5.982242 \times 10^{27} \times 6.66328 \times 10^{-8}/10^9 = 3.986135 \times 10^{11}$ ergs

The impact energy of a gram mass falling from satellite height is also the energy needed to cause it to ascend to that height by coasting against gravity after an initial acceleration to maximum velocity at the earth's surface. Since the lofting energy of a gram mass to orbit height is equal to the difference between their escape energies, we can obtain it simply by subtracting the escape energy at orbit height from that at the earth's surface. It can also be obtained by averaging the force of gravity acting upon a mass through its flight, and then applying the formula in Section 309 for acceleration through a uniform force field. Using the first letters of mean, orbit and earth as subscripts, we have the formulas: $G_M = G_O \sqrt{G_O/G_E} = G_O \sqrt{R^4} = GR^2$. Mean gravity is therefore obtained by multiplying its force at orbit distance by the height ratio. The figures for a gram mass are:

$G_M = G_O R^2$ $398.61350 \times 1.5678233 = 624.955533$ dynes mean gravity

$E = mG_M H$ $1.0 \times 624.955533 \times 3.621700 \times 10^8 = 2.263420 \times 10^{11}$ ergs

Orbit radius	10000.0 km.	Escape e., Earth	6.249555 x 10" ergs
Earth "	6378.2 "	" " , orbit	3.986135 x 10" "
Height	3621.7 km.	Lofting energy	2.263420 x 10" ergs

The minimum energy needed to put a gram mass satellite in orbit is equal to orbital and lofting energies added. The velocity equivalents of these energies are obtained by the formula: $V = \sqrt{E/\frac{1}{2}m}$. The distance a free-falling mass will move before impact can be checked against its terminal velocity and mean gravity by the formula below. It gives us the orbit's mean height above the earth's surface.

$H = V^2/2G$ $(6.728180 \times 10^5)^2\ 2 \times 624.955533 = 3.62170 \times 10^8$ cm.
                                                                3621.70 kilometers

A mass falling through a uniform field of gravity accelerates at a uniform rate. The time of a free fall can, therefore, be defined by: $T = V/G$. The mean above gives a fair approximation for small differences in gravity, but the error in time becomes increasingly large with an increase of the difference, because a falling mass will spend a disproportionately long time in the low-gravity field.

Note that the ideal relations and proportions defined for orbital motions in gravitation are also applicable to the orbits of electrons in the electrostatic force fields of atoms. (See Sections 215 and 812 for comparison values.)

321 Eccentric Orbits. Earth and Moon.

Kepler's first law states that the orbit of each planet is an ellipse, with the sun at one focus. The point of a planet's orbit nearest to the sun is called its perihelion, and its farthest distance from it at the longitude opposite is its aphelion. The longest line which can be drawn through the ellipse runs from its perihelion through the sun to its aphelion. It is called the orbit's major axis. Its minor axis is the shorest line which can be drawn through the center of the ellipse at a right angle to its major axis. The point where the two lines cross, at the center of the ellipse, is equidistant to perihelion and aphelion. The distance between this point and aphelion or perihelion is called the orbit's semi-major axis. It defines the radius of a circular orbit with the same period as the eccentric orbit. An accentric orbit's mean radius can be obtained, therefore, by adding perihelion to aphelion distance; the mean radius equals one half their sum. If the sun's distance from the center of the semi-major axis is known, we add that distance to the orbit's perihelion distance or subtract it from its aphelion distance.

Since mean distance defines a circular orbit, eccentricity is an orbit's deviation from this ideal. If the eccentricity is zero, the orbit is a circle. Between zero and one the orbit is an ellipse, with one defining a parabolic orbit; a transition from the closed orbit of an ellipse to the open orbit of a hyperbola. The velocity of an object moving in a hyperbolic orbit is greater than escape velocity at its nearest approach to the sun. The eccentricity of the moon's orbit around the earth is defined below.

The term "helio" is reserved for the sun. Satellite minimum and maximum distances from their primaries are called perigees and apogees, respectively. When those of the moon are added and divided by two, as shown below, their corresponding distances in miles are: apogee 251,970.66, perigee 225,743.86, and mean orbit 238,857.26 miles.

Distance at apogee   405506.94 kilometers
Distance at perigee   363299.06 kilometers
        Added   768806.00/2 = 384403.00 km. mean distance.

The eccentricity of the moon's orbit is obtained by subtracting mean from aphelion distance, or perihelion from mean distance, thus giving us the earth's distance from the center of the ellipse as a first result. This figure is then divided by mean distance for eccentricity as shown.

Moon's distance at apogee   405506.94 kilometers
Mean distance   384403.00 kilometers
Earth to center of ellipse   21103.94/384403.00 = 0.05490056 eccent.

We can now obtain aphelion distance by adding one to the eccentricity and multiplying this figure by mean distance as shown.

1.05490056 × 384403.00 - 405506.94 kilometers aphelion distance.

322 Mass Ratio Reductions. Earth-Moon Orbit.

According to Newton's third law of motion, two gravitating bodies will circle a common center of inertia. It makes the radius of their orbits and their periods less than that of a relatively infinitesimal mass orbiting one of those bodies at the same distance. (See Section 315 for details.)

The earth's mass is equal to 81.53 moons, and the moon is 60.2665 equatorial radii from the earth's center. When the radius of the earth's orbit around their common center of inertia is subtracted from its equatorial radius of 6378.27 kilometers, we find the radius of its mean orbit to be 1663.404 km. (1033.7 miles) below its surface. The mean distances of their mass centers from the center of inertia of their orbits are:

Mean distance between earth and moon   384403.00 km.   238856.492 miles
Earth's orbit   384403.0/81.53 ratio =   4714.866 km.   2929.676 miles
Moon's orbit   379688.134 km.   235926.816 miles

A body with a relatively negligible mass, such as a man-made satellite, circling the earth at the moon's distance, will have a slightly longer period than the moon because the radius of its orbit is greater. Its four elements are in ideal proportions.

Terms   Earth
V Velocity 7.905413 ÷ 7.76322073 = 1.018316 km. sec. = 0.6327511 mi. sec.
r   Distance 6378.270 × 60.2675961 = 384403.0 kilom. = 238856.49 miles
p Period 5069.4192 × 467.870651 = 2371832. seconds = 27.451760 days
G Gravity 979.81983 ÷ 3632.18314 = 0.269761 dynes

The orbital period of this satellite can now be converted into the moon's sidereal period by the formula below. The conversion ratio is equal to the square root of the earth + moon mass in earth mass units as shown below.

$R = \sqrt{1 + (M/E)} = \sqrt{1 + (1/81.53)} = \sqrt{1.01226542} = 1.00611402$ period ratio
$p = p/R$ 27.451760/1.00611402 =   27.2849394 days in one sidereal month
         Increase due to sun   0.0367215 day
         Observed true period   27.3216609 days in one sidereal month

The increase of orbital period due to the sun is caused by its slightly greater attraction for the moon at new moon, when it is opposing the earth's, as compared with its attraction at full moon, when their forces combine. The difference is because the moon's distance from the sun at full moon is greater by the diameter of its orbit around the earth-moon center of inertia than at new moon. The sun's attraction for the moon, therefore, appears as a slight reduction of the earth's attraction for that body. This three-body problem has never been completely solved, and scientific estimates range from 52 minutes to about one hour. Since the difference between its theoretical and observed period is 0.0367215 day by my figures, I postulate the corresponding increase of 52.87896 minutes as being due to the sun.

The force of attraction between the earth and the moon and that attraction per gram mass which produce the moon's orbit around their common center of inertia, are defined below.

$$F = \frac{gm_E m_M}{r^2} \quad \frac{6.666561 \times 10^{-8} \times 5.979298 \times 10^{27} \times 7.333863 \times 10^{25}}{(3.844030 \times 10^{10})^2} = 1.978387 \times 10^{25} \text{ dyne}$$

$$F = \frac{g(m+m)}{r^2} \quad \frac{6.666561 \times 10^{-8} \times (5.979298 \times 10^{27} + 7.333863 \times 10^{25})}{(3.844030 \times 10^{10})^2} = 0.273069 \text{ dyne}$$

The gravitational attraction of one mass which causes another mass to accelerate toward it is: $F = gm/r^2$. This formula is valid for the earth's attraction for a relatively infinitesimal mass, but not for a large one, such as the moon, because that body's attraction for its primary must be included. The formula for the attraction between two large masses, per gram mass, which causes them to circle a common center of inertia, is: $F = g(m + m)/r^2$. (See the second formula above.) While it takes a negligible mass 27.451765 days to circle the earth at moon distance, it takes the moon only 27.284945 days to do so, because the attractive force is slightly greater per unit mass.

323 Solar Surface Orbit from Earth's Orbit.

The sun's theoretical force of gravity at one centimeter is defined in Section 317 as 1.324633×10^{26} dynes. When this force is divided by a planet's distance from the sun's center in centimeters squared, we obtain its attraction for each gram of its mass in dynes. This attraction is also the sun's acceleration of a free-falling mass in centimeters per second at that distance (See Section 309). As it acts upon the transverse motions of the planets, the sun's attraction causes them to recurve into their observed periodic orbits. (See Section 318 for symbols and conversion formulas.)

The figures for the sun's mass and surface orbit were obtained from the observed distances and orbital periods of the planets. The elements of the earth's orbit have been determined with great accuracy. The gaussian gravity constant $k = 0.017202099$, is defined by the Nautical Almanac as the acceleration due to the sun's attraction at the earth's mean distance in one solar day, with the formula $2\pi/k$ defining the orbital period, in days, of a body of negligible mass moving in a circular undisturbed orbit at that distance. This period can also be obtained by multiplying the earth's sidereal period by an orbital ratio equal to the square root of sun plus earth in solar mass units. Note that the sun's mass is equal to 332310 earth masses and 328284 earth plus moon masses (See Sections 304).

$= \sqrt{(E+S)/S} = \sqrt{1+(E/S)} = \sqrt{1+(1/332310)} = \sqrt{1.00000304} = 1.00000152$ ratio
$= 2\pi/k$ 6.28318531/0.017202099 = 365.25690 days in one sidereal year
$= Rp_0$ 1.00000152 × 365.25690 = 365.25690   "   "   "   "   "
            1.00000152 × 31558149.5 = 31558196. seconds in one "   "

The sun's radius has been estimated at about 696,500 kilometers (432,784.2 miles). By multiplying this figure by the ratio 214.650683, we obtain the radius of the earth's mean orbit, 149.5042 million kilometers, as defined by the Nautical Almanac. The square root of the mean orbit radius ratio gives us their velocity ratio, and this ratio cubed, their period ratio. By dividing the sidereal year in days or seconds by the period ratio we obtain the period of a solar surface satellite orbit. The force of gravity at the sun's surface is greater than at the earth's orbit by the distance ratio squared. Their observed values are related by these formulas from Section 318: $G = gm/r^2$, $V = \sqrt{Gr}$, $p = 2\pi r/V$, $G = F = mV^2/r$. From these relations we obtain the sun's theoretical gravity at one centimeter, and from that its mass as defined by Section 304. The four elements of two ideal proportion orbits are defined below:

Ratio, symbol and term	Surface of sun orbit.	Ratios of orbits.	Earth distance orbit of a satellite with negligible mass.
R^1 V Velocity	436.101149 ÷ 14.6509619 = 29.766042 km. per second		
R^2 r Radius	696500.000 × 214.650683 = 1.4950420 × 10^8 kilometers		
R^3 p Period	10034.9164 × 3144.83897 = 3.1558196 × 10^7 seconds si. p.		
	.116144866 × 3144.83897 = 365.25690 days, sidereal p.		
R^4 G Gravity	27305.7017 ÷ 46074.9157 = 0.5926370 dynes acceleration		

324 Idealized Reference Orbit. Million Km.

For the purpose of reference it is desirable to have one orbital element which is simple, and unchangeable by definition. By postulating an ideal circular orbit of one million kilometers, the planetary distances in this unit are also their distance ratios. The sun's gravitational attraction at that distance is less than its theoretical force at one cm. by 10^{22}, but their digits are the same.

Ratio, symbol and term.	10^6 km. solar orbit.	Ratios of orbits	Earth distance orbit of a satellite with negligible mass.
R V Velocity	363.955086 ÷ 12.2271911 = 29.766042 km. per second		
R r Radius	1000000.00 × 149.504202 = 1.4950420 × 10^8 kilometers		
R p Period	17263.628 × 1828.01645 = 3.1558196 × 10^7 seconds si. p.		
	.199810513 × 1828.01645 = 365.25690 days, sidereal period		
R G Gravity	13246.329 ÷ 22351.5065 = 0.5926370 dynes acceleration		

325 Lofting and Escape Velocities. Energy.

Formulas and examples of lofting and escape velocities appeared in Section 320 for earth satellites. The base values used to obtain the figures of the table are defined above. We can obtain the escape energy of a gram mass for any distance from the sun's center by dividing its theoretical gravity at one cm., 1.324633×10^{26} dynes, by distance. The gravity constant for the same distance is that figure divided by distance squared. For a million-kilometer orbit the divisors are 10^{11} and 10^{22} for the escape energy of a gram mass and gravitational acceleration, respectively. Orbital energy is the escape energy halved. The energy difference between two distances in space (the energy liberated or absorbed in a change of orbit) is the difference between their escape energies. Converting it into velocity by the formula: $V = \sqrt{E/\tfrac{1}{2}m}$ gives us the velocity of a free fall toward the sun from the greater distance as it passes the lesser. Compare the table below with that of Section 320.

Velocities in cm. per second.	Sun's radius. Basic orbit.	Million km. rad. reference orbit.	Earth's mean orbit. Astronimical consts
Escape velocity	6.167402×10^7	$5.1471021S \times 10^7$	4.2095540×10^6 cm.s
Orbit velocity	4.361011×10^7	3.63955086×10^7	2.9766042×10^6 "
Lofting velocity	0.0	2.40251757×10^7	6.1530137×10^7 "
Base vel. to orb.	4.361011×10^7	4.97900711×10^7	6.1602143×10^7 "
Energy of a gram mass moving with the velocities above:		$E = \tfrac{1}{2}mV^2$.	
Escape energy	1.901842×10^{15}	$1.32463304 \times 10^{15}$	8.8601726×10^{14} ergs
Orbit energy	0.950921×10^{15}	$0.66231652 \times 10^{15}$	4.4300863×10^{14} "
Lofting energy	0.0	$0.57720907 \times 10^{15}$	1.8929820×10^{15} "
Total L+O energy	0.950921×10^{15}	$1.23952559 \times 10^{15}$	1.8974120×10^{15} "

326 Idealized Planetary Orbits.

Ideal proportion orbits are used as a reference base for the analysis of deviations from this ideal in actual orbits. They are defined as relatively infinitesimal masses, such as spaceships, moving around the sun in undisturbed circular orbits at planetary distances. Their ratios were selected to bring them into accord with the observed distances and periods of the planets after the reduction of their periods, due to the displacement of the center of inertia from the sun's center by each planet, as defined in Section 322. True periods are defined in the next section.

The ratios below are related to the one-million-kilometer orbit of the preceding sections. It follows that distance ratios are also the planetary distances in million-kilometer units, and both are therefore defined by a single column. For convenience, ratios are always greater than unity. A distance less than unity, such as the solar surface orbit, gives us the proper ratio by taking the reciprocal of distance. The conventional symbols below are defined in Sections 312 and 327.

	Velocity in orbit Ratio R^1	km. sec.	R^4=Radius $\times 10^6$ km.	Sidereal period Ratio R^3	in days	Gravitational for Ratio R^4	in dyr
☉s	1.1982279	436.1011	1/.696500	1.7203560	.1161449	2.0613786	27305.
☿k	1.0	363.9551	1.0	1.0	.1998105	1.0	13246.
☿	7.6074030	47.84222	57.872580	440.26004	87.96858	3349.2355	3.9550
♀	10.399096	34.99872	108.14120	1124.5707	224.7011	11694.519	1.1326
⊕	12.227191	29.76604	149.50420	1828.0164	365.2569	22351.506	.59263
♂	15.092988	24.11418	227.79830	3438.1571	686.9799	51892.066	.25526
♃	27.889801	13.04976	777.84100	21693.831	4334.655	605036.62	.02189
♄	37.763700	9.637696	1426.0930	53854.548	10760.70	2033747.0	.00651
♅	53.552140	6.796275	2867.8317	153578.52	30686.60	8224458.6	.00161
♆	67.034770	5.429348	4493.6604	301231.49	60189.22	20192984.	.00065
♇	76.788225	4.739725	5896.4315	452776.51	90469.51	34767904.	.00038

327 Conversions to True Planetary Periods.
The sun's family of nine planets circles it in slightly eccentric orbits in the same direction on nearly the same plane, as defined in Section 312. The masses, distances and periods of the planets in that section's table are defined below in solar masses, grams, kilometers and days.

To obtain the reduction of a planet's period, caused by the displacement of its orbit's center of inertia relative to the center of the sun, we use a ratio equal to the square root of the sun's plus the planet's mass in solar mass units. The ideal proportion periods in the preceding section are then divided by the figure thus obtained for the observed sidereal periods of the planets.

The agreement between orbit radii and periods are good for the first six planets and poor for the remaining three. Because I have given the greatest weight to an integration of periods, the distance ratios of Uranus, Neptune and Pluto in my ideal proportion table are not in accord with those below. A better understanding of the effects of perturbations on orbital periods will obviously necessitate a revision of the ideal proportion table.

ame of lanet	Orbit. Radius ×10⁶km.	Mass. Gram ×10¹⁷	Ratio in Sun mass R = P/⊙	Sidereal ideal p. in days	Mass to period R. √(P+⊙)/⊙	Sidereal true pe. in days	Reduction of period I = p-p̣ .
ercury	57.3726	.33133	.000000167	87.9686/1.00000008	= 87.9686	0.6 sec.
enus	108.141	4.3724	.000002451	224.701/1.00000122	= 224.701	23.7 "
arth-M.	149.504	6.0552	.000003046	365.257/1.00000152	= 365.256	48.0 "
ars	227.793	.64262	.000000323	686.930/1.00000016	= 686.930	10.8 "
upiter	777.341	1898.1	.000954786	4334.66/1.00047728	= 4332.59	2.07 days
aturn	1426.10	567.73	.000285584	10760.7/1.00014278	= 10759.2	1.54 "
r&nus	2869.13	86.928	.000043727	30686.6/1.00002186	= 30685.9	0.67 "
eptune	4495.59	102.93	.000051776	60189.2/1.00002589	= 60187.6	1.56 "
luto	5908.11	5.5221	.000002778	90469.4/1.00000139	= 90469.3	0.13 "

Chapter 4

ELECTRICAL SYSTEMS

The systems of units in this chapter form a bridge between atomic theory, experimental verification and the practical use of electricity. The guassian system, combining electrostatic and electromagnetic units, is used by most physicists throughout the world. Its fundamental units of action have been idealized by relating them to the ideal and ultimate systems of units as outlined in the preceding chapters and defined in Chapter 10. The greater units of the mks system are used by industry and commerce. Their values are abstracted from the cgs units of action on which the esu and emu systems of electrical and magnetic units are based.

401 Electrodynamic Systems. esu, emu, mks. (25C, 32B, 27K.)

There are three systems of measurement in general use among scientists for the definition of electrical and magnetic phenomena. They are: the electrostatic, electromagnetic and practical systems, usually abbreviated to esu, emu and mks, respectively. The mks stands for meter-kilogram-second; the units of action of the practical system. Its units of force and energy are the newton and joule. (See Sections 209 and 507).

The emu and esu systems are based on the cgs (centimeter-gram-second) units of force and energy, called the dyne and erg. (See Sections 206-8). The guassian system uses the esu system for the definition of electrostatic forces and the emu system for electromagnetic phenomena. The difference between them is equal to the speed of light in centimeters per second, symbolized by c, as defined in Sections 210 and 213. The electromagnetic system is related to the practical system through changes of exponents, as defined by the table below. There are small differences between the units of the practical and international systems. They are defined in Section 409.

The prefix "ab" is added to emu terms, thus giving us abvolts, abamperes, etc. The prefix "stat" is used with esu terms, such as statamperes, statcoulombs, etc. The terms of the second column are described and defined in Chapter 5.

nversion factors for three electrodynamic systems.

mbols and finitions.	Practical units.			Ab- units.			Stat- units.		
	mks	emu	esu	emu	mks	esu	esu	emu	mks
Quantity	1 coulomb	} 0.1	$c/10.$	1 Q	} $10.$	c	1 Q	} $1/c$	$10/c$
Current	1 ampere			1 I			1 I		
Potential	1 volt	10^8	$10^8/c$	1 V	10^8	$1/c$	1 V	c	$c/10^8$
Resistance	1 ohm	} 10^9	$10^9/c^2$	1 R	} 10^{-9}	$1/c^2$	1 R	} c^2	$c^2/10^9$
Inductance	1 henry			1 B			1 B		
Capacitance	1 farad	10^{-9}	$c^2/10^9$	1 C	10^9	c^2	1 C	$1/c^2$	$10^9/c^2$

402 Electrostatics.

The electrostatic charge on an isolated hollow metal sphere acts as if it was concentrated at its center. When the charges on spheres of different sizes have been made identical by contact and separation, it is found that their charges have the same value at the same distances from their centers. It follows that the surface density of charge on each sphere is inversely proportional to its radius and, therefore, proportional to the curvature of its surface. This relationship to curvature appears on irregular shapes as an increase of density on curved areas, with maximas at edges and points which makes them behave like conductors.

When a ground-connected body is brought near an electrostatic charge, a charge of opposite sign is induced on its surface, and the density of the primary charge increases in its vicinity. This condenser effect increases when the air space between opposite charges is filled with an insulating substance, such as glass or mica. There is a corresponding decrease in the charge (voltage) necessary to effect a particular electron density. This increase of condenser capacity per unit charge is called the capacitance of the medium. Its numerical value, defined in comparison with capacitance in a vacuum, is symbolized by K in algebra. The force between two charged spheres is proportional to the product of their charges and inversely proportional to the square of the distance between their centers, provided that they are small enough compared to distance to eliminate the condenser effect.

403 Electrostatic System of Units. esu

The electrostatic unit of force, a statcoulomb, is defined as that electrostatic charge which produces a repulsion of one dyne between two similar point charges one centimeter apart. It is a quantity unit, defining the number of electrons needed to produce this effect. (Compare it with emu coulomb, Section 504.)

An electrified body in an electrostatic field is repelled or attracted according to its relative charge-sign, force and distance. A statvolt is defined as the charge difference between two parallel plates with opposite charges, thus producing a uniform field between them, when it requires an expenditure of one erg of energy to cause a unit charge to move from one to the other against their charges.

The statampere is defined as that current which carries one electrostatic unit of electricity past a given section of a conductor in one second. It is to be contrasted with the abampere, in emu, which is defined in terms of the electromagnetic field produced by moving charges. It is less than the statampere by the velocity of light. Since current is reciprocally related to volts, one statvolt is smaller than one abvolt by the same difference. The table in Section 401 shows that all esu values differ from those in emu by the velocity of light, and that velocity squared.

404 Electrodynamics.

Electrodynamics is the science of electrons in motion. The state of stress produced by an electrostatic charge tends to resolve into a reduction of local stresses by a dispersal of similar charges, or into a neutral state through its union with an opposite charge. In both cases we find electrons accelerating or moving through conductors from relatively negative charges. A moving electron produces a magnetic field proportional to its velocity. A current of electrons passing through a conductor produces a magnetic field whose lines of force circle the wire; they are, therefore, at a right angle to both current and electrostatic lines of force. When a conductor is made into one or several parallel circular loops (a solinoid), the magnetic field produced by its current has a concentration of lines of force at its center; they pass through a north and south pole of equal strength at a right angle to the loops. When a paramagnetic substance is inserted in the solinoid, an increase of magnetic field strength occurs. Other substances, such as bismuth and antimony, are called diamagnetic because they oppose penetration by a magnetic field. There is a strong increase in magnetization when a ferromagnetic metal, such as iron or nickel, is inserted in the solinoid. The magnetic permeability of a substance is given a numerical value relative to the permeability of a vacuum. Its algebraic expression is μ.

There is a momentary transfer of energy from coil to magnet during magnetization, which appears as an opposition to the current. This energy is liberated to the coil as an opposition to a reduction or reversal of the current. It can also appear in a second coil, independent of the first, as a current induced by a changing magnetic field. A changing magnetic field is produced mechanically in dynamos and generators; the current induced is proportional to its rate of change, and to the number of magnetic lines of force cut by a conductor.

405 Electromagnetic System of Units.   emu.   (E)

The electromagnetic unit of force is defined as a magnetic repulsion of one dyne between two similar poles one centimeter apart. A unit of magnetic force is produced when one abampere is passed through a single turn of wire one centimeter in radius. The point value of this magnetic field at the center of the circle is 2π oersted (6.283 dynes). One abampere can also be defined as that current which produces an attractive force of one dyne per unit length between two conductors one unit distance apart, when the currents are similar and in parallel. This dimensionless definition is possible because the force gradient of a long conductor decreases inversely as the distance. The abcoulomb is a quantity unit equal to one abampere-second; i.e., the quantity of electricity passing through a conductor at a given point in one second. Since an electron's electrostatic charge is 1.602×10^{-20} emu, the number of electrons is the reciprocal of this figure, or 6.242×10^{19} units. (See Tables 19B and 32G.)

A comparison between water flowing through a pipe and an electric current tells us there is a direct relationship between flow and quantity per unit time, and that both are related directly to pressure and inversely to resistance. Flow is in amperes, quantity in coulombs, pressure in volts and resistance in ohms. It gives us the formula: $I = E/R$, or amperes = volts/ohms.

The unit of resistance, the abohm, is defined as that resistance which will cause one erg of heat per second to develp in a conductor when one abampere is flowing through it. The unit of potential difference, the abvolt, is defined as that electrostatic force which will cause one abampere to flow through a conductor having a resistance of one abohm. The unit of inductance is assigned the same value as the ohm, and the unit of capacitance is the reciprocal of their assigned value. (See the table in Section 401.)

406 Gaussian System of Units. emu-esu.

The gaussian system is the one preferred by most scientists. It uses the esu system of units for electrostatic quantities and the emu system of units for electromagnetic quantities. Its use was made possible by the discovery that the corresponding values in the two systems differ from one another by the velocity of light; hence its symbol "c" appears in all conversion formulas from one system into the other (Table, Section 401).

Maxwell worked out a formula (Section 213) showing that a dynamic relationship between the dielectric constant, K (Section 402), and the magnetic permeability constant, μ (Section 404), defines the velocity of an electromagnetic wave through the ether, and he proved that this velocity should be the same as that of light in a vacuum. The corresponding difference between quantity units (coulombs) in esu and emu is measurable and definitive. An esu coulomb gives us the number of electrons needed to produce a dyne of electrostatic force, while the emu coulombs gives us the number of electrons which must be moving past a given point in one second to produce the same force as a magnetic effect.

Although electrons move with high velocities within a conductor, their motions through it as an electric current are comparatively slow. However, the directional pressure to which they respond as an electric current is transmitted through the conductor and the surrounding space with the speed of light. Electrons, being pure negative electrostatic charges, react instantaneously to the directional forces of other charges. It follows that the electrostatic force needed to effect the transfer of one erg of energy to the electrons as a current is less than the electrostatic unit of force by the velocity of transmission through the conductor; since this force, by definition, acts as an accelerator through one second of time. The electromagnetic unit of force is, therefore, the esu unit of charge at one centimeter, divided by the speed of light in centimeters per second, because the abcoulomb is the action of that charge through one second. The electrostatic energy transferred to an electromagnetic field as motion is less, per unit charge, in the same proportion. It defines the esu-emu relationship on which the gaussian system of units is based. (See Section 213.)

407 Gaussian Units: Sequence and Table.

The algebraic sequence in Section 217 appears above the table as an integrated series of nine gaussian units. The simple relationship between rest masses, emu and esu energies and wavenumbers, as defined by Section 218, makes it possible to convert each of these atomic constants into three other values, as defined by the two tables below the sequences. The figures in these tables were then used to rationalize and integrate the figures in the large table, Chapter 11, into accord with their observed values. (Note that many are useless equivalents.)

The units of the sequence were selected after comparing numerous experimental values from standard physics texts. They were assigned different weights according to my best judgment. Among them, Rydberg's wavenumber appears to be the most reliable constant.

Gaussian system sequence of units.

	m_e	c	m' emu$_{17}$	$\dot{v}$ wl.	h emu$_{27}$	2π
Numbers	$9.108325^{-28} \times$	$2.997930^{10} =$	$2.730612^{17}) \times$	$2.425998^{10} =$	$6.624461^{27})/$	$6.283185=$
Log 10	$-28.959438 \times$	$10.476822 =$	$-17.436260) \times$	$-10.384890 =$	$-27.821150)/$	$0.798180=$
Log 2	$-89.826801 \times$	$34.803248 =$	$-55.023553) \times$	$-31.940702 =$	$-86.964255)/$	$2.651496=$

	Continued h emu$_{17}$	c/ϕ	e^2 esu$_{19}$	e esu$_{10}$	$4\pi\bar{v}$	μ emu
Numbers	$1.054316^{-17}) \times$	$2.187554^8 =$	$2.306373^{19})^{1/2} =$	$4.802471^{10})/$	$5.179876^{10} =$	9.271402
Log 10	$-27.022970) \times$	$8.339959 =$	$-19.362930)^{1/2} =$	$-10.681465)/$	$10.714319 =$	-21.9671
Log 2	$-89.615752) \times$	$27.704744 =$	$-61.911008)^{1/2} =$	$-30.955504)/$	$35.592197 =$	-66.5477

Table of gaussian atomic units.   (Location of constants from Section 1004.

		Mass in grams	Ergs emu	Ergs esu-cgs	Wavenumbers
1	$\hbar$	$3.5168121 \times 10^{-38}$	$1.0543157 \times 10^{-27}$	$3.1607645 \times 10^{-17}$	0.1591549
2	h	$2.2096782 \times 10^{-37}$	$6.6244606 \times 10^{-27}$	$1.9859669 \times 10^{-16}$	1.0
3	μ	$3.0926013 \times 10^{-31}$	$9.2714023 \times 10^{-21}$	$2.7795015 \times 10^{-10}$	1.3995709×10^6
4	e	$5.3434506 \times 10^{-31}$	$1.6019291 \times 10^{-20}$	$4.8024713 \times 10^{-10}$	2.4182031×10^6
5	m_e	$9.1083250 \times 10^{-28}$	$2.7306121 \times 10^{-17}$	8.1861839×10^{-7}	4.1220142×10^9
6	Q	$1.1126460 \times 10^{-21}$	$3.3356349 \times 10^{-11}$	1.0	5.0353306×10^{15}
7	E	$3.3356349 \times 10^{-11}$	1.0	2.9979300×10^{10}	1.5095569×10^{16}
8	G	1.0	2.9979300×10^{10}	8.9875843×10^{20}	4.5255458×10^{36}
9	R	$2.4248415 \times 10^{-32}$	$7.2695050 \times 10^{-22}$	$2.1793467 \times 10^{-11}$	1.0973732×10^5

Gaussian units in basic logarithms.

		Mass in grams	Ergs emu	Ergs esu	Wavenumbers
1	$\hbar$	-124.418999	-89.615751	-54.812503	-2.651496
2	h	-121.767503	-86.964256	-52.161007	0.0
3	μ	-101.350950	-66.547701	-31.744454	20.416553
4	e	-100.562000	-65.758752	-30.955504	21.205503
5	m_e	-89.826801	-55.023553	-20.220305	31.940702
6	Q	-69.606496	-34.803248	0.0	52.161007
7	E	-34.803248	0.0	34.803248	86.964256
8	G	0.0	34.803248	69.606496	121.767503
9	R	-105.023808	-70.220560	-35.417312	16.743695

408 Practical System of Units. mks units

A system based on the meter-kilogram-second units of force and energy; the neuton and the joule. This is sometimes called the absolute system, the mks system, or the practical system of units. This last term is derived from the fact that its units of action are within the range of ordinary physical phenomena. The newton is equal to 10^5 dynes, and the joule is equal to 10^7 ergs (See Section 209).

The mks system is never used as a complete system. Its secondary units are related to the gaussian system through changes of exponents, as can be seen by an inspection of the table in Section 401. The changes are integrated in such a way that it eliminates the duality of the gaussian system. The units of the mks system were originally used in the development of the practical international system, but the units of the latter now differ slightly from the mks system because their values must be expressed in physical terms that can be duplicated anywhere. Those originally adopted contain small errors that have been preserved by convention and legislative fiat.

409 International System of Units.

A system of physical and electromagnetic units used by science and industry everywhere to measure commercial quantities and qualities. It was derived from the practical system. To make it possible to reproduce the units of electricity anywhere on earth with a minimum effort and error, the ohm and the ampere were defined by science in physical terms; the ohm by a resistance column, and the ampere by electrolysis. The original intention was to make them identical to the practical units; but after their adoption small errors were discovered which makes the international units differ slightly from those of the mks system.

The international ohm is the resistance to an electric current by a column of mercury of unvarying cross-section with a length of 106.300 centimeters, a mass of 14.4521 grams and a temperature of 0 degrees centigrade. It is equal to 1.00051 absolute ohms.

The international ampere is that current which will deposit 0.001118 gram of silver per second when it is passed through a solution of silver nitrate in water. It is equal to 0.99995 absolute amperes.

The international volt is that electric pressure which produces a current of one ampere against a resistance of one ohm. It is equal to 1.00046 absolute volts. It can also be determined by a normal Weston cell. This type of cell tends to maintain a constant charge of 1.0183 international volts at a temperature of 20 degrees centigrade, over a long period of time.

410 Various Systems of Units.

A large number of units were proposed during the last half of the nineteenth century; most of them were based on the second, and on the metric system. Among them were the following:

Kelvin: The centimeter-gram-second system (cgs).

Giorgi: The meter-kilogram-second system (mks).

Moon: The decimeter-kilogram-second system.

Strout: The 10^9 centimeter- 10^{-9} gram-second system.

Weber and Gauss: The millimeter-milligram-second system.

The English system: Foot-pound-second. Force unit: one poundal.

All these systems were suggested to provide the theoretical and practical scientists with a useful viable frame of reference. Their use in theoretical physics is based on the proposition that the true dimensions of nature, if they exist, are beyond definition and discovery, and that they do not influence the formal relations and their observable results. But my own researches prove that both propositions are untenable in the light of facts.

My discovery of the true unit of length in nature led to a number of formal relations in which it is an essential part. When these formulas are worked out in gaussian units, their results differ from those anticipated by the difference between the centimeter and the natural unit of length, or that difference raised to a higher power. But when the natural unit of length is used to define the constants of a system, the elimination of this ratio leave us with simple proportion formulas whose results are identical with those obtained by conventional reductions. This identity is not affected by the changes which occur when a system's mass and time units are changed. I have worked out a large number of systems in which the length unit is a constant and the mass and time units are changed to produce an identity of two constants, or a specific difference between them. The most significant of these appears in the chapter on proof (Chapter 10).

411 New International Reference System.

In this system the unit of length is increased by 1.0419584 centimeters to one natural length unit, while the international units of mass and time—the gram and second—remain unchanged. The change of length makes it possible to idealize a large number of atomic constants by bringing out their simple natural proportions. The gaussian constants are then idealized by using the nl/cm length difference as conversion ratio. (See Sections 221 and 222.)

In anticipation of an extensive use of this new system of units by science, I make the following suggestions. Since the new length unit is close to one centimeter it seems advisable to retain the terminology of the metric system, with notations such as cm*, km*, cl*, to show the accompanying figures are in new centimeters, kilometers or centiliters. The term "new" can be used with the text to distinguish this new system from the gaussian system.

The mathematical sequence and the constants of the two tables are arranged and grouped like those of the gaussian system in Section 407. Note that many of the figures in the tables are meaningless equivalents which have been included for comparison. (For example: An electrostatic charge does not have a mass or wavenumber.) Figures which normally appear in tables of atomic constants have been underlined.

New international system.   (Mathematical sequence from Section 217.)

	m_c (Å)	c (T)	m' emu	v̇ (L)	h emu	2π
ters	9.108325^{-28}	× 2.877207^{10} = 2.620554^{-17})	× 2.328306^{-10} = 6.101685^{-27})/6.283185 =
10	-28.959438	× 10.458971 = -17.418410)	× -10.367040 = -27.785450)/0.798180 =
2	-89.826301	× 34.743950 = -55.082851)	× -32.000000 = -87.082851)/2.651496 =

	$\hbar$ emu	c/φ	e^2 esu	e esu	4πv̇	μ emu
ters	9.711133^{-29})	× 2.099464^8 = 2.038818^{-19})½ = 4.515327^{-10})/5.397215^{10} = 8.366031^{21}
10	-28.987270)	× 5.3221085 = -19.309378)½ = -10.654639)/10.732170 = -21.922519
2	-89.734347)	× 27.045446 = -62.038901)½ = -31.044451)/35.651496 = -66.695947

able of new international atomic units. (See table, Section 1004.)

	Mass in grams	Ergs emu	Ergs esu	Wavenumbers
$\hbar$	$3.3751944 \times 10^{-38}$	$9.7111328 \times 10^{-28}$	$2.7940940 \times 10^{-17}$	0.1591549
h	$2.1206972 \times 10^{-37}$	$6.1016847 \times 10^{-27}$	$1.7555810 \times 10^{-16}$	1.0
μ	$2.9076918 \times 10^{-31}$	$8.3680313 \times 10^{-21}$	$2.4070804 \times 10^{-10}$	1.3711019×10^6
e	$5.4544001 \times 10^{-31}$	$1.5693433 \times 10^{-20}$	$4.5153270 \times 10^{-10}$	2.5719844×10^6
m_o	$9.1083250 \times 10^{-28}$	$2.6206536 \times 10^{-17}$	7.5401630×10^{-7}	4.2946730×10^9
Q	$1.2079746 \times 10^{-24}$	$3.4755928 \times 10^{-11}$	1.0	5.6961200×10^{15}
I	$3.4755928 \times 10^{-11}$	1.0	2.8772070×10^{10}	1.6388916×10^{26}
G	1.0	2.8772070×10^{10}	8.2783201×10^{20}	4.7154305×10^{36}
R	$2.4248412 \times 10^{-32}$	$6.9767700 \times 10^{-22}$	2.0073612×10^{11}	1.1434172×10^5

lew international units in basic logarithms.

	Mass in grams	Ergs emu	Ergs esu	Wavenumbers
$\hbar$	-124.478297	-89.734347	-54.990397	-2.651496
h	-121.826801	-87.082851	-52.338901	0.0
μ	-101.4398965	-66.6959465	-31.9519965	20.3869045
e	-100.5323505	-65.7884005	-31.0444505	21.2944505
m_o	-89.826801	-55.082851	-20.338901	32.0000000
Q	-69.487900	-34.743950	0.0	52.338901
I	-34.743950	0.0	34.743950	87.082851
G	0.0	34.743950	69.487900	121.826801
R	-105.023809	-70.279859	-35.535909	16.802992

412 Formulas of New International System.

The conversion formulas below are in basic logarithms for easier checking. They are conventional formulas which obviously form a web of algebraic proportions. The significance of such a web is noted in Sections 119 and 222. With all its physical dimensions in natural lengths, it is obvious that the wavelengths, wavenumbers and radii defined below must be the same for all systems using this length unit. These figures can be checked against the figures of the table in Section 1023. Readers evaluating the significance of my figures should not overlook the fact that their conversions do not approximate, but give results whose values are the exact figures expected.

Electron's mass wavenumber.

$$\tilde{v} = \frac{mc}{h} \qquad \frac{-89.826801 \times 34.743950}{-87.082851} = 32.0$$

Electron's rest mass.

$$m_c = \frac{h\tilde{v}}{c} \qquad \frac{-87.082851 \times 32.0}{34.743950} = -89.826801$$

Electron's radius wl. $r = e^L / mc^L$.

$$\frac{(-31.0444505)^L}{-89.826801 \times (34.743950)^L} = -41.75$$

Electron's static charge. $e = \sqrt{hc/2\pi\phi}$

$$\sqrt{\frac{-87.082851 \times 34.743950}{2.651496 \times 7.098504}} = -31.0444505$$

Rydberg's wavenumber. Hydrogen electron's K orbit radiation potential.

$$R = \frac{2\pi^L me^4}{ch^3} \qquad \frac{1 \times (1.651496)^L \times -89.826801 \times (-31.0444505)^4}{34.743950 \times (-87.082851)^3} = 16.802992$$

Bohr magneton. Hydrogen electron's K orbit magnetic field.

$$\mu = \frac{he}{4\pi mc} \qquad \frac{-87.082851 \times -31.0444505}{3.651496 \times -89.826801 \times 34.743950} = -66.6959465$$

De Broglie wavelength. Circumference of hydrogen electron's K orbit.

$$\dot{v}\phi = B = \frac{1}{2R\phi} \qquad -32.0 \times 7.098504 = -24.901496 = \frac{0}{1 \times 16.802992 \times 7.098504}$$

Equated forces on hydrogen K orbit electron. Centrifugal and electrostatic.

$$\frac{mV^L}{r} = F = \frac{e^L}{r^L} \qquad \frac{-89.826801 \times (27.645446)^L}{-27.552992} = -6.982917 = \frac{(-31.0444505)^L}{(-27.552992)^L}$$

Waveratio constant. $ch/e^L = C = F/2mc^L (\tfrac{1}{2}\pi)^4$.

$$\frac{34.743950 \times -87.082851}{(-31.0444505)^L} = 9.75 = \frac{-6.982917}{1 \times -89.826801 \times (34.743950)^L \times (0.651496)^4}$$

Note: Its gravity constant appears in the table, Section 1023.

Chapter 5

ELECTRICITY MAGNETISM

The system of electrical and magnetic units defined in this chapter is the practical international system used to measure the quantity of electricity produced and consumed throughout the world. It is the meter-kilogram-second (mks) system of units made experimentally verifiable, as defined in Section 409.

501 Electrostatic Unit Charge. $e = 4.802471 \times 10^{-10}$ dyne/cm

One dyne = 2.082261×10^9 electrons

The absolute unit of electrostatic charge is defined as the repulsion of one dyne between two equal point charges one centimeter apart. The atomic unit of force—an electron's electrostatic charge at one centimeter—is equal to the reciprocal of the number of electrons needed to produce one dyne of force as defined above. Both have been obtained by experiments. (See Sections 511, 706; Fig. 19C and 25G).

502 Volt as Energy.

There is a clear distinction between the force of an electrostatic charge and the energy which it brings into being by acceleration. Volt is a force which can also be defined as an energy term for work done. One abvolt is equal to the expenditure of one erg of energy when a unit of positive charge is caused to move from one point to another against an attracting negative charge. One international volt is equal to 10^8 abvolts and 299.7930 statvolts (Section 401).

503 Volt. (V or E) $E = R \times I$. $\qquad$ V = 299.7930 statvolts

10^8 abvolts

The international unit of electromotive force: the force with which similar charges repel each other and opposite charges attract, redefined as the energy with which movable masses are accelerated through one second of time. It is the electrostatic acceleration needed to overcome the resistance against electrons moving through a conductor, thus producing a constant current of one ampere (I) against a resistance of one ohm (R). Note: In comparison with water flowing through a pipe, volt is pressure, ampere is its consequent volume of flow, and ohm is the resistance to that flow.

504 Coulomb. $\qquad$ (Q) $Q = I \times T = E \times T/R$. $Q = 6.242474 \times 10^{18}$ electrons

1/10th abcoulomb

A unit of electrical quantity: the number of electrons passing through a conductor in one second when the current is one ampere. It is equal to 1/10th of a reciprocal of an electromagnetic unit charge, 1.601929×10^{-20} emu, as defined in Section 702. The number of electrons in one abcoulomb can be obtained by multiplying the number of electrons in an electrostatic unit by the speed of light, as defined below. See Sections 210, 501, Figs. 19B and 32G. Symbols: T is time, c is the speed of light, and U is the unit charge in electrons. The abcoulomb is obtained by the formula: Q = Uc. 10 coulombs =2.082261×10^9 $\times 2.99793 \times 10^{10} = 6.242474 \times 10^{19}$ electrons.

505 Ampere. (I) I = E/R   1/10th abampere

A unit of electric current: the motion of electrons through a conductor from negative to positive terminal; a current of one coulomb of electrons passing a wire cross section in one second; the current induced by one volt acting against a resistance of one ohm. The electromagnetic unit of current—the abampere—is defined as that current which produces a turning force of 2π dynes on a unit magnetic pole at the center of a circular wire, one centimeter in radius, when its axis is on the plane of the circle. The international ampere is one-tenth of this unit.

506 Ohm. (R) R = E/I $R = 1.112646 \times 10^{-12}$ statohms
                                                                                    10^9 abohms

A unit of resistance: the opposition of a conductor to an electric current; that opposition which reduces a current to one ampere when the pressure is one volt. When the current is increased above unity, the resistance of its conductor increases as the current squared. It will, therefore, take a pressure of 4 volts to produce a current of 2 amperes through a wire with unit resistance. The loss of energy reappears as work done, in the form of a raise of temperature, a chemical reaction, physical motion, etc.

507 Joule. (J or W) 10^7 ergs

The meter-kilogram-second (mks) unit of energy, power and work: the energy expended in the acceleration of a two-kilogram mass to a velocity of one meter per second. It is equal to one watt-second (see Section 209 Fig. 27K).

508 Watt. (W) $W = E^2 \times T/R = I^2 \times R \times T$ 10^7 ergs

A unit of energy, power and work: work done at the rate of one joule per second; power consumed or expended at the rate of one volt-ampere-second. One kilowatt is 1000 watts. One kilowatt-hour is this figure times 3600 seconds, or, 3.6×10^6 watts or joules. One English-American horsepower is equal to 746 watts, and a continental horsepower is 736 watts (see Fig. 30K and 33K).

509 Farad. (C) 10^{-9} abfarad

A unit of electrical capacitance: a condenser with a capacitance of one coulomb when it is charged with a potential of one volt. This unit is too large for practical use, so the international unit is the microfarad. It is equal to one millionth of a farad, or a capacitance of 6.242474×10^{12} electrons (see Section 504).

The attraction of a positive charge for electrons, and the repulsions between electrons due to their similar charges, causes the electron density to increase when two plates with opposite charges are near each other. One type of charge is induced by its opposite. This condenser effect reduces the charge value of the general field to near-zero. A thin insulating substance between two condenser plates increases capacitance, due to its transmission of electron displacements within its molecules.

510 Henry. (B) 10^9 abhenry
A unit of induction: the rate at which a changing electromagnetic force resolves into the energy of an electric current; a transfer of energy from a primary to a secondary electric circuit by causing the magnetization current passing through a solinoid to increase or decrease in power, thus inducing a current in another solinoid in proportion to its rate of change. A changing electromagnetic field can also be produced by a moving magnet, as in dynamos and generators.

A circuit has one henry of induction when the inducing current, varying at the rate of one ampere per second, produces an electromotive force of one volt in the secondary circuit. A henry of induction can also be produced by a magnet by causing its field to change at the rate of one ampere-second near a solinoid through motion.

511 Faraday. (F)   Physical unit = 1.00027497 chemical units
Physical u.   9651.39856 abcoulombs = 96513.9856 coulombs.(See 504.)
Chemical u.   9648.74576 abcoulombs = 96487.4576 coulombs.

A quantity unit in electrolysis: the number of ampere-seconds (coulombs) needed to transport a gram-mole of singly ionized atoms through an electrolytic solution. It is equal to the number of atoms in a gram mole (Avogadro's number. See Figs. 28M, 28N and 34E), divided by the number of unit charges moving through the solution in one ampere-second (see Sections 504 and 505). It follows that doubly ionized atoms require twice the current per gram mole. The faraday in abcoulombs is obtained by multiplying a unit of electromagnetic charge by Avogadro's number. The difference between a physical and chemical faraday is abstracted from their different definitions of a gram mole, as described in Section 903.

N Avogadro's number. 902, 28M, 28N   C Chemical faradays
Q Electrons in one coulomb. 504, 32G   P Physical faradays

$= N/Q$ $6.024860 \times 10^{23} / 6.242474 \times 10^{18} = 96513.9856$ coulombs physical u.
$= Ne$ $6.024860 \times 10^{23} \times 1.601929 \times 10^{-20} = 9651.39856$ abcoulombs physical u.
          $6.023204 \times 10^{23} \times 1.601929 \times 10^{-20} = 9648.74576$ abcoulombs chemical u.

512 Magnetic Unit Pole. (m^1)
A unit of magnetic force: that magnetic pole strength which causes one unit pole to repel a similar unit pole with a force of one dyne at a distance of one centimeter. A magnet's intensity of magnetization is defined as its number of unit poles per square centimeter. Magnetic intensity decreases as the inverse square of the distance from a north or south magnetic pole.

513. Magnetic Moment. (I)

The turning force acting upon a magnet in a vector field. It is greatest when the magnet's axis is on the plane of a magnetizing current and, therefore, is at a right angle to the axis of its poles. The turning force is equal to the magnet's length in centimeters times the strength of one of its poles. It is 2π dynes (6.2832) for a unit pole when its centimer-long magnet is on the plane of maximum turning force in a single turn wire one centimer in radius through which a current of one ampere is passing.

514 Oersted. (H)

A unit of magnetic field strength: the intensity of a magnetic field when it acts upon a unit magnetic pole with a force of one dyne; the strength of an undisturbed magnetic field one centimer from a unit pole. One oersted is defined as one line of force per square centimeter in the air.

515 Gauss. (B)

A unit of magnetic flux density and magnetic induction. (Flux density is the number of tubes of force per square centimeter of cross section normal to the tubes.) One gauss is one line of magnetic flux passing perpendicularly through one square centimeter.

Note that unperturbed lines of force are in oersteds, while lines perturbed by induction and the presence of permeable masses, such as iron, are in gauss. Since the number of such lines define the potential induction of an electric current in henrys, (510), they are also called lines of induction.

516 Maxwell. (Φ)

A unit of magnetic flux: the total number of lines of induction passing through a specific region; the flux density per square centimeter (in gauss) times the area of the region.

Example: A magnetized iron bar with a square cross section of two centimeters (four square centimeters), and a flux density of 200 gauss, has a total flux of 800 maxwells.

517 Ratio: Magnetic Flux to Pole Strength.

A unit pole produces a flux density of one gauss per square centimeter at a distance of one centimeter. Since the surface area of a sphere one centimeter in radius is 4π square centimeters, the total flux radiating from its magnetic poles is 12.56637 maxwells. The pole strength of any magnet is therefore its flux density in maxwells divided by 4π.

518 Magnetizing Current Formulas.

The unit of action in the formulas below is the magnetic field intensity at a distance of one centimeter from a conductor carrying a current of one abampere, as defined in Section 505. Since one abampere is equal to ten international amperes, the doubling of values in the first three formulas give us a field intensity of one gauss when five ordinary (international) amperes are passed through the conductor and coils.

H	Field intensity in dynes and gauss.			r Radius of coil.
n	Turns per centimeter length of solinoid.			I Current in amperes.
N	Turns of conductor wire in flat coil.			π Pi. Circle to diam.
Straight conductor.	Single turn coil.	Many turn coil.		Solinoid A long coil.
$H = 2I/r$	$H = 2\pi I/r$	$H = 2\pi NI/r$		$H = 4\pi nI$

519 Electromagnets.

When a soft iron bar is inserted in a conducting coil or solinoid, the magnetization increases greatly, because the iron acts as an accumulator of electromagnetic energy. There is a transfer of directed electron motions from the conductor to the atoms and molecules of the iron. The consequent inertia within the iron acts as an opposition to a rapid increase or decrease of magnetization. This opposition can be transferred to a secondary coil as an induced current proportional to the rate of change. Its direction is always such as to oppose the change of state (see Henry, Section 510).

Chapter 6

W A V E D Y N A M I C S

The possibilities and limitations of waves are of special interest to theoretical physics because ether waves, besides having the simple properties anticipated for first causes, also appear to be the phenomena into which matter and physical phenomena resolve, and from which, therefore, they might have been created. This subject is discussed in detail in Book Two. The first sections on physical wave phenomena outline their elementary properties. They are followed by a description of waves in the ether and their observed relations to the quantized masses and motions in the atoms.

601 Wavedynamics and Wave Phenomena.

The fundamental property of waves is their ability to transmit momenta through a medium. The speed of transmission across a measurable distance gives us a definable time and a natural relationship between wavelengths and pulsation periods. The interactions between wave momenta and the inertia of their transmitting medium produce effects which can be classified roughly as local momentary inversions of the momenta, and the continuity and dispersal of the waves thus produced along a gradient of descending power with an increasing distance from their origin. The energy of waves is the action potentials of contained, periodically inverting momenta.

Wave momenta have a theoretical continuity through space from their origins in accordance with Newton's laws of motion, as defined in Section 315. It follows that their conversion into periodic pulsations is a product of containment, and that the anticipated continuity is transferred to the medium as a deformation of its natural shape. The medium thus acts as a momentary container of the waves and as a potential momentum state. However, if the localization of periodic wave motions are of long duration, it is necessary to postulate their isolation by containing forces through actions transcending the possibilities of their medium's inertia, or we must postulate a continuous supply of new wave energy. (see Book Two for my theory of containment.)

The energy of periodic waves can be defined as local accumulations of contained and self-contained momenta. When the only containing force is the inertia of their medium, the periodic waves expand and diverge in accordance with the laws of momentum. The medium not only opposes this expansion, but its inertia also opposes a return to the original inert state after it has been set in motion by periodic waves. Note that the inertia of a medium increases the time during which an expanding momentum acts, but it does not reduce its total power as defined by the longer time value.

When the expansion and action gradient of a wave pattern is eliminated, there remains a group of stationary self-contained periodic waves. The stresses and motions they produce in their medium are paired opposite equal potential and kinetic energies, and their functional inversions through a period are, therefore, equal to the theoretically inactive state of the medium when added.

When a train of waves passes from one medium into another with a different density (inertia), their direction of motion is changed in proportion to the angle of transition. The waves are refracted because one side is retarded more than the other. When light waves are passed through a prism, short waves are bent more than long waves. White light is thus broken up into its component colors, as in the rainbow.

Waves bend around obstacles in their paths, and long waves bend more than short waves. This effect is used in the diffraction grating—a surface of parallel rulled lines—to convert light waves into a spectrum. When an obstacle causes a homogenous group of waves to divide and move in different directions in the same area, the consequent overlapping of their dynamic states opposes and reinforces each other at different points, thus producing an interference pattern of locally active and inactive states.

A physical structure with a latent ability to produce a particular wavelength, when energized, usually responds to waves transmitted by another source on the same wavelength by converting a part of that energy into a physical vibration. A violin string will tend to vibrate in consonance with the sound waves to which it is tuned. Atoms absorb light waves on their radiation wavelengths. The wavelengths of radio and T.V. receivers are changed by their tuning dials, thus making it possible to obtain the broadcast of a particular station.

The shape and natural periodicities of a confining physical medium can produce numerous different waves, such as Chladni figures and the quantizing waves in atoms; however, when they are free to expand through a large homogenous medium, such as the atmosphere or the ether of space, they are limited to longitudinal and transverse oscillations. Longitudinal waves vibrate in the same direction as their propagation, while transverse waves vibrate at right angles to their motion.

Sound waves are longitudinal and light waves are transverse. Water waves combine transverse pulsations with horizontal motions. Earthquakes produce both horizontal and transverse waves. Because the former move nearly twice as fast as the latter, it is possible to estimate the distance of an observer from the origin of an earthquake by noting the difference in the waves' arrival time. Horizontal waves pass through gases, liquids and solids, while transverse waves are transmitted by solids only. Because transverse wave momenta must invert, they require an elastic medium or a containing force for their return and transmission as a directional motion.

Because light waves are transverse and matter is known to move through space without loss of energy, it is argued that the ether must be both a solid and a tenuous gas, and that the ether does not exist because it cannot be both. My theory in Book Two assumes that a contracting ether solves both problems.

602 Wave Terms Described and Defined.

Waves are periodically inverting dynamic actions in a medium. The waves in a train are equally spaced and of similar shapes. The following terms are used: *Wavelength:* The distance between successive maximas. *Amplitude*: The height of transverse waves, as contrasted with their length. *Wavenumber*: The number of waves in one length unit. *Frequency*: For waves moving with the speed of light, it is the number of waves passing a point in one unit of time; for stationary waves, it is the number of periodic pulsations in one unit of time. *Periodicity*: The time it takes one moving wave to pass a point in space, or the time it takes a stationary wave to pass through one full cycle of change. *Node*: The undisturbed parts of a stationary wave. *Loop*: The parts of a stationary wave vibrating with maximum amplitude.

In theoretical physics, wavelengths are in centimeters, and wavenumbers are the number of waves in one centimeter—the reciprocal of wavelength. Frequency is the number of periodic pulsations in one second, and periodicity is the time it takes a wave to pass through a cycle of change—the reciprocal of frequency. Wave frequencies are wavenumbers multiplied by the speed of light.

Light travels through space in photons with energies that do not change with distance. The energy of a photon of waves is its wavenumber multiplied by the energy of a centimeter wave—a wave-energy ratio discovered by Max Planck in 1901 (see Section 606). Wavelengths, therefore, decrease when the energy of a free photon increases. (See Physical Constants, page 152, columns C, T and U.)

603 Dynamics of Physical Periodicities.

The motions of a simple pendulum (Section 309) give us the basic relationship between force, length and time in wave dynamics. When its length is replaced by mass m, and its gravity by spring stiffness k, a formula defining the vibration period of a mass suspended by a spring is obtained. Its period in time: $T = 2\pi \sqrt{m/k}$.

The velocity of a transverse wave through a stretched wire is obtained by the formula: $V = \sqrt{t/m}$, with V the velocity through the wire, t its tension, and m its mass per unit length. Let V stand for centimeters per second, t for 10^5 dynes of force, and m for 0.04 gram per unit length, and the wave speed is:

$$V = \sqrt{t/m} \qquad \sqrt{10^5/0.04} = 1531.1 \text{ centimeters per second.}$$

A frequency of 120 vibrations per second gives its wavelength:

$$\lambda = V/f \qquad 1531.1/120 = 13.176 \text{ centimeters}$$

The natural period of a wire supported at both ends is obtained by this formula: $V = \sqrt{t/(m/L)}$, with L its length and m its mass. Since its end supports are nodes reflecting the standing waves, the distance between them is only half of the wavelength. Its fundamental wave, therefore, has the frequency: $F = V/2L$. Its first overtone is: $F = V/L$, and its second overtone is: $F = 3V/2L$. The complete formula for the frequency of a vibrating wire is compared below with that of a vibrating column of air, such as the pipes of an organ.

Stretched wire.

L   Distance in cm. between nodes.
F   Frequency per second.
m   Mass of wire in gram per cm.
t   Tension of wire in dynes.

$F = 1/2L\sqrt{t/m}$

Air column.

L   Length of air column.
K   Compressibility of the gas.
d   Density of the gas.
p   Pressure of the gas.

$F = 1/2L\sqrt{K(p/d)}$

604 Wave Velocity.

The velocity of a compression wave through a homogenuous medium in which the molecules are in contact, such as a solid or a liquid, depends upon its density and elasticity. When e is the volume modulus of elasticity of the medium and d its density, the formula for velocity is: $V = \sqrt{e/d}$. The speed of sound through iron is about 5,100 meters per second, and it is about 1,440 meters per second through water.

As a rule the speed of sound is greatest for solids, intermediate for liquids and least for gases. It is low for gases because the mean distances between their molecules are great in comparison with their physical sizes. A gas therefore transmits the momenta of sound waves through periodic collisions, with the speed of sound depending upon the molecular velocities of the gas. Because molecules with relatively small masses move faster at equal pressures and temperatures, they transmit sound waves with greater speed. Its speed, therefore, is high for hydrogen and low for air, and increases as the square root of the absolute temperature for all gases (see Sections 901 and 905). The speed of sound is about 1,270 meters per second through hydrogen and 331.5 through the air, at normal pressures and temperatures.

The density of an atmosphere has little influence upon the speed with which it transmits sound waves. Classical science assumes that the ether has the properties of a perfect gas, and that the mean velocity of its particles produces the observed velocity of light. My theory of a contracting ether in Book Two is based on this postulate.

605 Electromagnetic Waves.

In 1864 Clerk-Maxwell worked out a series of mathematical formulas from experimental determinations of electrostatic capacitance and magnetic permeability. He proved that electrostatic and electromagnetic forces are related through a velocity of interaction which turned out to be the speed of light in a vacuum (see Section 213). It is, therefore, the difference between esu and emu values, as defined by the table in Section 401 and the columns C and D in the large table of constants, Chapter 11, page 152. The implied electromagnetic nature of ether waves was proved by Hertz in 1887. It has also been proved and confirmed by atomic theory and countless experiments.

The observed inverse square gradient of electrostatic charges with distance from their origins implies a continuity of their action potentials to infinity in space. As long as an electron moves with uniform velocity, its negative electrostatic field accompanies it without radiation. But when a change of velocity or direction is imposed upon it, the distant parts of its field cannot change at once, because the change is transmitted with a finite speed. It follows that a quantity of its charge, proportional to the rate of change, is liberated as a radiation. Since maximum displacement occurs at a right angle to its line of motion, a maximum of energy is radiated in that direction.

The symbols in the radiation formula below are: c, the speed of light; f, acceleration of the electron; e, its electrostatic charge; and R, its radiation energy.

$$R = 1/6\pi(e^2 f^2/c^3).$$

The energy of a moving electron's negative charge field induces a magnetic field at a right angle to its line of motion and its plane of vibration. The periodic waves on its plane of vibration act as carriers of its charge-related, potentially reducible momentum to its magnetic field, or from that field to the charge, and a radiation as defined by the formula above.

606 Energy of a Centimeter Wave. $h = 6.624461 \times 10^{-27}$ erg emu
$$hc = 1.985967 \times 10^{-16} \text{ erg esu}$$

This unit of energy is also called Planck's quantum, after the scientist who discovered and defined it in 1901. It is the energy of a free (radiated) photon with a wavelength of one centimeter, in electromagnetic and electrostatic units (see Section 401). Because a free photon's wavenumber is directly proportional to its energy, the energy of any photon, such as a photon of light waves, can be obtained by multiplying its wavenumber in one centimeter by Planck's quantum of action in emu, or by dividing its wavelength by that quantum.

Max Planck obtained the energy of a centimeter wave by a mathematical analysis of light waves emanating from a cavity radiator—a hollow ball with a small hole through which some of the internally reflected light waves from an internal incandescence can escape. According to theory, a continuous radiation of energy by excited atoms within the cavity should be accompanied by a degeneration of wave energy and an increase of wavelengths, due to their countless reflections within the cavity before escape. It should produce a maximum of wave energy in the infrared wavelengths, while the actual radiation maximum is in the short wavelengths of the visible range.

Planck proved that the greater than theoretical energy of observed radiations can be explained by assuming that atoms absorb and radiate energy in quantized wave bundles. A comparison with waves transmitted by a physical medium, such as sound and water waves, caused physicists to believe that waves in the ether would disperse from their sources and, thus, lose energy with distance. In 1905 Einstein suggested that Planck's quantized wave bundles move through space without loss of energy as photons—that they have properties comparable to those of matter waves. He pointed out that this postulate would explain the photo-electric effect. It had been noted that electrons are ejected from a metal plate by irradiation. When a plate is irradiated by monochromatic light (light waves with the same wavelength and energy), the electrons were ejected with the same speed regardless of brightness, while the number of electrons ejected was proportional to brightness. An increase of energy by a reduction of wavelength increased the velocity of ejected electrons. When their wavelengths are the same, a photon which has traveled through space for countless light years will have the same energy potential as one which has traveled only a few inches. It is possible to obtain Planck's quantum from the photo-electric effect, as well as many other phenomena.

607 Energy-Wavelength of a Radiation.

When one of the electrons in an atom drops into a lower quantum orbit and/or state, a quantity of energy equal to the difference between them is liberated as a free photon of energy. The wavelength of this radiation is a reciprocal of its energy. From my definition of Planck's quantum in the preceding section, it is evident that the energy of a centimeter wave, multiplied by a free photon's wavenumber, gives us its energy in ergs.

Radiations by atoms range from cosmic rays through x rays and visible light to the relatively long wavelengths of heat rays. Molecular radiations and physical surges of electrons extend it through radar and radio waves to waves with long periodicities. Since most natural radiations occur in the visible range, the two examples below are for its longest and shortest wavelengths. In the large square table of constants, Chapter 11, we find the wavenumbers of red and violet to be about 14000 and 24000 waves per centimeter, respectively. (See fig 5., 15U and 16U.) Multipled by Planck's quantum their energies are:

$$= \bar{\nu}h \qquad 14000 \times 6.624461 \times 10^{-27} = 9.274245 \times 10^{-23} \text{ erg emu} \quad (15B)$$
$$24000 \times 6.624461 \times 10^{-27} = 1.589871 \times 10^{-22} \quad \text{"} \quad \text{"} \quad (16B)$$

Assuming that a red or violet light photon could unite with a stationary electron, its energy above becomes the electron's energy of motion. Its velocity is obtained by the formula: $V = \sqrt{2E/m}$. An electron mass of 9.108325×10^{-28} gram gives us a velocity of 451.2685 centimeters per second for a red light photon, and 590.8492 cm. per second for violet light. The absorption of a light photon by an atom adds its energy to the orbital energy of one electron (see Section 320).

608 Waves are Quantized.

A comparison with the dispersal of physical waves through their medium (such as sound waves through the air) caused classical physics to draw the erroneous conclusion that waves in the ether should also disperse from their sources. The behavior of electrostatic charges in gross phenomena led them to the conclusion that changes of velocity or direction, as defined in Section 605, cause electrons to radiate energy in proportion to the forces needed to effect the change. Such changes should cause the orbital electrons in atoms to lose energy and spiral into their nuclei, an assumption which was known to be erroneous.

Einstein's postulate, that radiations move through space as photons of energy, solved the first problem; Bohr's assumption that atomic electrons move in quantized non-radiating orbits solved the second. Both men left the problem of why and how unsolved. Bohr defined a non-radiating orbit as one in which the electron's mean orbital velocity produced an orbital (de Broglie) wavelength equal to the orbit's circumference or to a whole fraction of that circumference. Its smallest orbit has one wave, its second orbit has two, its third has three, and so on, with the wavelengths increasing with distance.

When an electron drops from one of these quantized orbits into a smaller one, the energy difference between them is radiated. When a free photon is absorbed by an atom, an electron with a corresponding energy difference jumps into the larger orbit. The internal quantizing of electron orbits and their energies are thus revealed by the energies and wavelengths of their radiations (see Section 812).

609 Rydberg's Wavenumber.   17U   R = 109737.320 waves per cm.

The orbital elements of a negative electron circling an atom's positive nucleus are comparable to those of a planet circling the sun's center of gravity. The ratio sequence: $-R^1$, R^2, R^3 and $-R^4$, defines the relative velocities, radii, periods and forces of attraction of two orbits in both cases (see Sections 215 and 316). In Section 320 the energy of orbital motion is shown to equal one half of the energy of escape from that orbit. The doubling of an orbiting body's energy of motion, therefore, accelerates it to its velocity of escape.

An electron, accelerated by a positive charge from a theoretically infinite distance to an orbital motion around its center, will liberate one half of the energy of acceleration as a radiation, and retain the other half as its energy of orbital motion. Rydberg's wavenumber is the energy equivalent of a hydrogen electron's orbital motion in its smallest (K) orbit. It is, therefore, also the equivalent of energy liberated by the transition above, and the reciprocal of the wavelength which will cause a hydrogen electron to escape from that orbit.

Rydberg's wavenumber is idealized by postulating an infinite mass—a stationary nuclear unit charge. The wavenumber obtained by experiments is smaller because the electron and proton circle a common center of inertia. The difference is equivalent to the reciprocal of a hydrogen atom's mass ($M_p + m_0$ = proton plus electron) in electrons plus one. Let D be the divisor and H a hydrogen atom in electrons, and we obtain the observed wavenumber by these formulas:

$D = 1/H + 1.$ 1/1837.114 + 1.0 = 1.00054433 reduction ratio

$R_o = R/D$ 109737.32/1.00054433 = 109677.62 wavenumber, observed

Rydberg's wavenumber for an infinite mass is defined in the table of constants, Chapter 11, by 17U, and a proton's mass in electrons by 23F. The conversions above can be compared with the formulas in Sections 322. The Rydberg wavenumber for singly ionized helium is one fourth of its observed value because of its positive nuclear charge, being twice that of hydrogen, increases the orbital energy of its K orbit electron by four. The energy equivalent in electron volts needed to strip their nuclei of electrons is obtained by dividing their wavenumbers by the wavenumber of one electron volt. The divisor is 8066.24253, as defined in Section 703 and by figure 14U.

Terms	Elec. volt	Wavenumber	Wavelength
Hydrogen. Infinite mass	13.604516	109737.32	911.26699 angstrom
Hydrogen. True value	13.597114	109677.62	911.76302 "
Ionized helium. (wn./4 =	13.602664	109722.39	911.39104 "
Ionized helium. True va.	54.410656	438889.55	227.84776×10^{-8} cm.

My idealizations of the fundamental units of physics makes it possible to obtain Rydberg's wavenumber by two different formulas. The first of these is the conventional formula; the second is an ideal proportion formula with a conversion from natural length units to centimeters. It is of special interest because it makes use of pi and the electronic constant in Section 614.

Velocity of light in cm/sec. 210, 52C	V	Electron volts. 703, 14H
Electrostatic unit, esu. 501, 19C	R	Rydberg's wavenumber. 17U
Planck's quantum unit, emu. 606, 8B	ϕ	Electronic constant. 614
Electron's mass in grams. 710, 21A	$\mathcal{t}$	Natural length, cm. 221, 7T

$$\frac{2\pi^2 me^4}{ch^3} \quad \frac{(6.283853)^2 \times 9.108325 \times 10^{-28} \times (4.8024713 \times 10^{-10})^4}{2.99793 \times 10^{10} \times (6.624461 \times 10^{-27})^3} = 109737.32 \text{ wn/cm.}$$

$$\frac{(\pi/2)^4 \phi^2}{\mathcal{t}} \quad \frac{(3.14159265/2)^4 \times (137.044809)^2}{1.0419584} = 109737.31 \text{ waves per cm.}$$

610 De Broglie's Momentum Waves. (B or λ)

In 1924 Louis de Broglie suggested that moving masses are accompanied by waves whose wavelengths decrease with increases of momenta in accordance with the formula: $B = h/mV$ (Planck's quantum divided by mass times velocity). Note that mv is the formula for momentum, and that the de Broglie waves of a mass change wavenumber in direct proportion to its changes of velocity. The momentum of a mass is to be contrasted with its energy of motion as defined by the formula: $E = \frac{1}{2}mV^2$. That the de Broglie waves of moving electrons and protons are their true wavelengths is proved by their quantizing of electron orbits in the atoms, and by many other phenomena.

Let us assume the speed of a mass is abruptly reduced to zero, and that the momentum of its velocity pattern becomes the momentum of a free photon moving with the speed of light. When the energy of motion of this photon is converted into its wavelength by the formula, $\dot{v} = h/E$, we find its wavelength greatly increased by the separation. The de Broglie wavelength of a hydrogen electron in its smallest (K) orbit is shorter than its Rydberg radiation wavelength by 2ϕ = 274.089618 ratio. It is defined by two formulas below. Symbols: m_o is an electron's rest mass in grams, v its velocity in centimeters per second, B its de Broglie wavelength, and h is Planck's quantum of energy (see Sections 606 and 708).

$$B = \frac{h}{mv} \qquad \frac{6.624461 \times 10^{-27}}{9.108325 \times 10^{-28} \times 2.187555 \times 10^{8}} = 3.324705 \times 10^{-8} \text{ centimeter}$$

$$B = \frac{1}{2\phi R} \qquad \frac{1}{2 \times 137.044809 \times 109737.32} = 3.324705 \text{ angstrom wavelength.}$$

611 Energy and Momentum Waves Converge.

When the momentum waves of a moving mass are converted into the energy waves of a free photon, the wavelength increases. The difference in wavelength decreases with an increase of velocity until a coincidence of values appears at twice the speed of light, assuming that the observed increase of mass with speed near the velocity of light is not included, since it makes the coincidence a physical impossibility. The converge is defined for idealized electron motions in section 1027.

To bring out the convergence in the simplest possible terms, I compare the conversion values and the ratio difference between an electron moving with the energy of one electron volt and one moving with the energy of a thousand electron volts. The energy difference is therefore equal to 10^3. The electron volt is defined in Section 703. The energy of an electron's rest mass equals 8.186184×10^{-7} erg esu. (See 710 and 21C.)

B	De Broglie momentum wl. 610	m₀	Electron's mass. 708, 21A
c	The speed of light. 210, 34B	P	Free photon energy wl. 607
E	Energy of motion. 703, 14C	R	Ratio of wavelengths. 1027
h	Planck's energy qu. 606, 8B	V	Velocity of electron. 703

$E = \frac{1}{2}mV^2$ $0.5 \times 9.108325 \times 10^{-28} \times (5.930856 \times 10^7)^2 = 1.601929 \times 10^{-12}$ erg esu
$\phantom{E = \frac{1}{2}mV^2}$ $0.5 \times 9.108325 \times 10^{-28} \times (1.875501 \times 10^9)^2 = 1.601929 \times 10^{-9}$ "   "

$B = h/mV$ $6.624461 \times 10^{-27}/9.108325 \times 10^{-28} \times 5.930856 \times 10^7 = 12.26294 \times 10^{-8}$ wl/
 $6.624461 \times 10^{-27}/9.108325 \times 10^{-28} \times 1.875501 \times 10^9 = 0.387738 \times 10^{-8}$ wl/

$P = hc/E$ $6.624461 \times 10^{-27} \times 2.997930 \times 10^{10}/1.601929 \times 10^{-12} = 1.239735 \times 10^{4}$ wl/
 $6.624461 \times 10^{-27} \times 2.997930 \times 10^{10}/1.601929 \times 10^{-9} = 1.239735 \times 10^{7}$ wl/

$R = P/B$ $1.239735 \times 10^{4}/1.226294 \times 10^{-7} = 1010.960$ wavelength ratio
 $1.239735 \times 10^{7}/3.877882 \times 10^{9} = 31.96937$ "   "

612 Planck's Quantum/Two Pi.   3B $\hbar = 1.054316 \times 10^{-27}$ erg emu
 3C $c\,\hbar = 3.160756 \times 10^{-17}$ erg esu

When a free photon is captured by an atom, its energy and momentum become associated with the motion of an orbiting electron. Its consequent conversion from linear to circular motion, with energy and momentum distributed along the electron's orbit, reduces the action potential of this energy by 2π. (It appears in the algebraic sequence, in the tables of constants and in a hydrogen electron's K orbit.) Its base value is obtained from Planck's quantum, Section 606.

ħ= h/2π $6.6244607 \times 10^{-27} / 2 \times 3.14159265 = 1.0543157 \times 10^{-27}$ erg emu.

613 Waveratio Constant.   C = 861.077930 ratio

This is a fundamental ratio in electron physics defining a difference in wavelength between the contained waves of matter and the free waves of their radiations. Its value, therefore, is independent of the system of units used to define the constants of physics. It can be obtained by comparing measurements using the same length unit.

Assuming that the wavelength of an electron's rest mass energy is equal to its radius, as defined by the ultimate system of units in Sections 115, 711 and 1021, the conversion of its rest mass energy into the energy of a free (radiation) photon increases its wavelength by the waveratio constant. When the idealized radius of a hydrogen electron in its smallest (K) orbit is multiplied by the waveratio constant, we obtain its orbital period in electron radius time units. A doubling of this period gives us Rydberg's wavelength for an infinite mass. Planck's constant of energy in the ultimate system of units is equal to the waveratio constant (see Sections 1021 and 1023). The constant C = $2\pi\phi$ = Log$_2$ 9.75, with ϕ being the electronic constant.

Since the waveratio and the electronic constants are in fixed proportions, any formula defining one of them can be used with 2π to obtain the other. The waveratio constant is defined by three formulas below.

```
El's K orbit radius in hy. 812       R  Rydberg's wavelength. 609, 17T
El's mass wavelength. 708, 21T       r  Electron's radius wl. 711
Electronic constant. 215, 614        2π Circumference in radii. 115
```

$= 2\pi\phi$ $2 \times 3.14159265 \times 137.044809 = 861.077930$ ratio.

$= R/2\delta$ $9.112670 \times 10^{-6} / 2 \times 5.291432 \times 10^{-9} = 861.077930$

$= \dot{v}/r$ $2.425998 \times 10^{-10} / 2.817397 \times 10^{-13} = 861.077930$

614 Electronic Constant.   ($\phi = 1/\alpha$) $\phi = 137.044809$ ratio

Fine Structure Constant. $\alpha = 7.29688346 \times 10^{-3}$ ratio

I use the term "electronic constant" for the reciprocal of the fine structure constant, because the latter is a meaningless term in theoretical physics. It was originally discovered by the splitting of lines in atomic radiation spectra, due to the interaction between orbital electrons electrostatic and electromagnetic fields. Its presence as a factor in numerous formulas shows that it is a fundamental ratio in nature. Its defined value does not change with changes of the fundamental units of action in physics, because it is a theoretically measurable or definable ratio between values using the same dimensional factor. It can be used, therefore, to determine the most probable value of those constants that do change with changes of the units of length, mass and time. See Sections 215, 220, 222, 813, 1021 and 1023. The electronic constant times 2 pi defines the waveratio constant of Section 613.

Since the electronic constant is the reciprocal of the fine structure constant, the formulas below are easily converted. The new sign was selected to go with the more appropriate term which I am using. The fine structure constant is the only quantity of zero dimension which can be formed from the three constants, e, h and c. They appear in the first reduction below. Besides the nine formulas below, additional formulas can be invented through ananalysis of the table of constants in Section 1023.

B	El's momentum wl. in hy. 610	ó	El's orbit radius in hy. 812
c	Speed of light. 210, 34B, 32C	r	Electron's radius wl. 711
C	Waveratio constant. 613	R	Rydberg's wavenumber. 609, 17
e	Electron's charge, esu. 701, 19C	Ȓ	Rydberg's wavelength. 609, 17
h	Planck's energy co., emu. 606, 8B	ṽ	Electron's mass wn. 709, 21U
2π	Circumference in radii. 115	V	El's speed in hy. K orbit. 81

$$\alpha = V/c = 2B/\bar{R} = 2\pi\tilde{v}r = 2\pi/C$$

$$\alpha = \frac{2\pi e^2}{hc} \qquad \frac{2 \times 3.14159265 \times (4.8024713 \times 10^{-10})^2}{6.6244607 \times 10^{-27} \times 2.99793 \times 10^{10}} = 7.2968835 \times 10^{-3}$$

$$\phi = C/2\pi \qquad 861.077930/6.28318531 = 137.044809 \text{ ratio}$$

$$\phi = \sqrt{\frac{\tilde{v}}{2R}} \qquad \sqrt{\frac{4.12201445 \times 10^9}{2 \times 109737.317}} = 137.044809$$

$$\phi = \sqrt{\frac{\delta}{r}} \qquad \sqrt{\frac{5.2914313 \times 10^{-9}}{2.8173967 \times 10^{-13}}} = 137.044809$$

615 Wavemechanics and Entropy.

The amount of energy available in a heat engine is determined by its temperature relative to its environment and the potential flow of energy from hot to cold areas. Work is done by equalizing temperatures, and thus increasing entropy. (Entropy is a measure of the unavailable energy in a heat system.) The entropy of the universe appears to be constantly increasing, because the stars are radiating away their masses. If matter is organization and radiation a first step toward chaos, an increase of entropy can also be defined as an increase of disorganization in the universe.(See Sections 913-4.)

It will be noticed that a small part of the energy radiated by the sun is captured by the living processes on earth and converted into the potential energy of organic structures. The organic growth of living bodies is a local reduction of entropy, as defined above. Even though it is an infinitesimal part of the energy liberated by the stars, our recognition of life as a reversal of entropy is important because it symbolizes a process which converts chaos into organization under special conditions.

Our experience with waves of various kinds, from sound waves to the electromagnetic waves of radio and television, tells us that energy can be converted into periodic pulsations by containment. When energy is captured and converted into periodic waves within a hollow box, and caused to remain there, the waves will tend to fill the box and evolve structures and wavelengths which are determined by its shape and size.

The observed conversions of matter into radiant energy, and the conversion of the periodic waves of free photons into matter, leads to the conclusion that matter is organized waves. If these waves have evolved the specific structures defining the various forms of matter in containment, it is to be assumed there is a process of capture, containment and integration which increases the quantity of matter under special conditions. Such a process would increase entropy and reverse its observed direction. Those scientists who use entropy as time's arrow will find it reversed in organic processes and the integration of matter waves.

Chapter 7

ELECTRON PHYSICS

The importance of electrons in atomic research is enhanced by the fact that their masses are all-electric. The elements of their actions can, therefore, be integrated into a rational system of atomic units by formal algebraic idealizations and verifiable mathematical values and proportions. This also makes possible their reductions by integration to those simple proportions from which nature's unit of length is obtained.

701 Electrostatic Charge Unit. $e = 4.8024713 \times 10^{-10}$ dyne esu

The electrostatic force one centimeter from an electron, positron or proton. It appears as an attraction between an electron's negative charge and the positive charge of a positron or proton. Their identical charge values decrease as the inverse square of the distance from the supporting centers.

Because the formulas for an electron's radius in Section 711, $r = e^2/c^2 m_o$, defines the coincidence of an electron's charge and mass energy, it is assumed its mass is all-electric, and that its radius is the wavelength of a periodic pulsation pattern implementing both. The identical value of opposite charges implies a corresponding identity of electron and positron masses. A proton has the same charge as a positron, but its mass is equal to 1836.1141 electrons (see Section 815 and figure 23F). Atoms are composed of nuclei of positive protons circled by negative electrons at various varying distances.

The coincidence of an electron's mass and charge energy at its radius wavelength makes it possible to work out a system of units in which all three are unity. Other constants are in simple proportions, as defined by the ultimate system of units in Sections 215 and 1021. Its ideal proportions made possible the idealization of the gaussian system of units (see Sections 222 and 1023).

The value of a unit charge can be determined by experiments in various ways: by Millikan's falling drop method in Section 706, by the number of ions transported through a chemical solution (Section 511), and by its relationship to various constants through the unchangeable ratio of the electronic constant. The charge can be defined by: $e = \sqrt{Gc^2/2\pi\phi}$, $e = \sqrt{mc^2/2\pi\tilde{v}\phi}$, and by the three formulas below.

Speed of light. 210, 32C, 54B   m₀ Electron's mass. 708, 21A
Electrostatic charge unit. 19C   N Avogadro's number. 902, 28N
Faraday; phy. abcoulomb. 511   Q Electron's in abcoul. 504, 32G
Wavelength of gram mass. 54T   φ Electronic constant. 220, 614
Planck's energy qu. 606, 8B   2π Circumference in radii. 115

$= c/Q$ $2.997930 \times 10^{10}/6.2424735 4\times 10^{19} = 4.8024713 \times 10^{-10}$ dyne esu

$= Fc/N$ $9651.39856 \times 2.997930 \times 10^{10}/6.024860 \times 10^{23} = 4.8024713 \times 10^{-10}$

$= \sqrt{\dfrac{hc}{2\pi\phi}}$ $\sqrt{\dfrac{6.624461 \times 10^{-17} \times 2.997930 \times 10^{10}}{2 \times 3.14159265 \times 137.044809}} = 4.8024713 \times 10^{-10}$

702 Electromagnetic Force Unit. $e^1 = 1.6019291 \times 10^{-20}$ dyne emu
The electromagnetic force one centimeter from the center of an electron moving with a speed of one centimeter per second. The electromagnetic force produced by a positron or proton moving with the same speed is the same as that of an electron, but is oppositely directed due to their opposite charges. Because a proton's mass is 1836.1141 times greater than that of a positron, although their charges are the same, its opposition to an acceleration is that much greater, due to its large neutral mass which produces no electromagnetic field. A proton's inertia reduces its reaction to a specific acceleration charge (and,therefore, its acceleration and electromagnetic field) to less than that of an electron or positron by the difference in mass. (Compare the magnetons of electrons and protons in Sections 804 and 806; 13B and 18B.)

An electron's electromagnetic field is related to its momentum. Since a momentum is defined as mass times velocity, it follows that any increase of an electron's speed produces a corresponding increase of its electromagnetic field. Elementary logic leads to the conclusion that an electron's electromagnetic field value becomes identical with that of its electrostatic field at the speed of light, and that the difference between the two units of action is, by definition, equal to the speed of light. (That an electron cannot be accelerated to the speed of light, due to its increase of inertia as it approaches that velocity, is irrelevant. See Section 1027 for convergence.) An electron's electromagnetic field is obtained from its electrostatic field by the formula below. (See Fig. 19B).
$e^1 = e/c$ $4.8024713 \times 10^{-10}/2.997930 \times 10^{10} = 1.6019291 \times 10^{-20}$ dyne emu

703 Electron Volt. (Ve)   14C $E = 1.6019291 \times 10^{-12}$ erg esu
14U w=8066.24254 wavenumber/cm.
B = 1.226294×10^{-7} wavelength
S = 5.930856×10^7 cm/second.

A unit of electrodynamic energy. The energy of motion of an electron accelerated by an electrostatic field with a charge difference of one volt in the meter-kilogram-second (mks) system of units (See 408). The work done on an electron as it passes through a charge gradient of one volt. The figures above are the energy (E) of a volt electron and its corresponding wavenumber (w), its de Broglie wavelength (B) and the speed (S) with which it accelerates each second. (Compare with gravitational acceleration.)

The unit of electrostatic charge is defined in Section 501, and the volt in Sections 401, 408 and 503. Since the practical (mks) volt used in the definition of an electron volt's energy is equal to $c/10^8 = 299.7930$ in statvolts, the electron volt is obtained by dividing an electron's electrostatic charge by this ratio, as shown by the first formula below. The other four formulas give its energy equivalent wavenumber, the wave ratio from which the electron's true velocity wavelength and its velocity are obtained. Its first wavelength is that of a free photon; the second is the de Broglie wavelength of an electron with the same energy of motion.

B	De Broglie wavelength. 610	R	Wave and velocity ratio. 10.
c	Speed of light. 210, 32C, 34B	S	Electron's speed in cm/sec.
e	Unit charge in esu. 701, 19C	$\tilde{v}$	El's mass wavenumber. 709,
I	Acceleration energy, esu. 14C	V	Energy in electron volts.
h	Planck's quantum, emu. 606, 8B	$\tilde{w}$	Volt energy wavenumber. 14U

$$I = e/(c/10^8) \qquad 4.8024713 \times 10^{-10}/299.7930 = 1.6019291 \times 10^{12} \text{ erg esu.}$$

$$\tilde{w} = \frac{E}{hc} \qquad \frac{1.6019291 \times 10^{12}}{6.6244607 \times 10^{47} \times 2.99793 \times 10^{10}} = \begin{matrix} 8066.24254 \text{ wn. cm.} \\ = 1.239735 \times 10^{4} \text{ wl. c} \end{matrix}$$

$$R = \sqrt{\frac{2\tilde{v}}{\tilde{w}}} \qquad \sqrt{\frac{2 \times 4.1220142 \times 10^{9}}{8066.24254}} = 1010.96030 \text{ ratio}$$

$$B = 1/\tilde{w}R \qquad 8066.24254 \times 1010.96030 = \begin{matrix} 8.154651 \times 10^{6} \text{ wn. cm.} \\ 1.226294 \times 10^{7} \text{ wl. cm.} \end{matrix}$$

$$S = \frac{2c}{R} \qquad \frac{2 \times 2.997930 \times 10^{10}}{1010.96030} = 5.930856 \times 10^{7} \text{ cm. per second}$$

704 Radiated Photons in Electron Volts.

The electron volt defined by the preceding section is the energy of an electron accelerated by a one-volt electrostatic force (see Section 502-3). It is the energy liberated by an atom when one of its orbital electrons drops through a one-volt difference between two quantum states. The energy of light waves in electron volts can be obtained by dividing their wavenumbers by that of one electron volt. A free photon's energy in volts times the energy of a volt electron in ergs gives us its energy in ergs, a figure which can also be obtained by multiplying its wavenumber by Planck's quantum. The three types of energy of the longest and shortest visible light waves are:

Red light ph.	1.735628 volts	2.780354×10^{12} erg	14000 wn/cm.	15H-
Violet light	2.975363 volts	4.766321×10^{12} erg	24000 wn/cm.	16H-

705 Weight Supported by Volt Electron. $W = 1.633513 \times 10^{-15}$ gram mass. A unit of mass and force: the weight one electron can support against gravity when it is being pulled upward by a one volt difference between two large metal plates, one centimeter apart. (Note that large plates produce a uniform force field between them.) Its weight in grams is equal to the force acting on a volt electron, V (Section 703), divided by the earth's attraction for a gram mass, G (Section 305).

$W = V/G$ $1.601929 \times 10^{-12}/980.665 = 1.633513 \times 10^{-15}$ gram mass weight.

706 Determining an Electron's Charge. 19C, 701

The cloud produced by a liquid converted into a fine spray contains many particles with a small electric charge. A liquid which does not evaporate, such as oil or mercury, is used in the experiment. The rate at which each particle falls through the air increases with mass and decreases with size. Both can be determined from Stokes' law.

A cloud is produced between two horizontal metal plates one centimeter apart, and the rate at which individual particles fall is observed through a telescope. A particle is selected, and its mass and size are determined from its rate of fall. The plates are then given opposite electrostatic charges pulling against the force of gravity on the charged particle, thus reducing its fall or pulling it upward. The voltage can be adjusted to leave the particle stationary.

Abrupt changes of speed occur when the particle picks up or loses a part of its charge, and these changes are always multiples of a unit speed and charge. The number of electrons on the particle can be determined from this unit, and we can thus obtain its weight per unit electron. The voltage necessary to leave the particle stationary against gravity is noted, and the electrostatic force of one electron per volt is thus obtained. This value is multiplied by 299.793 for its charge value in esu (see Sections 703 and 705).

Millikan give the case history of one oil drop in a book describing his experimental determination of an electron's charge. From its speed in a free fall of 0.08584 centimeter per second and a density of 0.9199 (see Section 306), he determined its radius as 0.000276 centimeter and its mass as 8.103×10^{-11} gram. By charging the plates, he caused the oil drop to move against gravity or remain suspended. On occasion its speed would change abruptly as it picked up or lost electrons, thus increasing or reducing its charge. These changes of speed were always multiples of 0.005365 centimeter per second when the difference between the two plates was 3100 volts. He found that 16 units (electrons) of charge would cause it to remain suspended against gravity, and that 32 units caused it to ascend with the speed of a free fall.

D	Weight of drop in dynes	M	Mass of drop in grams
E	Electrons; number of charges	r	Radius of oil drop
G	Earth's gravity in dynes	v	Electron volt dynes
s	Speed of drop in free fall	V	Volt charge on plates

U   Unit rate of speed change σ Density of oil drop
$\frac{U}{K} = 4.1887902$ (See 115)   e   Electrostatic charge

$M = \frac{4}{3}\pi\sigma r^3$ $4.1887902 \times 0.9199 \times (2.76 \times 10^{-4})^3 = 8.103 \times 10^{-11}$ gram

$D = MG$ $8.103 \times 10^{-11} \times 980.664 = 7.9463 \times 10^{-8}$ dynes weight

$v = \dfrac{D}{EV}$ $\dfrac{7.9463 \times 10^{-8}}{16 \times 3100} = 1.6021 \times 10^{-12}$ dynes per volt

$e = v(c/10^8)$ $1.6021 \times 10^{-12} \times 299.783 = 4.8029 \times 10^{-10}$ dyne esu
Its accepted value in 701 and 19C $= 4.802471 \times 10^{-10}$ dyne esu.

We can obtain the mass of the drop above from W in 705 by:

$M = WVE$ $1.633513 \times 10^{-16} \times 3100 \times 16 = 8.102224 \times 10^{-11}$ gram mass.

707 Electron's Charge-Mass Ratio. $e^1/m_o = 1.7587527 \times 10^7$ ratio
An electron in an electrostatic field accelerates toward its positive charge (like the gravitational acceleration of an unsupported mass). An electron passing a charged plate is, therefore, deflected in proportion to the square of the time the electrostatic forces are acting upon it and in inverse proportion to its mass-inertia. But a magnetic field does not act upon a stationary electron. It deflects the electron in proportion to its velocity as it cuts the magnetic lines of force, and the direction of that deflection is at a right angle to those lines.

This difference makes it possible to obtain an electron's charge/mass ratio by causing a stream of electrons with a known velocity to pass through crossed electrostatic and magnetic fields, recording their deflections on a screen as a bright point. The simultaneous deflection of electrons by the two kinds of fields makes the determination of the e^1/m_o ratio very accurate. Its value is the difference between an electron's mass in grams and its electrostatic charge in emu. It is obtained by the formula:

$R = e^1/m_o$ $1.6019291 \times 10^{-20}/9.108325 \times 10^{-28} = 1.7587527 \times 10^7$ ratio

708 Electron's Rest Mass. 21A $m_o = 9.108325 \times 10^{-28}$ gram
An electron's mass in grams. The term "rest mass" is used to distinguish it from the apparent increase of an electron's mass at high velocities. An electron's mass can be obtained from its electrostatic charge divided by the e^1/m_o ratio (Section 707). Since any mass can be converted into energy in ergs by multiplying it by the speed of light in centimeters per second squared, and the ergs can be converted into wavenumbers through the energy of Planck's quantum, there are several ways to obtain an electron's rest mass by formula.

c   Speed of light. 210, 32C, 34B m_o Electron's rest mass. 21A
e   El's charge in esu. 701, 19C   R   El's charge/mass ratio. 707
h   Planck's qu. in emu. 606, 8B $\tilde{v}$ El's mass wavenumber. 709, 2

$m_o = \dfrac{e}{cR}$ $\dfrac{4.8024713 \times 10^{-10}}{2.997930 \times 10^{10} \times 1.7587527 \times 10^7} = 9.108325 \times 10^{-28}$ gram mas

$m_o = \dfrac{h\tilde{v}}{c}$ $\dfrac{6.6244607 \times 10^{-17} \times 4.1220142 \times 10^{9}}{2.997930 \times 10^{10}} = 9.108325 \times 10^{-28}$

709 Electron's Mass Wavenumber.   21U $\tilde{v}$ = 4.1220142 × 10⁹ wn/cm.

21T $\dot{v}$ = 2.4259984 × 10⁻¹⁰ cm. wl.

The wavenumber of a free photon with the energy of an electron's rest mass. It appears as one of two oppositely moving photons when an electron and a positron unite and resolve into radiant wave energy. It can be obtained from an electron's rest mass energy, $E = mc^2$, divided by Planck's quantum of energy. Its wavelength $\dot{v}$ is equal to its radius r divided by the waveratio constant C (see Sections 613 and 711).

$$' = \frac{mc}{h} \qquad \frac{9.108325 \times 10^{28} \times 2.997930 \times 10^{10}}{6.6244607 \times 10^{27}} = 4.1220142 \times 10^9 \ \text{wn/cm.}$$

$$' = rC \qquad 2.8173971 \times 10^{13} \times 861.07793 = 2.4259984 \times 10^{10} \ \text{centimeter}$$

710 Electron's Mass Energy.   21C $E = 8.1861839 \times 10^{-7}$ erg esu

21B $E^1 = 2.7306126 \times 10^{-17}$ erg emu

The potential energy of an electron's rest mass. It is the energy which appears when an electron is completely dissolved into its elements; usually as the energy of a free photon. It is defined by Einstein's formula for the energy equivalent of matter: $E = mc^2$. It can also be obtained by converting Planck's quantum of energy into its esu value, and then multiplying this figure by the electron's rest mass wavenumber. Or we can mutiply this wavenumber by Planck's quantum for its energy in electromagnetic units.

$$= mc^2 \qquad 9.108325 \times 10^{28} \times (2.997930 \times 10^{10})^2 = 8.1861839 \times 10^{-7} \ \text{erg esu}$$

$$= hc\tilde{v} \qquad 6.6244607 \times 10^{27} \times 2.997930 \times 10^{10} \times 4.1220142 \times 10^9 = 8.1861839 \times 10^{-7}$$

711 Electron's Radius Wavelength. $r = 2.81739707 \times 10^{-13}$ cm. wl.

This radius of presumably spherical electrons is called the electron's classical radius by relativity physics because it questions the postulated specific size. However, the ultimate system of units (Section 1023) proves it physically real by relating it to numerous constants. These relations, in conjunction with an electron's convertibility into radiation, give support to my belief that the radius defined above is also the wavelength of an electron's rest mass. It acts as a transmitter of charge-related momenta.

An electron's radius is defined on the assumption that its rest mass is all-electrical in nature. The mutual repulsions between negative electrostatic charges on the surface of a sphere appear as a tendency of the sphere to expand. Conversely, they oppose a contraction of the sphere, and energy must, therefore, be expended to effect its reduction. The electron's radius is defined as the point where the energy expended in reducing the size of a sphere with unit charge is equal to an electron's rest mass energy.

The force of an electron's electrostatic charge is defined in cgs units for a distance of one centimeter (see Sections 206 and 402-3). Since this force changes power as the inverse square of the distance, the charge squared is divided by the energy of an electron's rest mass ($E = mc^2$), for its radius given in centimeter(s).

An electron's radius can also be obtained from its rest mass radiation wavelength by the formulas: $r = \dot{v}/C = \dot{v}/2\pi\phi$, and by $2\dot{o}R/\tilde{v}$. The first two formulas define the change of wavelength when a free photon with an electron's energy is converted into an electron, and the third uses an electron's K orbit radius in hydrogen and Rydberg's wavenumber to obtain the reciprocal of C.

c Speed of light. 210, 32C, 34B   o K orbit radius in hy. 713,
C Waveratio constant. 220, 613   R Rydberg's wavenumber. 609,
e Electron's charge, esu. 701, 19C   v̇ El's mass wavelength. 709,
m₊ Electron's rest mass. 703, 21A   ∢ Electronic constant. 220, 6

$r = \dot{v}/C$ $2.4259984 \times \overline{10}^{10}/861.077930 = 2.8173971 \times \overline{10}^{13}$ radius waveleng

$r = 2\dot{o}\dot{v}R$ $2 \times 5.291431 \times \overline{10}^{-9} \times 2.4259984 \times \overline{10}^{10} \times 109737.32 = 2.817397 \times \overline{10}$

$r = \dfrac{e^2}{mc^2}$ $\dfrac{(4.8024713 \times \overline{10}^{10})^2}{9.108325 \times \overline{10}^{18} \times (2.99793 \times 10^{10})^2} = 2.8173971 \times \overline{10}^{13}$ radius wl

712 Electron's Charge-Gravity Ratio.

EE = 4.170140×10^{42} gravities
EP = 2.271172×10^{39} gravities
PP = 1.236942×10^{36} gravities

The electrostatic/gravity (e/g) ratios above are symbolized by E for electrons and positrons, and by P for protons. The electrostatic attraction between an electron and a positron is greater than their gravitational attraction, as shown by the first figure, when the gravity constant is equal to 6.666561×10^{-8} dyne per gram mass and the unit charge on an electron is 4.802471×10^{-10} dyne (see Sections 302 and 701). In the ratio formula: $e/g = ee/mmg$, or $e^2/m^2 g$ for equal charges and masses; the masses are symbolized by m.

Both theory and observation show that an electron's mass is all-electrical—that its electrostatic mass is identical with its rest mass—and that a positron has the same mass and charge potential as an electron. The repulsive force acting between two electrons, therefore, has the same value as the attraction between an electron and a positron. Because a proton's rest mass is greater than its charge mass by 1836.11810 electrons, the electron—proton and proton—proton ratios above are less by that difference and the difference squared, respectively.

Electrostatic and gravitational forces both decrease in power as the inverse square of the distance from their origins. It follows that their ratios above do not change with a change of distance for unperturbed field relations. There is, however, a significant difference; an electrostatic charge is an energy-related force acting through time against containing reactions by space, whereas gravity is a momentum-related product of a mass-induced timeless configuration (fourth-dimensional) space. (See Sections 302 and 1013, and Book Two.)

There is no change in the e/g ratio for identical mass values when a system's length or mass unit is changed, but it changes with a change of its time unit. The different origins and time relations of electrostatic and gravitational forces appear in the definition of the e/g ratio as a change of its value in direct proportion to the change of a system's time (speed of light) unit, provided that the length unit used in its definition is the natural length (see Sections 221 and 1012).

The e/g ratio below is obtained by two equations. The first of these is the conventional reduction formula from their accepted values, and the second is the same figure obtained from the gravity constant of the ultimate system of units; with the reciprocal of that figure multiplied by the difference in the time it takes a light wave to move one electron radius and one second. This ratio is obtained by multiplying two time units; the natural unit of length in electron radii, redefined as a time difference, and the number of natural length units traveled by a light wave in one second. When the second is in centimeters, the cm/nl ratio ϕ appears as a divisor in the formula. The figure for the ultimate system, 3.919018×10^{19} gravity units, is defined in Sections 302 and 1013, and in logarithms in Section 1026.

Speed of light. 210, 407, 32C	ϕ Natural length in cm. 221, 7T
Electrostatic unit. 701, 19C	*L Natural time in el. radius time.
Gravity constant. 301-2, 34A	R e/g ratio. Ultimate system.
Electron's rest mass. 708, 21A	R' e/g ratio. Gaussian system.

$$\frac{e^2}{m^2 g} \qquad \frac{(4.802471 \times 10^{-10})^2}{(9.108325 \times 10^{-49})^2 \times 6.666561 \times 10^{-8}} = 4.170140 \times 10^{42} \text{ e/g ratio}$$

$$\frac{RLc'}{\phi} \qquad \frac{3.919018 \times 10^{19} \times 3.6983015 \times 10^{12} \times 2.99793 \times 10^{10}}{1.0419584} = 4.170140 \times 10^{42}$$

$$= \text{Log}_2 \quad 41.75 = 3.6983015 \times 10^{12} = \text{nl/Er ratio.}$$

713 Orbital Equality of Forces.

The inertia of a mass is a tendency to move in a straight line with constant velocity. When a force acts upon a mass to change its direction or velocity, the inertia of that mass becomes a counter force proportional to the rate of change.

An orbiting mass evolves a functional equality between the centrifugal force opposing its continually recurring motion and the gravitational or electrostatic attraction of its primary mass. For a circular orbit these forces are continually equal, and the periodic dominance of one over the other when a mass is moving in an eccentric orbit can be reduced to the equality of a circular orbit, as defined in Section 321. The formula for centrifugal force of a recurring motion is: $F = mV^2/r$. (Force equals mass times velocity squared, divided by the radius.) The corresponding force of attraction is $F = gmm/r^2$ for gravity, $F = ee/r^2$ for electrostatic forces, and $F = H\grave{e}V$ for electromagnetic fields. (See Sections 318, and 801 and below.)

The velocity of a hydrogen electron in its lowest quantum orbit is equal to the speed of light divided by the electronic constant: $c/\phi = 2.997930 \times 10^{10}$ /137.044809 = 2.187555 $\times$ 10^8 centimeters (cm) per second. For its mean orbit radius of 5.291431 $\times$ 10^{-9} cm., the opposite forces equate at 8.237268 $\times$ 10^{-3} dyne. The first part of the double formula below defines the centrifugal force of orbital motion; the last part, the electrostatic attraction between a proton and an electron at mean orbit radius distance.

The last formula is included to show that the orbital motion of this electron can also be produced by an electromagnetic field of sufficient strength. However, the magnetic field strength of 2.350612$\times$10^9 gauss is impossibly large; however, it points up the fact that charged particles can be trapped by a magnetic field. The recurve of a free electron in a one gauss field is defined in Section 802 as a radius curve of 12.438102 centimeters for the same speed.

B	De Broglie Wavenumber. 606	m₀	Electron's mass. 708, 21A
e	El's charge in esu. 701, 19C	r	Radius of el's orbit. 312
e'	El's charge in emu. 405, 19B	c	The speed of light. 210, 32?
F	Force on electron. 207, 812	V	Electron's velocity. 215, 8?
H	Gauss, electromagnetic. 515	φ	Electronic const. 220, 614

$$mV^2/r = F = e^2/r^2 = H e'V$$

$$\frac{9.103325 \times 10^{-28} \times (2.1375546 \times 10^8)^2}{5.291431 \times 10^{-9}} = 0.00823727 = \frac{(4.8024713 \times 10^{-10})^2}{(5.2914310 \times 10^{-9})^2}$$

$$He'V = 2.350612 \times 10^9 \times 1.601929 \times 10^{-20} \times 2.1375546 \times 10^8 = 0.00823727 \text{ dyne}$$

714 Electrostatic Deflection of Electrons.

An electrostatic field exerts a continuous deflective force on a beam of electrons. Their negative charges are repelled by a negative field and attracted by a positive, thus producing an acceleration deflection of the beam in the form of a parabola. It is comparable to the deflection of horizontally moving projectiles in a field of gravity, as defined in Section 311. Their motions at any moment can be defined by unchanging horizontal velocities and a continuous acceleration toward or from the charge. By taking a small fraction of the curve thus produced, we obtain a close approximation to the arc of a circle with radius r. The deflective force E on the electron's charge e, mass m, and velocity V can then be defined by the formula: $Ee = m(V^2/r)$, for that fraction of the parabola.

If the velocity-recurve around a positive charge center is such as to leave the distance to that center unchanged, the electron moves in a circular orbit. Suppose we define such an orbit by postulating a nuclear charge large enough to cause a free electron to circle it at one centimeter with the speed of a hydrogen electron in its smallest orbit, as defined in the preceding section. With an orbit radius equal to unity, the electron's centrifugal force is equal to its mass times its velocity squared, and the attraction is its unit negative charge times the positive charge needed to equate its centrifugal force. The two formulas are:

$mV^2/r = F = ep/r^2$, with p defining the positive charge. The number N of positive charge units is obtained by: $N = p/e$. The other symbols are the same as those in the preceding section.

The first formula below defines the electron's centrifugal force; the second, the corresponding recurve (in dynes) by a magnetic field (H in gauss) producing a circular motion without a central charge; the third multiplies the negative and positive charges for the electrostatic attraction (in dynes); and the fourth formula defines the number of positive charges (protons) needed to produce an orbital motion of 2.1875546×10^8 cm/sec. at one centimeter. Note the reduction of gauss and increase of charge with an increase or orbit radius (see Sections 713 and 803).

$= mV^2/r$ $9.108325 \times 10^{-28} \times (2.1875546 \times 10^8)^2/1.0 = 4.358693 \times 10^{-11}$ dyne

$= HeV$ $12.4381025 \times 1.6019291 \times 10^{-20} \times 2.1875546 \times 10^8 = 4.358693 \times 10^{-11}$

$= ep/r^2$ $4.8024713 \times 10^{-10} \times 0.090759385/(1.0)^2 = 4.358693 \times 10^{-11}$ dyne

$= p/e$ $0.090759385/4.8024713 \times 10^{-10} = 1.889848 \times 10^8$ positive charges

Chapter 8

ATOMIC PHYSICS QUANTA

This chapter defines the electromagnetic fields produced by electron motions, in free flight and in atomic structures, and their quantizing. Magnetic field values are followed by relativity motions; among them the elements of a high velocity electron. Quantized hydrogen orbits are followed by wave-energy relations in complex atoms and molecules, with their possible states and terms defined. The terms used to describe the electrical and chemical states of atoms are given.

801 Magnetic Recurve of Electrons.

A magnet deflects a stream of electrons in a direction at a right angle to its lines of force and their line of motion, thus causing them to change direction but not velocity. In a uniform magnetic field the consequent recurve of the electrons is an arc with a definable radius r. Because a magnetic field acts upon an electron in proportion to the rate at which it cuts its lines of force, an unchanging magnetic field does not interact with stationary electrons. Its force on moving electrons is proportional to its number of lines of force per unit area (see Sections 514-6), their charges and velocities. The radius recurve produced by that force is inversely proportional to the momentum of each electron. The force and the radius recurve it produces are defined by: $F = He^1V$, and $r = \bar{v}/B$ respectively.

Magnetic lines of force run from a magnet's north to south pole. It follows that electrons passing between two opposite poles recurve in a direction at a right angle to their pole faces. The direction in which they recurve can be defined by comparison as follows: Wind an electric conductor around the circular part of a clock and send a current through it from the negative to positive pole of a battery, with the electrons circling the clock in the same direction as its hands. The magnetic field thus produced has a northern polarity at the clock face. A stream of free electrons passing across a magnetic north pole recurves in the opposite direction of the magnetizing electrons—counter-clockwise. But a stream of positrons or protons recurves in the direction opposite to that of electrons, due to their opposite (positive) electrostatic charges.

An electron's recurve in a uniform magnetic field can be described as an orbit with a specific radius. The electron inertia opposing its changes of direction appears in the equation as a centrifugal force whose formula is: $F = mV^2/r$ (see Sections 318 and 713). Note that the formula, $F = ee/r^2$, in Section 713, is replaced by HeV in the electromagnetic formula: $mV^2/r = F = HeV$, below. The figures used are for a one-volt electron (Section 703) in a one-gauss magnetic field (Section 515). Its radius recurve is defined in the next Section.

B **El's momentum wavelength.** 610, 703	m₀ **Electron's mass.** 708, 21A
₁ **Electron's charge in emu.** 702,19B	r **Orbit section radius.** 802
₁ **Equated forces on electron.** 713	v̇ **Unit charge wl.** 802, 19T
H **Magnetic field in gauss.** 515	V **Electron's velocity.** 703

$$= \frac{mV^2}{r} \qquad \frac{9.108325\times10^{28}\times(5.930856\times10^7)^2}{3.3721945} = 9.5008107\times10^{13} \text{ dynes}$$

$$= HeV \qquad 1.0\times1.6019291\times10^{20}\times5.930856\times10^7 = 9.5008107\times10^{13}$$

802 Gauss Recurve of Volt Electron.   r = 3.3721945 cm. radius

The radius curve of an electron moving with the speed and energy of one electron volt through a uniform magnetic field of one gauss. Its elements are defined in Section 703. Note that electrons in strong magnetic fields can be caused to move in circles without physical contact. This effect made the cyclotron possible, and it is fundamental to the magnetic plasma theory.

Orbiting electrons in the atoms produce magnetic fields in the same way as magnetizing currents (see Sections 404 and 518-9). The radius curve of an electron moving through a gauss field is obtained by two different formulas below. In the first of these, there is a conversion from abvolts to volts by including their difference, 10^8, as a factor. The second formula is of great theoretical importance because it makes use of the difference between two wavelengths: the energy of a unit charge at one centimeter in terms of a wavelength (Fig. 19T), divided by the de Broglie (momentum) wavelength of a volt electron. The momentum wavelength of a hydrogen electron in its smallest orbit is used to show the recurve of a free electron moving with the corresponding speed through a gauss field, for comparison and a check on the validity of this formula (see Sections 713 and 812). In column G, Section 1026, the radius recurves of electrons with various velocities are defined. The symbols used below are defined in the preceding section.

$$\sqrt{\frac{2m_0 \cdot 10^8}{e'}} \qquad \sqrt{\frac{2\times9.108325\times10^{28}\times10^8}{1.6019291\times10^{20}}} = 3.3721945 \text{ cm. radius curve}$$

v̇/B
0   electron volts $4.135302\times10^{-7}/1.226294\times10^7 = 3.372195$ cm. rad.
3045   "   " $4.135302\times10^{-7}/3.324705\times10^8 = 12.433102$ "   "

803 Electron with c/φ Speed in Cm. Ring.

The orbital motion of an electron circling an atom's nucleus produces a magnetic field similar to that which appears when a current of electrons is caused to flow through a single loop of wire (see Sections 404 and 518). To bring out the relationship between an electric current and a magnetic field, the orbital speed of a single electron circling a wire ring with a radius of one centimeter will be assumed to equal that of a hydrogen electron in its smallest orbit.

Dividing its speed of 2.1875546×10^8 centimeters per second by the circumference of the ring, we find the electron passing the same point in the wire 3.481601×10^7 times each second. The definition of a coulomb in Section 504 tells us that the number of electrons passing a given point does not change when the electron's speed is divided between the countless electrons in the conductor. This is because their speeds and momenta, when added, are equal to that of the postulated electron in its direction of motion; the frequency with which an electron pass a given point is, therefore, also the same. The magnetic field induced by a moving charge is directly proportional to its momentum. When the frequency with which an electron passes a given point is divided by the number of electrons in an abcoulomb-ampere, we obtain the current in abamperes. Its formula: $I = f/Q$, gives the same current value as $I = s/2\pi Q$ and $I = es/2\pi r$. The abamperes can then be converted into gauss by: $\mu = I\pi r^2$. By combining the last two terms into a single formula we get: $\mu = esr/2$.

e' Electron's charge in emu. 701, 19B   r Radius of centimeter orbi
f   Frequency in periods per second.   s Speed in orbit = c/φ. 812
I   Current in abamperes. 405, 505   μ Magnetism in gauss. 515
Q   Abcoulomb in electrons. 401, 504   π Pi. Circle in radii. 115

$I = f/Q$ $3.481601 \times 10^7 / 6.242474 \times 10^{11} = 5.577277 \times 10^{-13}$ abampere

$I = \dfrac{e's}{2\pi r}$ $\dfrac{1.6019291 \times 10^{-M} \times 2.1875546 \times 10^8}{2 \times 3.14159265 \times 1.0} = 5.577278 \times 10^{-13}$

$\mu = I\pi r^2$ $5.577278 \times 10^{-13} \times 3.14159265 \times (1.0)^2 = 1.752154 \times 10^{-12}$ gauss

μ e'sr/2 $1.6019291 \times 10^{-20} \times 2.1875546 \times 10^8 \times 1.0/2 = 1.752154 \times 10^{-12}$ g.

804 Bohr Magneton. 18B $\mu = 9.2714025 \times 10^{-21}$ gauss

The magnetic field of a hydrogen electron in its smallest (K shell) orbit. Its value in erg gauss can be obtained from the formulas for an electron circling a centimeter ring, and from the conventional quantum formula. My use of the electrostatic charge unit in these formulas makes it necessary to include the speed of light as a factor, thus changing them slightly in comparison with those above.

The electric current equivalent of a hydrogen electron's periodic motion in its smallest (K) orbit is obtained by: I es/2πr; its corresponding magnetic moment by: $\mu = esr/2c$. The conventional quantum formula is: $\mu = he/4\pi mc$. From Section 401, we find that one abampere is equal to 2.997930×10^{10} statamperes and ten international amperes.

Electron's charge, esu. 701, 19C	r Radius of hydr. orbit. 713, 812
Planck's quantum, emu. 613, 8B	R Rydberg's wavenumber. 609, 17U
Statamperes in esu. 401, 505	s Speed of electrons in orbit. 812
Electron's mass in grams. 708, 21A	$\tilde{v}$ El's mass wavenumber. 709, 21U

$$\frac{e}{r} \quad \frac{4.8024713\times 10^{-10} \times 2.1875546\times 10^{8}}{6.28318531\times 5.2914323\times 10^{7}} = 3.1598799\times 10^{6} \text{ statamperes}$$
$$1.0540206\times 10^{-4} \text{ abamperes}$$
$$1.0540206\times 10^{-5} \text{ Int. amperes}$$

$$\frac{er^2}{c} \quad \frac{3.1598799\times 10^{6}\times 3.14159265\times (5.2914323\times 10^{-9})^{2}}{2.997930\times 10^{10}} = 9.2714025\times 10^{-21}$$

$$\frac{he}{4\pi mc} \quad \frac{6.6244607\times 10^{-27}\times 4.8024713\times 10^{-10}}{12.5663706\times 9.108325\times 10^{-28}\times 2.99793\times 10^{10}} = 9.2714025\times 10^{-21} \text{ gauss}$$

The Bohr magneton can also be obtained by these wavenumber formulas: $\mu = 2\pi Rer^2$, and $\mu = e/4\pi\tilde{v}$. This last formula is of special interest because it is used by me in the sequence formula in Section 217. Because the natural length unit defining an electron's wavenumber is an invariable constant in nature, the divisor above becomes a constant of nature when its centimeter values are converted to a natural length ratio. Its centimeter formula gives the same value as above.

$$\mu = \frac{e}{4\pi\tilde{v}} \quad \frac{4.8024713\times 10^{-10}}{12.56637061\times 4.1220142\times 10^{7}} = 9.2714024\times 10^{-21} \text{ gauss}$$

This magnetic field is produced by the electron's orbital motion and changes its plane of rotation with the electron. The electron changes its orbital plane so rapidly that its position appears in experiments as an electron cloud of statistically distributed charges, like the blurred image of a rapidly rotating object. Its Bohr magneton, therefore, does not interact with an external magnetic field, because information-reaction time is relatively long, but it interacts strongly with the magnetons of other electrons.

There is also a weak couple between an electron's magnetic field and its spin field. By setting itself with or against this field, the spin field increases or reduces the electron's quantized orbital energy. It appears as a fine splitting of lines in the spectroscope.

805 Nuclear Magneton. 10B $\qquad\qquad \mu_o = 5.049470 \times 10^{-24}$ gauss

This is the reference unit of nuclear magnetic fields. It is obtained by dividing the Bohr magneton in the preceding section by a proton's mass in electrons. The mass ratio formula: $R = M_p/m_o$, equals 1836.11408 electrons (see Section 815 and Fig. 23F). When the Bohr magneton is divided by this ratio, we obtain the nuclear magneton in erg gauss: $\mu_0 = \mu e/R$.

An atom of hydrogen contains one electron and one proton circling their common center of inertia, as defined by Newton's law of motion (Section 315). The radius of the proton's orbit is less than that of the electron by their difference in mass, and its velocity in that orbit and the magnetic field produced by it is less than that of the electron by their mass ratio, according to theory. However, observation shows that a proton's nuclear magneton is nearly three times greater than the value defined above. The nuclear magneton, therefore, is used as a reference unit.

806 Proton Magneton.   13B $\mu = 1.408600 \times 10^{-23}$ gauss

$\mu / \mu_0 = 2.789600$ nuclear mag.

When the magnetic field of an orbiting electron interacts with that of a proton at an angle, a torque is produced which causes a precession of their dynamic planes comparable to the precession of a gyroscope when a force acts upon it to change its plane of revolution). The natural harmonics of this motion can be determined from their interactions with an external magnetic field. The observed precession harmonics of a proton's magnetic field gives us a ratio of 1/657.4685th of a Bohr magneton. It is called the 657th harmonic of a proton's precession frequency. (Note that my figure for a proton magneton may be too small, since it gives the ratio 1/658.2.)

807 Neutron Magneton.   11B $\mu = 9.770724 \times 10^{-24}$ gauss

$\mu / \mu_0 = 1.935000$ nuclear mag.

Since a neutral mass does not produce a magnetic field by motion or rotation, the magnetic moment of a neutron is an unsolved problem in theoretical physics. However, a comparison with the magnetic fields of neutral atoms leads to the conclusion that a neutron has a positive center surrounded by equalizing negative charges. It appears to be a proton circled by negative electron equivalents which do not penetrate to its positive center, thus leaving a charge difference whose motions resolve into its observed magnetic field. But the neutralizing effects of its negative charge make the energy of a neutron magneton less than that of a proton. When a proton's magneton is divided by that of a neutron's, we get the ratio 1.44165.

808 Deuteron Magneton.   9B $\mu_0 = 4.324871 \times 10^{-24}$ gauss

$\mu / \mu_0 = 0.856500$ nuclear mag.

A deuteron is twice as heavy as an ordinary atom of hydrogen because its nucleus contains a proton and a neutron. Assuming their magnetons interact and reduce each other's power, it follows that the energy of a deuteron magneton should equal the difference. My figures are not accurate, but the subtraction gives a fair approximation to the expected value.

Proton's magneton $14.036000 \times 10^{-24}$ erg gauss

Neutron's magneton 9.770724×10^{-24} "   "

Deuteron magneton 4.315276×10^{-24} "   "

809 Velocity Increase of Mass.   (See the table in Section 1026.)
Relativity theory assumes that the mass-inertia of moving bodies increases asymmetrically with increasing velocities, and becomes infinitely great at the speed of light. My theory in Book Two assumes that all motions, including those of light waves, are composed of stationary energy states and momenta transmitted through the ether with twice the speed of light, with actual motion a compromise.

The implication of the relationship defined in this section is that all energy, regardless of its form or nature, has a mass equivalent which appears as an increase of the inertia of a rest mass when it unites with it as motion. The energy absorbed by a mass during acceleration, therefore, increases its opposition to additional increases of speed. For low velocities, it is negligible, but as the energy of motion approaches the rest mass energy of a moving mass, it increases rapidly as the corresponding velocity approaches that of light. The inertia of a mass, being theoretically infinite at the speed of light, makes it impossible for a rest mass to attain that velocity. An electron's mass-inertia increases to three times that of its rest mass when its velocity is 94.28 per cent that of light, and it is nine times greater at 99.38 per cent the velocity of light. (See E2 in Section 1026.)

There are two formulas at the end of this section which give the same increase of mass with motion. If the electron's energy of motion is known, the second formula gives its increase of mass by adding it to its rest mass energy. The ratio increase is obtained by dividing this total mass by the electron's rest mass energy. If the moving body's velocity is known, its increase of mass with motion can be obtained by using the first formula. In both cases the increase is defined for an electron accelerated by a 100,000 volt electrostatic charge.

It will be noticed that the first reduction is the electron's velocity less light squared, with the ratio: $v^2/c^2 = 0.3005365$. By subtracting it from unity we get:

$$\begin{array}{r} 1.0000000 \\ \underline{0.3005365} \\ 0.6994635 \end{array}$$

The square root of this result is 0.8363393, and the reciprocal of this root is 1.195687, the increase of an electron's mass when it is moving with a speed of 1.6435016×10^{10} cm. per second.

In the second formula, the electromagnetic energy of a one-volt electron is multiplied by 100,000 for its energy of motion. By adding it to its rest mass energy in emu, and then dividing the sum by that energy, we get the electron's increase of mass-inertia. The simplicity of this reduction permits the use of any two comparable figures from lines 14 and 21 in the Table of Constants, page 152. When both are in terms of masses, the inertia $I = m_1 + m_o/m_o$.

c Speed of light in cm/sec.   L. Electron's rest mass energy. Erg e
I Inertia increase of mass.   E_I Electron's energy of motion. Erg e
v Velocity in cm/second.   V Electron volt energy. Erg emu.

$$I = \frac{1}{\sqrt{1-(v/c)^2}} \qquad \frac{1}{\sqrt{1-(1.6435015\times 10^{10}/2.99793\times 10^{10})^2}} = 1.1956869 \text{ increa}$$

E_o
E_I = 10^5 V_E $100000 \times 5.3434506 \times 10^{23} = \dfrac{27.3061208 \times 10^{18}}{5.3434506 \times 10^{18}}$ erg emu energy
                                                                   "   "   "
E_I + E_o $\overline{32.6495714 \times 10^{18}}$ "   "   "

$I = E_I + E_o / E_o$ $32.6495714 \times 10^{18} / 27.3061208 \times 10^{18} = 1.1956869$ inertia increase

810 Elements of a 100,000 Volt Electron.

1 E_I Energy of motion wavenumber   8.0662425 × 10^8 waves per centimeter
2 I   Velocity increase of mass   1.1956869 electron rest masses
3 r   Relativity reduction factor   0.9181697 of classical value
4 E_R Relativity energy of motion   7.4061792 × 10^8 relativity wavenumbe
5 R   Principal waveratio factor   3.6482229 energy-momentum wn. rati
6 V   Speed of electron in cm-sec.   1.6435015 × 10^{10} centimeters per sec.
7 B   de Broglie wavenumber of mo.   2.7019393 × 10^7 waves per centimeter
8 H   Radius curve in gauss field   1117.3335 centimeter radius

These are the elements of an electron accelerated by a hundred-thousand-volt electrostatic charge. They can be checked against the results of the subsection formulas, as numbered above. A high-energy electron was selected to bring out the relativity effects of masses moving with velocities near that of light. The formulas have been simplified by the use of wavenumbers, and they have been made more comprehensible by a step-by-step analysis using simple relations.

I have checked the figures below against results obtained by the more complex formulas conventionally used, and found them in full agreement. My formulas were used to obtain the figures appearing in the table of the elements of high-velocity electrons, Section 1026. The table shows a rapid increase of inertia near the speed of light and a negligible increase at low velocities. By ignoring this apparent increase of mass at all velocities, the simple ideal ratios at low velocities have been continued in another table, Section 1027, to show a convergence of wavenumbers at the speed of light. The increase of mass in sub-section 2 below, is the same as that defined by Section 809.

1 **Energy of motion wavenumber.**   E_I = V_o E_v

The energy wavenumber of one electron volt (703, 14U) is multiplied by acceleration volts for electron's energy of motion

$8066.24253 \times 100000 = 8.06624253 \times 10^8$ waves per centimeter.

2 **Velocity increase of mass.**   I = $m_I + m_o / m_o$

The electron's energy of motion is added to its rest mass
energy (70?, 21U) for its increase of mass-inertia. The sum is di-
ded by its rest mass energy for its ratio increase in electrons.

.2201417 × 10^8
.0662425 × 10^8
.2863842 × 10^8/41.2201417 × 10^8 = 1.1956869 ratio increase of mass.

Relativity reduction factor. $r = 1 + (1/I)/2$

One is added to the reciprocal of the relativity mass in
ectrons, and the sum is halved for relativity conversion factor.

/1.1956869 = 0.8363393
    Add 1.
    1.8363393/2 = 0.91816967 ratio relativity reduction.

Relativity energy of motion. $E_A = E_V r$

The electron's energy of motion is multiplied by the rela-
vity ratio decimal for its relative motion energy.

0662425 × 10^8 × 0.91816967 = 7.4061792 × 10^8 relativity energy wavenumber.

Principal wave ratio factor. $R = \sqrt{2(m_f m_c)/E_h}$

The electron's mass is doubled and divided by the relativity
ergy added to its rest mass. The square root of the sum gives us
e principal relativity ratio between de Broglie and energy wavenumbers.

.49.2863842 × 10^8/7.4061792 × 10^8 = 13.309530

13.309530 = 3.6482229 momentum-energy ratio and speed less twice light.

Relativity velocity of motion. $V = 2c/R$

The velocity of light is doubled and divided by the principal
tio for the electron's velocity. When the result is divided by the
eed of light, we obtain its speed in per cent of that velocity.

< 2.997930 × 10^{10}/3.6482229 = 1.6435015 × 10^{10} centimeters per second.

0 × 1.6435015 × 10^{10}/2.997930 × 10^{10} = 54.821211 % of the speed of light.

de Broglie's momentum wavenumber. $B = E_A R$

The relativity energy of motion wavenumber is divided by the
incipal ratio for the electron's de Broglie momentum wavenumber of
tion. (It is defined in section 610.)

4061792 × 10^8 × 3.6482229 = 2.7019393 × 10^9 waves per centimeter.

8 **Radius curve in gauss field.** $H = B/e_q$

The electron's de Broglie wavenumber is divided by its elect static charge wavenumber (Figure 19U) for its radius curve in a gaus field. (See Sections 515, 801 and 802 for definition.)

$2.7019393 \times 10^7 / 2.4182030 \times 10^6 = 1117.3335$ centimeter radius curve.

811 Relativity Motions.

When the experiments of Michelson and others proved that the velocity of light is the same in all directions on the moving and revolving earth, it became necessary to explain why physical motions through the postulated ether apparently cannot be observed. Lorentz did so by postulating an electromagnetic contraction of matter along its line of motion. He developed the formula in Section 809 and the first of the three below as its mathematical expression. It converts classical absolute motions into relative motions. Since the increase of mass is infinitesimal at low (ordinary) velocities and approaches the infinitely great at velocities near that of light, there is a natural transition from the absolute relativity of light waves and the non-relativistic motions of moving objects on the earth. The second formula is Lorentz's transformation formula for relative motions, and the third is Einstein's conversion formula for variable time. Both deal with a subject outside the purpose of this book.

c	Velocity of light	m_o	Rest masses
v	Classical velocities	m'	Increase of mass
x	Relative velocities	y,z	Dimensions which are not
t	Time factor		affected by motion

$$m' = \frac{m_o}{\sqrt{1-(v^2/c^2)}} \qquad x' = \frac{x-vt}{\sqrt{1-(v^2/c^2)}} \qquad t' = \frac{t-(v/c^2)x}{\sqrt{1-(v^2/c^2)}}$$

812 Electron Orbits in Hydrogen.

Elements of the smallest hydrogen orbit, with reductions to larger orbits

Shell terms for orbits	K shell	K	L	M	N	
Quantizing waves along orbit	1.0	1.	2.	3.	4.	
Momentum wavelength cm.	•3.324705×10^{-8}	1.	2.	3.	4.	
Velocity. Fractions of light	$1/137.044809$	1.	1/2	1/3	1/4	1
Velocity in centimeters sec.	2.187555×10^8	1.	1/2	1/3	1/4	1
Momentum in dynes per second	1.992496×10^{19}	1.	1/2	1/3	1/4	1
Energy in ergs per second	2.179347×10^{11}	1.	1/4	1/9	1/16	1/
Ionization potentials. Volts	13.604515	1.	1/4	1/9	1/16	1/
Radiation wavelength in cm.	911.2670×10^8	1.	4.	9.	16.	2
Circumference of orbit cm.	•3.324705×10^8	1.	4.	9.	16.	2
Radius of orbit cm.	0.529143×10^8	1.	4.	9.	16.	2
Radiation. Frequency in sec.	3.289848×10^{15}	1.	1/4	1/9	1/16	1/
Els' orbital frequency sec.	6.579696×10^{15}	1.	1/8	1/27	1/64	1/1
Attraction in dynes sec.	8.237268×10^{-3}	1.	1/16	1/81	1/256	1/6

The orbital elements of a hydrogen electron have been idealized for the purpose of the table. Actual values differ slightly from those given, due, primarily, to the motion of electron and proton around a common center of inertia (see Section 609). Note that energy related gradients are steeper than those associated with momentum.

The radius of each orbit is determined by the minimum number of waves which can be accomodated along its circumference without fractional wavelengths. The wavelengths, in turn, are determined by the velocity which the electron must have in order to equate centrifugal force and electrostatic attraction (Section 713). Note that orbital frequency plus the number of orbital waves is always twice that of the radiation frequency for that orbit. This is deceptive, since actual radiation frequencies are determined by the quantum of energy released during an electron jump from a larger to a smaller orbit. The electron can jump between any two orbits, and the energy difference between the two states determines its radiation wavelength.

813 Formulas Using Electronic Constant. (ϕ)   (Section 614.)

My theoretical definition of the electronic constant in Section 220, in conjunction with its use in the sequences in Section 215-17, has made possible a rational integration of the system values of the atomic constants. The interrelated accuracy of my figures is obvious from the formulas. Its definition (Sections 613-14), by conventional reduction formulas, lends support to my contention that the value I have adopted is true. The numerous formulas in which the electronic constant appears make it possible for the sceptical physicist to work out a statistical mean by using his own figures.

The ten formulas below are limited to atomic constants with dimensions defined by the unit of length, because their true values within an arbitrarily selected unit must, of necessity, have the same ratio to nature's unit, unlike such abstractions as charges, magnetism, volts, etc. The symbols used in the ten formulas are electron elements and the elements of an electron circling a hydrogen proton in its smallest orbit; all its elements have been idealized. The last two formulas are of special importance because they are, though dimensionless, giving results in natural length units which can be reduced to centimeters by including the ratio difference (see Section 221).

__adius to mass wavelength.__ $\dot{v} = 2\pi\phi r$.   709, 711, 61$\clubsuit$, 21T.
.2831853 × 137.044809 × 2.8173971 × 10^{13} = 2.4259984 × 10^{10} **mass wavelength**.

__elocity in orbit to velocity of light.__ $c = v_{\ast}\phi$.   210, 812, 34B.
.1875546 × 10^{8} × 137.044809 = 2.997930 × 10^{10} **centimeters per second**.

__ass wavelength to De Broglie orbit wl.__ $\lambda = \dot{v}\phi$.   610, 709, 812, 21T.
.4259984 × 10^{10} × 137.044809 = 3.3247047 × 10^{8} **momentum wavelength**.

__lectron's radius to orbit radius.__ $r_{N} = r\phi^{2}$.   711, 812, 61$\clubsuit$.
.8173971 × 10^{13} × $(137.044809)^{2}$ = 0.5291432 × 10^{8} **centimeter radius**.

__rbit radius to Rydberg's wavelength.__ $\dot{R} = 4\pi\phi r$.   609, 812, 17T.
2.5663706 × 137.044809 × 0.5291432 × 10^{5} = 911.267040 × 10^{8} **energy wl**.

__e Broglie orbit wl. to Rydberg's wl.__ $\dot{R} = 2\phi\lambda$.   609, 610, 812, 17T.
× 137.044809 × 3.3247047 × 10^{8} = 911.267040 × 10^{8} **wavelength**.

Mass wavelength to Rydberg's wavelength. $\dot{R} = \dot{v}(2\phi)^4/2.$ 709, 17T, 2

$2.4259984 \times 10^{-10} \times (2 \times 137.044809)^2/2 = 911.267040 \times 10^{-8}$ **wavelength.**

Electron's radius to Rydberg's wavelength. $\dot{R} = 4\pi\phi^3 r.$ 609, 711, 17

$12.5663706 \times (137.044809)^3 \times 2.8173971 \times 10^{-13} = 911.267040 \times 10^{-8}$ **waveleng**

Electronic constant to Rydberg's wavelength. $\dot{R} = \dfrac{\dot{\phi}}{(\pi/2)^4\,\phi^4}.$ **221, 7**

$\dfrac{1.0419584}{(3.14159265/2)^4 \times (137.044809)^2} = 911.267040 \times 10^{-8}$ **energy wavelength**

Electronic co. to De Broglie orbit wl. $\lambda = \dfrac{\dot{\phi}}{2(\pi/2)^4\,\phi^3}$ 610, 614.

$\dfrac{1.0419584}{2 \times (1.59079633)^4 \times (137.044309)^3} = 3.3247047 \times 10^{-8}$ **momentum wavelen**

814 Statom Nucleon. (M_o) amu   22A $M_o = 1.659790 \times 10^{-24}$ gram
                                          22U $= 7.511454 \times 10^{12}$ wn.
                                          22F $= 1822.2775$ electrons

The nucleon is the mass unit of atomic nuclei; the statom is an atom's mass divided by its number of nucleons. These units are also symbolized by amu (atomic mass unit). A nucleon's mass equals 1/16th of an oxygen atom's nucleus with isotopic number 16; the average mass of its 8 protons and 8 neutrons by definition. The statom is 1/16th of an oxygen atom's mass. The chemical statom is larger than the physical by 1.000275 physical units because chemists divide oxygen as it is found in nature by 16, and natural oxygen is a mixture of isotopes 16 and 18. The figures above define the mass of a physical statom in gram, wavenumber and electrons.

815 Proton's Mass. (M_p) 22A $(M_p) = 1.672392 \times 10^{-24}$ gram
                                        23U $= 7.568488 \times 10^{12}$ wn.
                                        23E $= 1.007593$ statoms

It is defined as the rest mass of a free proton and as the nuclear mass of a hydrogen atom with isotopic number one. It is greater than a statom because a proton's mass is reduced by radiation when it unites with neutrons and other protons to form atomic nuclei heavier than hydrogen. The energy equivalent of these losses appears as a force binding the nuclear particles together against their electrostatic repulsions. A proton's mass is equal to about 1836.1141 electrons, as defined in Section 1010 (see also Section 818 and Fig. 23F).

My theory of a proton's quantized rest mass postulates two stages, with each state increased by its fourth power times a pi factor. With this in mind, we can obtain its mass wavenumber with this formula: $(M_p) = (4^4\pi)^4\,6\pi/\phi.$ Its theoretical value of 7.568505×10^{12} waves per centimeter is slightly greater than that above. It gives us a mass equal to 1836.11809 electrons.

A hydrogen atom's mass is heavier than that of a proton's by its orbital electron. It is, therefore, equal to 1837.1141 electrons. When an electron's mass in statoms, 0.00054876, is added to that of a proton, we find that a hydrogen atom's mass in statoms is 1.008142. Its weight is, therefore, equal to 1.673309×10^{-24} gram.

816 Neutron's Mass. (M_n) 24A $M_n = 1.674698 \times 10^{-24}$ gram

24U $= 7.578922 \times 10^{12}$ wn.

24E $= 1.008982$ statoms

The rest mass of a neutron in free space. It is equal to about 1838.645 electrons. Neutrons are stable only in atomic nuclei with the right proportion of protons. A neutron in free space will resolve into a proton and a high velocity electron in about 18 minutes. The tendency of free neutrons to enter atomic nuclei is far greater than that of protons because, being electrostatically neutral, they are not repelled by its positive charge. A neutron's mass is less in a nucleus than in free space because a part of it is radiated as it enters the nucleus. The difference represents a bonding force which prevents its expulsion until a corresponding quantity of energy is recaptured and converted into a velocity of recession and an increase of mass. A combination of casual and integrated motions within an unstable nucleus may, momentarily, leave an excess of directed energy which can cause the expulsion of a neutron or proton.

817 Energy Equivalent of Mass. $E = mc^2$ $M_o = 0.001491750$ erg

$M_p = 0.001503077$ erg

$M_n = 0.001505149$ erg

Any mass can be converted into its equivalence of energy by using Einstein's conversion formula; energy equal mass times the velocity of light squared. Since the velocity of light squared is equal to 8.9875843×10^{20} --the energy in cgs ergs of a gram mass—any mass in grams multiplied by this figure gives us its energy equivalent in ergs (see Sections 211 and 34C). Note that the tendencies and forces which created atomic particles are now acting to prevent their destruction. Their organizations are energy equivalents which require the expenditure of energy to destroy, but organization is not energy; hence, it causes the liberation of energy.

818 Mass Defect. Packing Fraction.   *142691*

Mass defect is the difference between an atom's mass and the mass it would have if each nuclear particle had the mass of one statom. Packing fraction is the mass defect of one nuclear particle.

In all atomic phenomena there is a tendency toward organization which appears as the replacement of energy by functional processes and structures. The lowest energy states attained by protons and neutrons during the formation of atomic nuclei are also the most stable. The energy liberated during the formation of an atom of oxygen, isotopic number 16, from an equal number of protons and neutrons is obtained from the difference in mass between their free and bound states; it is called mass decrement: $8 \times (1.007578 + 1.008947) = 16.1322) - 16. = 0.1322$ statoms. $0.1322 \times 1.4917499 \times 10^{-3} = 1.972093 \times 10^{-4}$ erg.

Since the mass of an oxygen isotope 16 is taken as unity, other atoms can have positive or negative mass defect. The binding energies of atomic nuclei are often given in millions of electron volts (see Section 703 and Fig 14H).

819 Atomic Number.

The number of protons in an atom's nucleus; the number of electrons in a neutral atom; the number of positive electrostatic charges on an atom's nucleus. Note that a proton's positive charge has the same value as the negative charge of an electron. Atomic numbers range from one for hydrogen, two for helium, three for lithium, and so on to about 100 for as many different elements. All elements above 83 are radioactive, with instability increasing until the heaviest elements can exist for only a brief moment of time. Light elements with the proper number of neutrons in their nuclei are stable and can apparently exist indefinitely (see Section 835).

820 Isotope.

The number of protons and neutrons in an atom's nucleus. The chemical properties characteristic of an element are produced by the orbital electrons in its atoms and these, in turn, by their invariable nuclear charge. The number of protons in an element is fixed by its atomic number, while its number of neutrons can vary without affecting its electro-chemical properties; furthermore, its physical properties are only slightly affected by an increase or reduction of neutrons. The physical changes are greatest for hydrogen, whose mass is doubled when a neutron is added to its nucleus. Hydrogen with isotopic number two is also called deuterium. Triterium, which is hydrogen with isotopic number three, has an unstable nucleus.

The nuclear stability of the elements vary with their isotopic numbers, and all elements become unstable (radioactive) when their isotopes range beyond certain limits. Some elements have only one or two stable isotopes, while others have as many as ten or more.

821 Radioactivity.

The radioactivity of an element is defined in terms of its half-life, i.e., the time it takes one half of its mass to disappear through disintegration. In the process it may convert protons into neutrons or neutrons into protons, with the expulsion or capture of electrons or positrons to effect the change of charge. Protons or neutrons may be expelled or captured, or the radioactive nucleus may divide into two new elements. Positrons are either recaptured at once by other nuclei, or disintegrate into radiation through a merger with electrons. Radioactivity liberates large quantities of energy in the form of heat and radiation.

Radiactivity, therefore, changes one element into another, or it changes the isotopic number of an element. A long series of isotopes and elements may appear, each with its own distinct half-life, until the process ends with the appearance of a stable element. The two principal radioactive families are the uranium and thorium series. Uranium, with atomic number 92 and isotopic number 238, has a half-life of four billion years. One of its intermediate products, before it ends up as lead, is radium with a half-life of 1600 years.

Most isotopes of the elements in nature are stable, but science can now change the isotopic number of such elements, thus making them radioactive. Scientists can also cause chain reactions in a radioactive substance, thus producing an atomic explosion.

822 Atomic Weights.

The atomic weight of an atom whose isotopic number is known is its number of nucleons times its mass defect. The atomic weight of oxygen, isotope 16, is 16 by definition (see Sections 814 and 820).

When dealing with the atomic weight of an element whose mass is composed of various isotopes, its average weight in statoms is used for reduction purposes. Since natural oxygen is composed of both isotopes 16 and 18, its atomic weight is 16.0044 physical statoms. In chemistry this last value is taken as an even 16 statoms. Its statom, therefore, is larger than the physical by 1.0002749. (See 5N.)

Using the chemical statom we find that neon, with atomic number 10, has the atomic weight 20.183; uranium, atomic number 92, weighs 238.14 statoms. Note that the number of neutrons to protons increases with increasing atomic numbers.

823 Atomic Radii.   0.5 to 3.0 angstroms

An atom's radius is the radius of its largest electron orbits. The rapidity of their motions makes them behave statistically as a negative electron cloud, repelling the negative clouds of other atoms. An atom's radius is increased by excitation and by an increase of electrons in negative ionizations; its size is reduced when a loss of electrons convert it into a positive ion.

With the increase of nuclear charge as we pass from element to element, it is evident that the filled electron shells, beginning with the K shell, contract in proportion. There is an abrupt increase of size with the beginning of a new shell, and a gradual decrease as the shell becomes filled with electrons. This rough outline does not account for the sizes actually observed, because it is too general. The atomic radii range from about 0.5×10^{-8} to 3.0×10^{-8} centimeter, or roughly one angstrom on the average.

824 Nuclear Radii.   From 10^{-13} to 10^{-12} centimeter.

Experimental determinations of the radii of atomic nuclei show a rough agreement between the number of particles they contain and the size they would have if the particles were distributed uniformly within a sphere; with each particle occupying about the same space as an electron. In the present case its radius is assumed to be one half of that defined in Section 711, or $1.4086985 \times 10^{-13}$ centimeter. Observation shows that, in spite of the apparent crowding of particles as postulated, they have considerable freedom of movement within the nucleus, as indicated by preferred groupings and pairings, and by the quantizing of interrelations.

The table below is based on the assumption that protons, neutrons and electrons have the same size. A nuclear cross-section is not the same as target area, because nuclear attractions and repulsions produce apparent changes of size when a nucleus is bombarded by high velocity particles. The figures below are for unit size.

r   Radius $= 1.4086985 \times 10^{-13}$ centimeter
a   Target area $\pi r^2 = 6.2342753 \times 10^{-26}$ square centimeter
s   Surface area $4\pi r^2 = 2.4937101 \times 10^{-25}$ square centimeter
v   Volume $\frac{4}{3}\pi r^3 = 1.1709619 \times 10^{-38}$ cubic centimeter
d   Density $M/v = 1.4174582 \times 10^{14}$ gram per cubic cm.

An argon atom with mass (isotopic) number 40 has a nuclear radius of 4.8177×10^{-13} centimeter. The radius of its neutral atom is 1.54×10^{-8} centimeter. The radius of its largest electron orbits is, therefore, about 32,000 times greater than its nucleus. (Pluto is 8,600 solar radii distant.) The reduction from volume to radius is:

$$r = \sqrt[3]{\frac{vN}{\frac{1}{3}\pi}} \qquad \sqrt[3]{\frac{1.1709619 \times 10^{-38} \times 40}{4.1887902}} = 4.81768 \times 10^{-13} \text{ centimeter}$$

825 Atom's Quantized Orbits.   N = 1, 2, 3, 4 vel. waves circumf.
                                           K, L, M, N shell term of orbit

An atom is composed of a positive nucleus circled by negative electrons. A proton's positive electrostatic charge has the same force and action potential as an electron's negative charge. It follows that the number of protons in an atom's nucleus is the same as its units of charge and the number of orbital electrons needed to produce a neutral state. Because the number of nuclear charges does not change in stable nuclei, its defines the atomic number of an element (see Sections 819 and 835).

All atoms heavier than hydrogen contain protons and neutrons in their nucleis. Since a proton's mass equals about 1836 electrons, and a neutron's mass is slightly heavier, it follows that nearly all of an atom's mass is concentrated in its nucleus. Observation shows it to be small in comparison with the radii of its electron orbits (see Sections 824 and 825). As a first approximation we postulate electrons circling a stationary center, like planets circling the sun.

The size of an atom's quantized electron orbits is determined by two inter-related sets of equalizing factors for each orbit. The orbital velocity of an electron must be such as to produce a centrifugal force equal to the nuclear electrostatic attraction at mean orbit distance, while the momentum (de Broglie) wavelength produced by that velocity must equal the orbit's circumference for its lowest quantum (K) state, and be a whole fraction of the circumference for its higher states (larger quantum shells), as shown by the sequence above, and in Section 812. These conditions, in conjunction with the quantizing of electro-static charges, anticipate specific orbit distances and identical orbit radii and energy potentials for identical nuclear charges (see Section 713).

An increase of velocity, as electrostatic attraction accelerates electrons approaching an atom's nucleus, causes a corresponding reduction of their momentum (de Broglie) wavelengths (Section 610). But the theoretical circular orbits defining their natural quantum shells decrease twice as rapidly, while the orbital increase of velocity is only half of that produced by the acceleration. To attain a stable orbit the excess energy is radiated. When an electron in a K orbit, where wavelength and circumference have the same values, absorbs the energy difference between that and an L orbit, it will accelerate and then lose velocity as it recedes against electrostatic attraction until its velocity in the L orbit is half of its previous value. Its wavelength has doubled; however, it now takes two waves to equal the circumference of its new orbit, because it is four times longer than before. Since attraction decreases as the inverse square of the distance, it is now only 1/16th of its previous value. The relative radii of K, L, M and N orbits are 1, 4, 9, and 16, respectively; their quantizing waves are 1, 2, 3, and 4, respectively (see Section 812).

826 Hydrogen to Helium Quantas.

When a neutron is added to the nucleus of an ordinary atom of hydrogen its weight is doubled; but its charges and the orbits of its single electron are the same, except for a small difference due to the greater inertia of the deuteron (heavy hydrogen) nucleus (Section 808). The union of two deuterium nuclei gives us a helium nucleus composed of two protons and two neutrons, orbited by two electrons when its atom is in its normally neutral electrostatic state.

The orbital motions of singly ionized (one electron) helium atoms are comparable to those of hydrogen atoms. Its two electrostatic nuclear charges double the orbital velocity of its single electron, thus halving its de Broglie wavelength and the circumference and radius of its K orbit. It follows that the electron's centrifugal force and its equalizing electrostatic attraction at that distance are increased by four, and that the energy binding it to that orbit is four times greater than for a hydrogen electron in its K orbit. It takes four times more energy to cause it to jump from its K to L orbit, and to expel it from its atom. The radius of its L orbit is twice that of the K orbit in hydrogen.

Since a neutral helium atom contains a double positive nuclear charge and two orbital electrons, its two-unit positive charge is the same in all directions. It is, however, reduced by a mutual repulsion between its two electrons, and by their local momentary reductions of its positive charge in longitude. Because electrons have identical masses and charges, they can exchange energy and wave functions without a loss or gain of energy by their atom. The ionization potential of neutral helium should, therefore, be less than for singly ionized helium and greater than for hydrogen. It takes 24.48 and 54.16 electron volts to produce a single and double ionization of helium, and 13.59 volts to ionize hydrogen, when all are in their K orbits.

It will be noticed that the radii of quantized electron orbits decrease with an increase of nuclear charge and increase with an increase of electrons. A comparison between singly ionized and neutral helium shows that the former's mean electron orbit is one half that of hydrogen, and the latter's is slightly greater than hydrogen. Because a K orbit can contain only two electrons, an atom of lithium, with three nuclear charges and three orbital electrons in its neutral state, therefore, has one electron moving in the four-times larger L orbit, this is proved by its ionization potential, which is only 5.36 electron volts. An L shell can contain eight electrons; an M shell, eighteen.

827 Electron Orbits and Wavemechanics.

In 1910 Rutherford made some experiments which proved that the atoms are composed of relatively small, heavy, positively charged nuclei, circled by negative electrons. Three years later Bohr explained the Balmer series of hydrogen wavelengths by postulating a series of non-radiating electron orbits, quantized as defined in Section 825. Photons of energy are radiated when an electron drops from a larger to a smaller orbit. His theory failed to explain, however, the complex radiations of atoms with more than one electron, among them the sub-division of the principal quantum states which appears in the spectroscope as groups of parallel lines. Sommerfeld explained some of these lines by assuming that electrons can move in eccentric orbits. Since they normally have the same energies as circular orbits, he argued that they acquired additional energy by relativity motions near the atomic nuclei, quantized to equal $h/2\pi$ or its multiples (see Section 829).

In 1927 Schrodinger proposed a wave-mechanical theory of radiation which gave a better mathematical definition of observed energy relations and transitions within the atoms. It is based on the observed behavior of contained waves, which tend to fill all available space with periodic waves whose shapes, periods and energies are determined by the motions, energies and momenta of electrons. The energy which can be absorbed and released by an atom is determined by the possible transformations of these distributed periodic waves and by the possible motions and transitions of its electrons.

The theory of wave mechanics converts the specific orbital electron motions postulated by Rutherford and Bohr into a probability distribution, by assuming a constant change of orbit shapes and orientations, thus producing a statistical cloud effect when the time unit used covers numerous orbital periods. The probability of finding an electron at a specific point or orbital plane is proportional to the atom's wave mechanical energy at that point or plane, as defined by its local cloud density. This distribution is assumed to occur through a constant exchange of energy between electrons and between each electron and its waves, with the conversions being such that no energy is liberated or absorbed until a wave mechanical transition between two possible primary energy states occurs within the atom.

828 Quantized Energies and Orientations.

We know that visible objects can have any mass and can move with any speed in any direction; however, in the atoms all masses, electrostatic charges and other quantities, such as spin fields, orbits and their relative orientations, have specific values—they are quantized. The quantizing of electron and proton rest masses and charges causes a quantizing of the elements of orbital electrons through a functional balance between centrifugal force and attraction, de Broglie wavelength and orbit circumference. (See Sections 713 and 825.)

The table in Section 812 defines the possible orbits of a hydrogen electron. When it drops from a larger to a smaller orbit, the energy difference between the orbits is liberated as a free photon with a specific energy and wavelength. The revolution of an electron's mass and charge around its axis produces a half-quantum momentum and a quantized magnetic spin field. The fields of two electrons tend to unite and produce a zero or unit spin field momentum. The energy difference between these two states appears in radiations as a splitting of spectrum lines. This energy is comparatively large. There is also a fairly large splitting of spectrum lines due to a coupling of the magnetic fields of orbital momenta; but the difference in energy (wavelength) between the two states produced by a couple between an electron's spin field and its orbital momentum is small.

In the spectroscope there are groups of lines that can be explained by postulating a series of half and unit momentum values for electron spin and an electron's orbital and sub-quantum states. By letting each de Broglie wave in the hydrogen sequence of orbits (defined in Section 813) be assigned unit momentum value, the angular momenta of the principal quantum numbers have the following sequence values: N = 1, 2, 3 . . . Each number defines the possible division of the principal quantum numbers into sub-states, as shown by the table below. The angular momenta of these states are L = O, 1, 2, . . . In an external magnetic field they become space quantized, with each unit value splitting into two parts because they can be both positive and negative orientations in space, relative to the intruding plane. The L states therefore split into M = 1, 3, 5, . . . groups of spectrum lines as shown by this table. (See tables, Sections 834 and 837.)

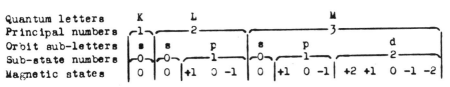

Quantum letters	K	L			M						
Principal numbers	1	2			3						
Orbit sub-letters	s	s	p		s	p		d			
Sub-state numbers	0	0	1		0	1		2			
Magnetic states	0	0	+1 0 -1		0	+1 0 -1		+2 +1 0 -1 -2			

The half-quantum electron spin fields will set themselves with or against an external magnetic field. Within the atoms they pair to produce a zero or unit spin value. Atoms with an odd number of electrons must, therefore, contain an extra half-quantum spin in addition to their paired values. The total momenta of atomic sub states and spin fields, called their J momenta, include this half value. By adding the unit values of L states and half-quantum spin fields together, we get the sequence: J = 1/2, 3/2, 5/2, 7/2 . . . angular momenta for odd electron atoms and: J = 0, 1, 2, 3 . . . angular momenta for atoms with even numbers of electrons (see Section 837).

829 Sub-Quantum States.   3B $L = h/2\pi = 1.054316 \times 10^{-27}$ emu.

Sub quantum terms   s   p   d   f   g
Angular momentum   0   1   2   3   4

When the spectrum of hydrogen is magnified, we find some of its single lines to be composites of several equidistant parallel lines. An electron's velocity in its smallest hydrogen orbit is $\propto = 1/137.044809$th of the speed of light, and the separation of lines in the fine structure above is less than the corresponding primary lines by this fine structure constant squared: $\propto^2 = 1/18781.28$.

Bohr's theory of circular non-radiating electron orbits did not explain the fine structure of hydrogen. In 1916 Sommerfeld suggested that these lines could be explained by postulating elliptical orbits. The increase of velocity when the electrons pass near the atomic nucleus produces a momentary increase of mass and orbital energy, in accordance with Einstein's relativity theory. Quantum theory anticipates a difference equal to $h/2\pi$, or its multiples. The possible eccentricities are related to the number of de Broglie waves in the principal quantum orbits, as defined in Section 825. The smallest one-wave hydrogen orbit is circular; the second two-wave orbit can be circular or have one eccentricity; the third three-wave orbit can be circular or have a small or large eccentricity. The momentua of its three possible orbits differ by 0, $h/2\pi$ and $h/4\pi$, respectively.

Accepting his postulate, this theory is a logical extension of Bohr's theory of quantized orbits. It has, however, been replaced by Schrodinger's theory of wave mechanics. This theory, developed by Schrodinger, Dirac and others since 1925, is in better accord with the observed energies, and it can also account for the observed intensities of spectrum lines; however, its complex mathematical base goes beyond the purpose of this book. It will be noticed that my theory of contained waves in Book Two may combine the two theories.

830 Electron Spin. $s = \frac{1}{2}j = h/4\pi = 5.271580 \times 10^{-28}$ erg emu

$\mu = he/4\pi mc = 9.271402 \times 10^{-21}$ gauss

In 1925 Goudsmit and Uhlenbeck suggested that several anomalies in the atomic spectra can be explained by postulating a half-quantum electron spin. Assuming an electron is a small sphere with a finite radius spinning around its axis, an angular momentum of $h/4\pi$ should cause its rotating electrostatic charge to produce a magnetic moment equal to $he/4\pi mc$ (see Section 804). This half-quantum spin of one electron tends to set itself with or against that of another, the pairing of spins thus producing a full-quantum spin or a reduction of both fields to zero—the usual state of paired electrons in neutral atoms. An external magnetic field will cause an electron to set itself with or against its magnetic momentum, or in a space-quantized angle to it, as defined by the p, d and f states (see Section 828).

The total angular momentum of an atomic electron is defined by the symbol j. The pairing of electrons in atoms with even numbers of electrons means that their values can be j = 0, 1, 2, 3 . . . , while atoms with odd numbers of electrons have the momenta j = ½, 1½, 2½, 3½ . . . , because all have one unpaired spin.

The orbital angular momentum of a hydrogen electron in its p state is $1(h/2\pi)$. Combined vectorially with an electron's half-quantum spin momentum, with the spin added or subtracted, its j value is either $\frac{3}{2}(h/2\pi)$ or $1/2(h/2\pi)$. The difference is the energy it takes to turn its spin from parallel to anti-parallel rotation. The difference appears as two parallel lines in the spectroscope.

All electrons, protons and neutrons have half-quantum spin fields with angular momenta equal to $\frac{1}{2}(h/2\pi)$. The interactions of nuclear particles give each atomic nucleus a spin and, therefore, a magnetic moment. Its interactions with those of orbital electrons produce an ultra-fine splitting of spectrum lines.

831 Magnetic Moment. (m)

The orbital motion of an electron's mass produces the physical momentum L; that of its negative electrostatic charge, the magnetic field moment m. Both are specific quantities because the orbital factors producing them (the electron's mass, charge and velocity) are quantized. Despite this common origin, their different reactions to external electromagnetic forces make them different phenomena.

An electron with charge e and mass m has the angular momentum $h/4\pi$ and the magnetic moment $eh/4\pi m$. (See the Bohr magneton in Section 804.)

832 Zeeman Effect. Magnetic.

In 1896 Zeeman discovered that single spectrum lines split into groups of parallel lines when radiating atoms are in a magnetic field. Their differences in wavelength increase with an increase of magnetization. This effect is interpreted as a turning of electron orbits and the planes of free spin electrons with or against an external magnetic field, or to a right angle or any angle which preserves their natural quantum states in such a field. Space quantizings in the atoms can be positive or negative.

The number of lines into which a single line of known origin will divide in a magnetic field makes it possible to identify the quantum states in the atoms. The polarization of a magnetic field produces a difference in the splitting of spectrum lines. In the normal Zeeman effect, limited to certain simple lines, light radiated on the plane of a magnetic field splits into two lines which are circularly polarized in opposite directions; light radiated at a right angle to the field splits into three equally spaced plane polarized lines, with the middle one perpendicular to the magnetic field, and the other two parallel to it.

From the table in Section 828, it will be noticed that each principal quantum (shell) number is also the number of sub-quantum states which can exist in that shell. When the total quantum number j of the sub-states 1, m and s is unity or its multiples, then the s, p, d and f states produce 1, 3, 5 and 7 line groups of Zeeman spectrum lines, respectively. However, when the j momenta include a half value, due to a free spin electron, their spectra can have 2, 4, 6 or 8 lines in a group, respectively. Section 837 gives the j values of 32 neutral elements.

The Zeeman splitting of a s state, in which 1 = 0 and s = ½, gives us a double line because the electron sets its spin with or against the magnetic field, thus increasing or reducing its atom's radiation potential. A p state, with 1 = 1 and s = 0, splits into three lines (+1, 0, -1), because the electron can set its orbit, or its spin field, with or against the magnetic field or at a right angle to it.

833 Stark Effect. Electrostatic.

In 1913 Stark discovered that the spectra of radiating atoms and molecules split into symmetrically spaced components in a strong electrostatic field. Some of its photons were plane polarized perpendicular to the direction of the field, and others parallel to it. This Stark effect is comparable to the transverse Zeeman effect, but the separations are larger.

The number of Stark lines in the spectroscope increases with the principal quantum (shell) number, but does not depend upon the components of the sub-quantum states. They are, therefore, of little value in the analysis of complex spectra. In metals the Stark effect usually appears as a displacement of unresolved components toward shorter or longer wavelengths.

834 Pauli's Exclusion Principle.

This principle was discovered by Pauli in 1925. It states that no two electrons in an atom can have the same four quantum numbers: n, l, m and s. These are: The principal quantum number n (Section 825); the orbital quantum number 1 (Section 829); the magnetic quantum number m (Section 831), and the spin quantum number s (Section 830). The possible combinations are defined by the table below.

```
n  Principal quantum letters K, L, M, N, O... Numbers 1, 2, 3, 4, 5.
l  Sub-quantum letters         s, p, d, f, g... Numbers 0, 1, 2, 3, 4.
m  Magnetic quantum states   s = 1;  p = 3;  d = 5;  f = 7.
s  Half-quantum spin + or −
T.l. Electrons in each sub quantum state:  s = 2;  p = 6;  d = 10;  f = 1
T.n. Electrons in each shell:  K = 2;  L = 8;  M = 18;  N = 32.
T.e. Electrons in filled shells:  K = 2;  KL = 10;  KLM = 28;  KLMN = 60.
```

nl	Ks	Ls	Lp	Ms	Mp	Md	Ns
n	1 1	2 2	2 2 2 2 2 2	3 3	3 3 3 3 3 3	3 3 3 3 3 3 3 3 3 3	4 4
l	0 0	0 0	1 1 1 1 1 1	0 0	1 1 1 1 1 1	2 2 2 2 2 2 2 2 2 2	0 0
m	0 0	0 0	+1+1 0 0-1-1	0 0	+1+1 0 0-1-1	+2+2+1+1 0 0-1-1-2-2	0 0
s	+½-½	+½-½	+½-½+½-½+½-½	+½-½	+½-½+½-½+½-½	+½-½+½-½+½-½+½-½+½-½	+½-½
T.l.	2	2	6	2	6	10	2
T.ne	2	4	10	12	18	28	30

Note that the number of electrons which can exist in each substate and shell is determined by the Pauli principle. The inner states and shells tend to fill up before electrons appear in the higher quantum states. The K, L and M shells are completed in sequence up to 18 electrons, but the Md sub-state does not begin to fill until the two Ns orbits are filled, because the bonding force in this latter state is slightly greater. The total number of electrons in each completed shell is obtained by doubling the shell number squared. Let each vertical line stand for one electron and one nuclear charge, and we get the sequence of elements in the next section. Completed shells plus 8 electrons in the next shell give us the atoms of inert gases, as shown in Section 836.

The Pauli principle not only limits the number of electrons which can exist within a shell, it also limits the type of electron jump which can occur between two possible orbits (shells) in an atom. The sub-quantum states are defined by combining shell numbers and sub-states in sequence: 1s; 2s 2p; 3s 3p 3d; 4s 4p 4d 4f; 5s 5p, and so on.

835 The Elements.   *Inert gases.

Hydrogen	21 Scandium	41 Columbium	61 Illinium	81 Thallium
Helium	22 Titanium	42 Molybdenum	62 Samarium	82 Lead
Lithium	23 Vanadium	43 Masurium	63 Europium	83 Bismuth
Beryllium	24 Chromium	44 Ruthenium	64 Gadolinium	84 Polonium
Boron	25 Manganese	45 Rhodium	65 Terbium	85 Astatine
Carbon	26 Iron	46 Palladium	66 Dysprosium	*86 Radon
Nitrogen	27 Cobalt	47 Silver	67 Holmium	87 Francium
Oxygen	28 Nickel	48 Cadmium	68 Erbium	88 Radium
Fluorine	29 Copper	49 Indium	69 Thulium	89 Actinium
Neon	30 Zink	50 Tin	70 Ytterbium	90 Thorium
Sodium	31 Gallium	51 Antimony	71 Lutecium	91 Protactinium
Magnesium	32 Germanium	52 Columbium	72 Hafnium	92 Uranium
Aluminum	33 Arsenic	53 Iodine	73 Tantalum	93 Neptunium
Silicon	34 Selenium	*54 Xenon	74 Tungsten	94 Plutonium
Phosphorus	35 Bromine	55 Cesium	75 Rhenium	95 Americum
Sulphur	*36 Krypton	56 Barium	76 Osmium	96 Curium
Chlorine	37 Rubidium	57 Lanthanum	77 Irridium	97 Berkelium
Argon	38 Strotium	58 Cerium	78 Platinum	98 Californium
Potassium	39 Yttrium	59 Praseodymium	79 Gold	99 Einsteinium
Calcium	40 Zirconium	60 Neodynium	80 Mercury	100 Fermium

The 100 elements above are listed in the sequence of their atomic numbers. The rare earths appear between 57 and 72. All elements above 83 are radioactive. The last of the series are so unstable they can exist in laboratories for only a fraction of a second. Structure-related properties of the first 32 elements appear in Section 837.

836 The Inert Gases.

AN	Shell K-2 Sub s. 1s	L -8- 2s 2p	M -18- 3s 3p 3d	N -32- 4s 4p 4d 4f	O -50- 5s 5p 5d 5f 5g	P-72 6s 6p
2 Helium	2					
10 Neon	2	2 6				
18 Argon	2	2 6	2 6			
36 Krypton	2	2 6	2 6 10	2 6		
54 Xenon	2	2 6	2 6 10	2 6 10	2 6	
86 Radon	2	2 6	2 6 10	2 6 10 14	2 6 10	2 6

These six inert gases give us an insight into the relationship between atomic structure and its electrostatic, physical and chemical properties. The elements immediately preceding an inert gas are non-metals and non-conductors; those immediately following are metals and good conductors. The former tend to complete their outmost eight electron shells by capture or sharing, while the latter may be stripped of electrons in excess of this number, or they may remain within the metal as a cloud of semi-bound quantum exchange states. The inert state of the gases is obviously caused by the maximum integration effected by eight electrons in an atom's outmost shell.

837 Composition and States of 32 Elements.

1	2	3	4	5	6	7	8	9	10	11	12
	Nucleons			Atomic	K shell	Shell and		Electron	Radi-	Valence	Normal
Sy	AN	N	I	weights	X rays	sub states	T	volts	tions	Ions	states
H	1	0	1	1.00814	911.76	K1s	$^2S_{1/2}$	13.595	1215.7	-1	Non met
He	2	2	4	4.00387	524.	"2s	$^1S_0$	24.580	584.4	0	Inert g
Li	3	4	7	7.01823	235.	L1s	$^2S_{1/2}$	5.390	6707.9	+1	Light m
Be	4	5	9	9.01506	133.	"2s	$^1S_0$	9.320	2348.6	+2	Lt. met
B	5	6	11	11.0128	84.	"2s 1p	$^2P_{1/2}$	8.296	2497.7	+3	Semi me
C	6	6	12	12.0038	49.3	"2s 2p	$^3P_0$	11.264	1657.0		Non met
N	7	7	14	14.0075	36.5	"2s 3p	$^4S_{1/2}$	14.540	1200.7	-3+5	Non met
O	8	8	16	16.0000	24.6	"2s 4p	$^3P_1$	13.614	1302.3	-2	Non met
F	9	10	19	19.0044	18.6	"2s 5p	$^2P_{3/2}$	17.418	954.7	-1	Non met
Ne	10	10	20	19.9988	14.5	"2s 6p	$^1S_0$	21.559	735.8	0	Inert g
Na	11	12	23	22.9971	11.5	M1s	$^2S_{1/2}$	5.138	5895.9	+1	Lt. met
Mg	12	12	24	23.9927	9.511	"2s	$^1S_0$	7.644	2852.1	+2	Lt. met
Al	13	14	27	26.9901	7.947	"2s 1p	$^2P_{1/2}$	5.984	3961.5	+3	Lt. met
Si	14	14	28	27.9858	6.73	"2s 2p	$^3P_0$	8.149	2524.1		Semi me
P	15	16	31	30.9838	5.758	"2s 3p	$^4S_{3/2}$	10.550	1787.5	-3+5	Non met
S	16	16	32	31.9822	5.012	"2s 4p	$^3P_1$	10.357	1807.4	-2+4+6	Non met
Cl	17	18	35	34.9800	4.384	"2s 5p	$^2P_{3/2}$	13.010	1347.2	-1	Non met
A	18	22	40	39.9751	3.866	"2s 6p	$^1S_0$	15.755	1048.3	0	Inert g
K	19	20	39	38.9761	3.435	"8sp N1s	$^2S_{1/2}$	4.339	7699.0	+1	Lt. met
Ca	20	20	40	39.9753	3.063	"8sp "2s	$^1S_0$	6.111	4226.7	+2	Lt. met
Sc	21	24	45	44.9702	2.752	"1d "2s	$^2D_{3/2}$	6.538	3911.8	+3	Lt. met
Ti	22	26	48	47.9632	2.494	"2d "2s	$^3F_2$	6.818	3653.5	+4	Metal
V	23	28	51	50.9602	2.265	"3d "2s	$^4F_{3/2}$	6.743	4379.2	+3+5	Heavy m
Cr	24	28	52	51.9570	2.065	"5d "1s	$^7S_3$	6.763	4254.2	+2+3+6	Hv. me
Mn	25	30	55	54.9555	1.889	"5d "2s	$^6S_{5/2}$	7.432	4030.8	+2+3+7	Hv. me
Fe	26	30	56	55.9527	1.738	"6d "2s	$^5D_4$	7.900	3581.2	+2+3	Hv. me
Co	27	32	59	58.9519	1.602	"7d "2s	$^4F_{9/2}$	7.862	3465.8	+2+3	Hv. me
Ni	28	30	58	57.9538	1.489	"8d "2s	$^3F_4$	7.633	3524.5	+2+3	Hv. me
Cu	29	34	63	62.9496	1.379	"10d "1s	$^2S_{1/2}$	7.724	3247.6	+1+2	Hv. me
Zn	30	34	64	63.9495	1.296	"10d "2s	$^1S_0$	9.391	2138.6	+2	Hv. me
Ga	31	38	69	68.9476	1.190	N2s 1p	$^2P_{1/2}$	6.000	4172.1	+3	Hv. me
Ge	32	42	74	73.9445	1.115	"2s 2p	$^3P_0$	7.880	2709.6	-4+4	Semi m

1	Sy	Symbols of the elements	8	T	Normal electronic terms
2	AN	Atomic numbers. Protons	6 & 9		Wavelengths in angstroms
3	N	Neutrons in nucleus	11		− capture, + lose electrons
4	I	Most abundant isotopes	11		Many valencies are non-electric

The purpose of this table is to show the relationship between atomic numbers, electronic states and a few of the observable states of the elements. The first column gives the chemical symbols of the elements; the second, their atomic numbers (Section 819). Since the latter is also the number of protons in the nucleus of that element, the addition of neutrons from the third column give us its isotopic number (fourth column). The most abundant isotope of each element was selected, and it will be noticed that its number of neutrons are even in all cases, with only two exceptions. This preference appears also in the remainder of the elements; the evidence thus indicates that a pairing of neutrons in atomic nuclei tends to produce stable configurations.

Since the atoms of an element in nature are mixtures of isotopes, its atomic weight obtained by chemical analysis differs slightly from the isotopic number of its most abundant species (column 5). The atomic weight of oxygen is 16 by definition (see Section 822).

Assuming that the circumference of an electron's orbit is identical with its de Broglie wavelength, as defined for hydrogen in Section 812, it is evident that an increase of nuclear charge increases its orbital velocity, and that there is a consequent reduction of wavelength and orbit radius. When an electron is knocked out from an atom's K orbit and is replaced by another, the consequent x ray radiation increases in energy and decreases in wavelength as defined in column 6. This sequence was discovered by Moseley. The wavelengths are in angstrom.

Since the inner shells and sub-states are filled with electrons and normally inactive, only one or two external states are defined for each atom (column 7). Letters are used to define the shell terms; ordinarily, they are numbered. For example, oxygen and iron (atomic numbers 8 and 26) appear as $2s^2 2p^4$ and $3d^6 4s^2$, respectively. The complete term for iron is: $1s^2 2s^2 2p^6 3s^2 3p^6 3d^6 4s^2$, with only the last two sub-states chemically active.

A proper explanation of column 8, in the table, giving the lowest spectrum terms of the atoms, is beyond the purpose of this book. The combination of three quantum terms can be represented by ML_J, with M defining the multiplicity of quantum states which appear as a splitting of spectrum lines; L is an orbital momentum quantum number with $S = L_o$, $P = L_1$, $D = L_2$, $F = L_3$; and J is the total angular momentum when the unit values of L have been added to the electrons' positive or negative half spin values. Hence $J = L \pm s$. It will be noticed from the table that odd-numbered atoms all have an extra half-spin. In a two-electron s shell, opposite orbital momenta and opposite spins are paired and, therefore, zero; J is, therefore, also zero.

The ionization voltage necessary to remove an electron from a neutral atom, as shown in column 9, is closely related to the shell numbers and sub-quantum states. It is also related to column 10. That column gives the radiation wavelengths which are the last to disappear when excited atoms return to the inactive state. The valencies of the elements are also related to the electronic states and the ionization potentials in electron volts. It is evident from columns 9 and 10, that firmly bound electrons produce non-metals, while those with loosely bound electrons are metals (column 12). These two types of atoms are separated by the inert gases. Check also column 7 against 11.

838 Ions.

An ion is an atom with a positive or negative electrostatic charge. A neutral atom becomes negative when it gains electrons, and positive when it loses some;

an ionic state is described in terms of the number of electrons by which it deviates from the neutral atom. Neutral atoms with a few electrons short of completing their eight-electron shells, as shown by the table in Section 836, tend to capture the lacking number; thus acquiring a singly, doubly or greater ionic negative state. When the number of electrons in a neutral atom are in excess of eight in the outmost shell, the excess are feebly bound because they must move in a larger orbit or exist in a sub-quantum state. Such atoms may lose electrons and become positive ions.

In some liquid mixtures, atoms with negative and positive ionic tendencies may exchange electrons and become permanent ionic states, a mixture of positive and negative ions. Such liquids are conductors of electricity, and a current will cause negative ions to move toward its positive pole and positive ions toward its negative. It will be noticed that it takes twice as much current to transport a doubly ionized atom as one that is singly ionized. (See Section 511 for definition of the Faraday—the quantity unit of electrolysis.)

839 Valency.

It is an exchange of electrons or a pairing of electromagnetic and spin fields between atoms, thus producing a cohesive bonding force by integrations. In an electrostatic bonding a non-metal captures electrons from a metal and the cohesive force is the mutual electrostatic attraction between atoms. Atoms with similar properties, such two atoms of oxygen, can also produce adhesion by an exchange of orbital momenta and electron spins. This is called a homopolar bond. This form of exchange is possible because the identity of electrons makes a conservation of energy and momenta possible within the complex.

Because the electrons of a completed shell or sub-state have zero free-spin and momentum potentials, the simplest valency bonds of incomplete sub-shells are effected by the same electrons as those of the ionic states. (See table, Section 837). However, the electrons of two interacting atoms can also exchange free spins and momenta without an exchange of electrons, thus producing cohesion by functional integrations that leave the atoms electrostatically neutral. An atom of carbon, for example, can gain or lose four electrons to form an electrostatic bond; but this reaction probably never occurs, and its four-electron valence is effected by an exchange of spin and momenta that leaves it electrostatically neutral.

840 Molecules.

One neutral atom and the union of two or more into systems with consequent cohesions of indefinite duration. The number of atoms in a molecule ranges up to tens of thousands for complex organic structures. The possible combinations of the elements in nature in molecular structures are to be counted by the billions.

Elementary compounds composed of a few atoms can be defined by matching valencies. An atom of oxygen with a valence of two may unite with two atoms of hydrogen to form a molecule of water, while a carbon atom with a valence of four can unite with four atoms of hydrogen as a molecule of methane. The valencies of the elements were originally discovered by noting the number of hydrogen atoms each element would combine with or replace in a chemical reaction.

The chemical symbols for 32 elements appear in section 837; their names in section 835. A molecule's composition is described by chemical symbols followed by subscript numbers defining the number of each kind of atom. Water and methane have the formula: H_2O, and CH_4, respectively. Pure hydrogen (H_2) and oxygen (O_2) is converted into water by the chemical formula: $2H_2 + O_2 \rightarrow 2H_2O$. A sample of more complex molecules is the conversion of nitrate ($NaNO_3$) and sulfuric acid (H_2SO_4) into nitric acid (HNO_3) and sodium sulfate (Na_2SO_4). The formula is: $2NaNO_3 + H_2SO_4 \rightarrow 2HNO_3 \uparrow + Na_2SO_4$.

The structure equivalent of energy liberated during the formation of a molecule must be broken before a reorganization can occur. It can be broken by functional replacements and by intrusive forces; usually by a combination of both during the molecular collisions effected by heat. At the absolute zero temperature of 273.18 degrees centigrade below the freezing point of water, all molecular motions cease and all matter exists in the solid state. With increasing temperatures, the molecules pass through a liquid state, because disruptive forces are repeatedly destroying reforming molecules. At still higher temperatures, the liquids become gases and the gaseous molecules are atomized. Finally, the atoms are stripped of their orbital electrons in the centers of the stars, where temperatures are in millions of degrees.

841 Diatomic Molecules.

The outer electrons of a diatomic molecule are shared by both atoms. When one of these electrons is excited, it changes orbit and speed in accordance with the quantum rules, and it also causes the molecule to vibrate and rotate with quantized energy in a quantized orbit. As the electron returns to a lower quantum orbit the energy it liberates is increased or reduced by quantized vibration or rotation changes. The radiations of diatomic molecules, therefore, appear in the spectroscope as a series of parallel lines, each defining a particular combination of energies and the corresponding wavelength.

Chapter 9

GASES SUBSTANCE PHYSICS

The importance of gases in the development of atomic theory is enhanced by the existence of proportions which remain unchanged, or changes in simple arithmetic or geometrical ratios, when some factors in an experiment are changed. It implies a corresponding consistency of the atomic constants and ratios on which the gas laws are based. The sections on gases are followed by comments on entropy and its use as an age-indicator of the universe.

901 Gas Laws. (Boyle, Charles and Avogadro.)

Boyle's law: "The volume of a gas is inversely proportional to pressure when the temperature is constant."

Charles' law: "The volume of a gas varies directly as the absolute temperature when the pressure is constant." (All gases have the same coefficient of expansion.)

Avogadro's law: "Equal volumes of gases have the same number of molecules when the temperature and pressure is the same."

All three laws can be deduced from the molecular motion theory of heat, and a mean kinetic energy of the moving particles. The mean velocity of a gas is obtained by the formula: $v = \sqrt{3P/D}$, with P the pressure of the gas in dynes per square centimeter, and D its density in grams per cubic centimeter.

902 Avogadro's Number. (N) 28M   Chemical = 6.023204×10^{23} statoms
                                       28N, 34E   Physical = 6.024860×10^{23} statoms

The number of statoms in a gram mass; the number of molecules in a gram mole. These two definitions were derived from Avogadro's law of gases and the gram mole postulate. When the atomic weights of the atoms or molecules composing a particular mass are known, we can obtain the number of such bodies by dividing Avogadro's number by their atomic weights. Thus, the number of oxygen atoms in a gram mass is Avogadro's number divided by sixteen, and its number of molecules is one half of the result, because oxygen molecules are composed of two atoms. (The difference between physical and chemical statoms is defined under gram mole. See section 814 for statom.)

903 Gram Mole.

A mass in grams equal to the atomic weight of its atoms or molecules. Since atomic weights are in statoms, it follows that the number of units in such a mass is equal to Avogadro's number. Because the atomic weight of oxygen is 16 by definition, its molar weight is 16 grams, and that of its molecule (O_2) is 32 grams. A gram mole of water (H_2O) weighs 18.016283 grams—the combined weight of two hydrogen atoms and one atom of oxygen in statoms.

In nature, oxygen atoms are composed of two isotopes, 16 and 18. Because the physicist is interested in the properties of individual atoms, he defines the statom as 1/16 of oxygen, isotope 16; while the chemist, dealing with oxygen as it appears in nature, takes the natural mixture and divides it by 16. The difference between the physicist's and the chemist's statom is 1.000275 physical statoms.

904 Centigrade. (C)   One $C° = 1.8$ fahrenheit

$0° c = 32$ farhenheits

A unit of temperature. A one-hundredth part of the temperature difference between the freezing and boiling points of water, with the melting point of ice defined as zero, and the condensing point of steam as 100 degrees centrigrade. Temperature is a motion or vibration of molecules. The energy of these motions can be expressed in terms of ergs, and their momenta in dynes.

Heat is to be distinguished from temperature. Heat can be both latent and active energy while temperature gives the active state only. Both are the energy of molecular motions, transmitted by collisions and through the forces binding atoms and molecules together; heat exists also as the latent energy of such states.

905 Absolute Zero Temperature. (k)   k = -273.18 centigrade

The natural unit of temperature. The temperature at which all molecular motions cease and all matter is in the solid state. It is the zero point on the Kelvin scale of temperatures, with degrees scaled as in the centigrade system.

Absolute zero can be obtained from Charles' law (Section 901) by noting the rate at which the volume of a gas changes with a change of temperature. It can also be deduced from the decreasing velocities of gas molecules with a decrease in temperature. (See Section 901 for formula.)

906 Gas Constant. (R)   Total energy = 1.247080×10^8 erg

Ch. Active energy = 8.313870×10^7 erg

The kinetic energy of molecular motions in a gram mole of perfect gas for a temperature increase of one degree centigrade. The energy which appears as an expansion pressure is two thirds of the translational energy of the gas molecules. The figures above are on the chemical scale. (See Section 903 for definition.)

The difference between total and active energy is defined as a doubling of molecular momenta by reflection on one of their three planes of motion (in three dimensions). The average velocity of the molecules vary in proportion to the square root of the absolute temperature, but the actual velocity of any one molecule ranges widely from this average. Note that energy is action and potential action within the complex, and that momentum is the expansion pressure of a contained gas. Since the ratio of momentum to energy is the difference between velocity and velocity squared, the wide range of velocities among the molecules produces a difference between the energy of mean molecular velocity and the root mean square of actual motions (see Section 117). This difference increases with temperature.

907 Boltzmann's Constant. (k)   Total energy = 2.070460×10^{-16} erg
66 Active energy = 1.380307×10^{-16} erg

The kinetic energy of each average molecule in a perfect gas, for each degree centigrade increase of temperature. It is equal to the molar energy of the gas constant divided by Avogadro's number (Sections 902-3). The average translational energy of each molecule—its total energy—is Boltzmann's constant times 3/2. Let symbol R be the gas constant and N Avogadro's number, and we have the formula:

$$k = \frac{R}{N} \qquad \frac{8.313870 \times 10^7}{6.023204 \times 10^{23}} = 1.380307 \times 10^{-16} \text{ erg}$$

908 Ideal Gas at Zero C. Temperature.

The energy of a gram mole of ideal gas at the freezing point of water. The figures below were obtained by multiplying the four constants in Sections 906 and 907 by the temperature above absolute zero as defined in Section 905.

Boltzmann's constant	times 273.18 =	3.770723×10^{-14} ergs
Its translational energy	" "	5.656084×10^{-14} "
Gram mole gas constant	" "	2.271183×10^{10} "
Its translational energy	" "	3.406775×10^{10} "

909 Gas Volume of Gram Mole. (v)   v = 22414.1 cubic centimeters
$1/v = 4.46148 \times 110^{-5}$ gram cm^3.

The volume occupied by a gas having Avogadro's number of molecules; the space occupied by a gram mole of ideal gas at zero centigrade temperature under normal atmospheric pressure. Pressure is defined as 1.0132×10^6 dynes per square centimeter. Note that the weight of a gram mole is the average atomic weight of the gas molecules, redefined as grams (see Section 903). One gram is, therefore, Avogadro's number in statoms, and the reciprocal of volume gives us their weight in grams in one cubic centimeter.

Each kind of gas molecule in a mixture of gases behaves as if the other kinds were not present. We can, therefore, obtain the behavior of each kind by treating it as a pure gas. By multiplying its atomic weight by the reciprocal of volume, we obtain a mass in grams per cubic centimeter which must then be reduced by its percentage value in the mixture. If one out of four molecules in a mixture is of that kind, its contribution to the total mass is one fourth of that defined for a pure gas.

The atomic weight of an oxygen molecule (O_2) is 32 by definition, and its weight as a pure gas in the atmosphere is obtained by the formula: $A_w/v = 32/22414.1 = 0.0014277$ gram per cubic centimeter. The atomic weight of water is 18.016283, and its atmospheric density as a gas is, therefore, 0.00080379 gram per cubic centimeter. The density of air, a complex mixture of different kinds of molecules, is about 0.00129 (see Section 307).

910 Loschmidt's Number. (N/v)   2.687239 X 10^{19} molecules

The number of molecules in one cubic centimeter of ideal gas at zero centigrade temperature under the normal atmospheric pressure of 1.0132 X 10^6 dynes per square centimeter. It is obtained by dividing Avogadro's number by the volume of an ideal gas. Note that all gases, regardless of mixture, have the same number of molecules under identical conditions of temperature and pressure. The density of the gas must, therefore, be directly proportional to the atomic weight of its molecules. A chemical reaction that halves the number of molecules doubles the density. A doubling of pressure doubles the density and the molecules per cubic cm. A halving of absolute temperature also doubles the density and the number of molecules per unit volume.

911 Gram Calorie. (c) 28C   c = 4.184761 X 10^7 ergs

The quantity of heat energy absorbed in raising the temperature of a one-gram mass of water one degree centigrade, from 14.5 to 15.5 degrees. It is called the specific heat of the substance. The difference between heat and temperature is defined under Section 904.

The specific heat of a substance varies with temperature, due to quantum transitions of its molecular states and the chemical reactions which may accompany them. (See Section 841 for quantum relations.) As long as the temperature is below that necessary to effect a quantum transition, the absorption of energy is confined to an increase of molecular motions and vibrations. However, as it passes above that point, the molecules begin to absorb large quantities of energy as their orbital electrons jump into higher quantum states. Note that the available energy must be above the energy difference between two molecular quantum states.

The gram calorie defined above is too small for practical use. To designate the nutritive value of food the kilogram calorie (1000 calories) is used. The two units are sometimes referred to as "small" and "large" calories, respectively.

912 Calorie Mole. (c/N) 5C   c/N = 6.947733 X 10^{-17} erg

The quantity of heat energy absorbed by one water molecule per degree centigrade as defined for the gram calorie; the energy of one-gram calorie divided by Avogadro's number.

$c^1 = c/N \ 4.184761 \times 10^7/6.023204 \times 10^{23} = 6.947733 \times 10^{-17}$ erg per molecule

913 Entropy.

A measure of thermodynamic energy which was once available to a system, but is no longer potentially usable as energy, due to dispersal and the disappearance of a thermal gradient. There is a constant decrease of available heat energy in an active system, even though local and momentary reversals occur or appear to occur as potential energy becomes active, because the dispersal of thermal heat is unavoidable and irreversible. Since heat disperses by flowing from higher to lower temperatures, and never in the other direction, the entropy of a closed system is either static or increasing. The heat energy lost by dispersal or radiation can never again become available in the original concentrations.

914 Age and Evolution of the Universe.

The constant increase of entropy in the universe, due to the constant radiation dispersal of energy by the stars, leads to the following conclusions. Since more energy was available one moment ago, and immensely more a billion years ago, there must have been a time long ago when the available energy was at a maximum—a moment of time when the universe was born. Looking forward in time, the day must come, perhaps billions of years hence, when all the stellar energies have been dispersed and the temperature throughout the universe is the same everywhere: the heat death of the universe.

Astronomical observations of galaxies show an increase of their velocity of recession with distance. If these motions are real there must have been a time, about two to six billion years ago, when the galaxies were close together. Other kinds of age indications seem to point to a common origin at that time, although there are old rocks on earth that appear to be nearly ten times older than that.

915 Rationale of Evolving Universe.

Mathematics tells us a limited universe is more probable than one without limits in space and time. A first conclusion is, therefore, that our universe had a beginning and will eventually end, and that this sequence of events consists of a dynamic progression in which the emergence of matter preceded its present disintegration. This is also, roughly, the opinion held by most astronomers, since it accounts for the observed disintegration of stellar matter and the law of entropy.

Most physicists seem to prefer an explosive origin; however, it is my contention that anything occurring on such an immense scale must develop as a smooth dynamic progression in both space and time. I believe that matter is the end-product of organization, and that there exists in nature a bias toward both organization and disorganization, with local conditions determining which one will be dominant at a particular time at one point or another in the immensities of space, and that local changes are so slow and gradual as to be beyond our perception.

My theory of the evolution of the universe in Book Two brings the theory of entropy into question, because there must have been a time when casual waves integrated into matter. It is questioned by my theory of containment, because the integration of contained waves is a reversal of entropy. (See Section 615 for additional comments.)

Chapter 10

PROOF OF IDEALIZATIONS

In the first part of this chapter I show how algebra led to my discovery of the natural unit of length by its idealization of relations and proportions in atomic physics. It is followed by proof based on experimental determinations of the atomic constants by converting the constants of the ideal and ultimate systems of units into centimeter values. They idealize the gaussian system of units by eliminating the marginal errors of its experimental determinations of the atomic constants. The ratios of experimental wavelengths led to the idealizations of the electronic and waveratio constants, and through them to an idealization of electron motions in hydrogen and free space. The atomic constants of the ideal, ultimate, and other systems are defined and proved. The elements of an electron's relativity motions are defined and related to the simple ideal proportions of low velocity electrons.

1001 Introduction to Proof.

My work for a third of a century on the problems of theoretical physics obviously led to many erroneous conclusions and some highly irregular advances. To make it possible for the reader to follow my reasoning, my errors are ignored, and discoveries follow a rational succession of implications and conclusions. The idealizations of physical constants in the preceding chapters and the Table of Physical Constants, Chapter 11, were made possible by the mathematical idealizations of proportions in electron and atomic physics described in the following sections. A belief that natural phenomena are comprehensibly logical because they are abstractions from an ether of ultimate mechanical simplicity is the philosophical base upon which the following researches in atomic physics were conducted.

1002 Algebraic Idealizations.

The most significant fact in theoretical physics is that many interrelated algebraic formulas give specific information. When these are converted into figures, and their mathematical results are checked against those obtained by experiments, the agreements are within the margin of experimental error. Although I believe all living processes, unlike algebra and geometry, contain functional deviations from ideal proportions, observation shows that they are too small to affect experimental determinations, and logic tells us that we must postulate ideal states until the contrary can be proved. It is evident that nature's idealizations of its fundamental phenomena anticipate corresponding idealizations in the mathematical expressions of its algebraic formulas. To discover the true proportions in nature, we must seek out factors whose values are independent of the arbitrary units of mass, time and length on which the accepted systems of physical constants are based.

1003 Nature's Mathematics.

The observations above lead to the conclusion there is a mathematics of nature, with proportional values related to a specific unit of length, and to Planck's energy for that unit, because the facts of physics are specific and related. Logic tells us nature's mathematics must be the simplest possible; that it probably acts through primary structural and velocity differences having a one-to-two ratio at the base and geometrical differences for its higher states. These are defined by multiplications and divisions, roots and powers, abstracted from the original differences by repeated doublings and halvings. (See Section 222 for the algebraic web.)

These postulates lead to the conclusion that the mathematics of nature can best be expressed by a logarithm, and that the binary-number (basic) logarithm is the one best fitted to bring out the ideal proportions anticipated by idealized algebra. It is obvious that we can select one significant value in atomic physics and express it in terms of an idealized power of two. If this selection is in simple proportion to other constants, that relationship is brought out by basic logarithms. It helps us recognize the true dimensions of physical phenomena from observations.

1004 Square Table of Atomic Constants.

A square table shows the relationship between atomic constants more effectively than a group of formulas. The table below was used by me as a guide in the development of simple formulas that were subsequently integrated into the sequence of units in the next section. It is evident that some of the values in the table, such as the mass of an electrostatic charge, are meaningless equivalents.

The arrangement of its four columns and their ratio values were developed from Einstein's formula: $E = mc^2$; Maxwell's formula: $emu = esu/c$, with esu and cgs values identical; and Planck's definition of the energy of a unit wave. The energy relations of a wavenumber can also be obtained from the wavenumber of an electron's rest mass. (See Sections 212, 213, 606 and 709 for definitions.)

Mass unit	Erg emu	Erg esu	Wave number		
–	ħ	–	-2π	1.	Quantum unit.
–	h	–	$1\tilde{v}$	c	Velocity of light.
–	μ	–	–	ħ	Planck's constant divided by two pi.
–	–	e	–	h	Planck's energy quantum. A wave unit.
m_c	m'	–	$\tilde{v}$	μ	Bohr magneton. In hydrogen K orbit.
$-o^\lambda$	$-c$	$1Q$	–	e	Electron's electrostatic charge.
$-c$	$1E$	c	–	m_c	Electron's mass. $\tilde{v}$ Its wavenumber.
$1G$	c	c^λ	–	Q	Electrostatic and cgs unit of action.
				E	Electromagnetic unit of action.
				G	Unit of mass and inertia.
	–	–		R	Rydberg's wavenumber. Hy. K orbit rad

1005 Mathematical Sequence of Units.

A quick, easy and certain way to obtain a large number of the atomic constants of a particular system of units is highly desirable, because it permits extensive exploratory changes of the accepted arbitrary units of action—mass, time and length. From the table above, I have worked out the following simple formulas:

$$m_o = h\tilde{v}/c \qquad h = m/\tilde{v} \qquad e^1 = \hbar c \propto \qquad \mu = e/4\pi\tilde{v} \qquad e^1 = hc/C = \hbar V$$
$$m' = mc \qquad \hbar = h/2\pi \qquad e = \sqrt{hc\propto} \qquad \propto = 1/\phi \qquad V = c/\phi$$

These formulas were recombined into the sequence of atomic units below. As a guide in the selection of sequence units and as a check on the validity of my choice, I halved one of the three fundamental units of action and noted its effects on the conventional reduction formulas. A halving of the mass unit doubles an electron's mass value; a halving of time halves the speed-of-light value; and a halving of the length unit doubles the speed-of-light value and halves all wavenumbers. The three sequences below show the changes that occur, in numbers and fractions, relative to a selected sequence, when one of its three units is halved:

	m_o	$\times c$	$= m')$	$\div \tilde{v}$	$= h)$	$\div 2\pi$	$= \hbar)$	$\times c/\phi$	$= e^1)^{1/2}$	$= e)$	$\div 4\pi\tilde{v}$	$= \mu$.
./2 mass	2.	1.	2.	1.	2.	1.	2.	1.	2.	$\sqrt{2}$	1.	$\sqrt{2}$
./2 time	1.	1/2	1/2	1.	1/2	1.	1/2	1/2	1/4	1/2	1.	1/2
./2 length	1.	2.	2.	1/2	4.	1.	4.	2.	8.	$\sqrt{8}$	1/2	$\sqrt{32}$

The algebraic terms of the sequence below were defined in the preceding section: The sequence appears also in Section 217.

$$mc = \dot{m})/\tilde{v} = h)/2\pi = \hbar \times c/\phi = e^2)^{1/2} = e)/4\pi\tilde{v} = \mu$$

1006 Proving the Sequence.

The simplest way of testing the reliability of the sequence is to use the figures appearing in any standard physics text; use its most reliable figures as key values in the sequence, work it forward and backward until completed, and then obtain as many atomic constants as possible by using the sequence figures in conventional formulas. Since books on physical constants do not agree on such figures as an electron's mass and wavenumber, the speed of light and the fine structure constant, the results will not show agreement with my figures, but they will be in reasonable agreement within their own frames of reference.

Since small changes produce small deviations, a test of the sequence's reliability can be made by changing the mass and time units greatly, and then use the abstracted values in conventional formulas for the purpose of obtaining the system's unchanged wavelengths and wavenumbers. I have done so by making the electron's rest mass and/or the speed of light unity, as defined in Sections 215, 1014-16, 1020-23 and 1024. The sequence values were also tested by the conventional formulas appearing in Section 407, 411 and 1011, and were found reliable.

The existence of a fundamental unit of length in nature is proved by the discovery of new relations that simplify conventional formulas, and by their conversion to conventional values by including the difference between that unit and the centimeter. Conventional formulas are more complex because they include factors whose only purpose is the elimination of errors caused by its arbitrary length unit. The waveratio and electronic constants in Sections 220, 614 and 1008, also have unchangeable numerical values in nature.

1007 Idealized Electron Wavelengths.

I have discovered several ways to obtain nature's unit of length and, through it, an electron's mass wavenumber. This number can also be obtained by taking the difference in area between a circle and a sphere (Section 116), raising it to its fourth power by two stages: $(4)^4 = 256)^4 = 4.294967296 \times 10^9$; and in powers of two: $(2)^4 = 8)^4 = 32$. The last figure is an electron's rest mass wavenumber in one natural unit of length according to my theory in Book Two. When it is compared with its experimentally obtained value in one centimeter, I found the natural unit of length to equal about 1.042 cm. A comparison with Rydberg's wavenumber and other constants gave me this improved ratio: 1.0419584 cm., $\log_2$ 0.059298 (see Sections 221 and 1010).

My theory also led to the conclusion that the wavelength we observe when an electron's rest mass is resolved into the energy of a free photon is longer than its wavelength in the mass, and that the difference is comparable to the difference between the radius of a hydrogen electron's smallest orbit and its Rydberg wavelength. This ratio is obtained by the formula: $R = 4\pi\phi r$. The radius of an electron's mass is converted to its free photon wavelength by this formula: $\dot{v} = 2\pi\phi r$. The similarity is obvious.

In *FUNDAMENTAL CONSTANTS OF PHYSICS*, a book by Cohen, Crowe and Dumond, Interscience Publishers Inc. (1957), the values of nearly a hundred atomic constants are listed. Their figures for an electron's rest mass wavelength and its classical radius are compared with my idealized centimeter values below.

```
Their:  Rest mass wl. 24.26260 x 10⁻¹¹ cm.  Radius wl. 2.81785 x 10⁻¹³
Ideal:    "    "    "  24.25998 x 10⁻¹¹ cm.    "    "   2.81740 x 10⁻¹³
```

```
Their el. radius  L-L ratio  Natural wl. radius  Basic logarithm
2.81785 x 10⁻¹³ cm.  /1.0423   =2.703492 x 10⁻¹³ nl.  Log₂ -41.69047
2.81735 x 10⁻¹³ cm.  /1.0419584 =2.704378 x 10⁻¹³ nl.  Log₂ -41.75024
```

```
Natural electron mass wavelength ratio to radius wavelength.
23.28306 x 10⁻¹¹ nl./861.07793 = 2.703944 x 10⁻¹³ nl.  Log₂ -41.75
```

The second set of figures above shows why $\log_2$ -41.75 was selected as the most probable electron radius wavelength. My theory of ideal proportions caused me to choose $\log_2$ 32 × 9.75 = 41.75, as the most probable value for an electron's mass wavenumber, waveratio and radius wavenumber. The difference between my ideal proportions and the values selected by the scientists above are obviously within the margin of experimental error. Since the waveratio is an invariable constant which can be obtained from the absolute value of the electronic (fine structure) constant by the formula: $C = 2\pi\phi$, its value does not depend on the system of length, mass and time units used.

My theories in Book Two show that an electron's radius is a contained, physically real wavelength, and not an unprovable concept, as postulated by modern science.

1008 Electronic and Waveratio Constants. ϕ = 137.044809 ratio
                                                        C = 861.077930 ratio

My theory of ideal proportions defines an electron's radius wavelength as $\log_2$ -41.75. When its mass is converted into the energy of a free photon, its wavelength is $\log_2$ -32. The difference of 9.75 is called the "waveratio constant." Because the transformation is from momentum waves, dispersed spherically around a point, to the energy waves of a photon, on a plane, the ratio must include the factor 2π, with the difference defining the electronic constant ratio.

It will be noticed that the fraction, $\log_2$ .75, is less than unity by .25—the fourth root of two. The reason for this fraction is found in the two-to-one difference between momentum and energy as defined by Sections 207-8, with momentum defined as mV and energy as $\frac{1}{2}mV^2$. It will be proved, in Book Two, that the base ratio for the two types of waves above is four-to-one, and that their space gradients are the inverse square and fourth power, respectively. The inverse fourth power of an electron's rest mass gradient makes its momentum equal to its energy at unit distance, when the latter is increased by the fourth root of two, or a unit momentum is reduced by that root.

Waveratio constant. ϕ **Electronic constant.**
Radiation wavelength. $\propto$ **Fine structure constant.**
Electron's radius wavelgt. m_e **Electron's rest mass.**
Velocity of mass. 2π **Circle's circumference in radii.**

tron's radius wavelength to radiation wavelength in basic logarithms.
e $\dot{v} = rC$ —41.75 $\times$ 9.75 = –32. wavelength in natural length unit.
o: $\dot{v} = r2\pi\phi$ —41.75 $\times$ 2.651496 $\times$ 7.098504 = –32. wavelength in nlu.
ce, $C = 2\pi\phi$ or $2\pi/\propto$.

versions from waveratio constant to fundamental ratio in figures.
ory $\phi = C/2\pi$ 861.07793/6.283185 = 137.044809   **Electronic constant.**
" $\propto = 2\pi/C$ 6.283185/861.07793 = 7.296883 $\times 10^{-3}$ **Fine structure co.**
ures from book below.   861.03127   7.29729 $\times 10^{3}$ "   "   "

Note that 861.03127 is the reciprocal of 1.161335 $\times$ 10^{-3}—the figure tabulated by Cohen, Crowe and Dumond in *FUNDAMENTAL CONSTANTS OF PHYSICS* (Interscience Publishers, Inc.). The second figure on the bottom line is their fine structure constant. Since the difference between their figures and mine is less than one part in ten thousand, my figures are within their margin of experimental error.

Because the electronic and waveratio constants are the same in all systems of units and appear in the formulas of numerous conversions to the atomic constants, their values can be determined with great accuracy. When the speed of light is divided by the electronic constant, we get the velocity of a hydrogen electron in its smallest (K) orbit. The two fundamental constants C and ϕ appear in nearly a hundred formulas in Sections 220, 222, 813, 1005, 1009, 1021 and 1023, confirming my ideal proportion theory.

1009 Hydrogen Orbit Idealized.

The idealizations of the preceding section make it possible to idealize other atomic constants by formal abstractions. Some of these are defined below. Theory shows that periodic energy waves are the transmitters of directed momenta, and that an electron's radius is a wavelength determined by the momentum it transmits. However, the wavelength of a free photon with the same energy is longer by $\log_2 9.75$. These factors appear in the formulas defining the elements of a hydrogen electron's motion in its smallest (K) orbit around a nuclear mass with infinite inertia and a unit positive charge.

The electron's orbital velocity is: $V = c/\phi$, and its momentum (de Broglie) wavelength is: $B = \dot{v}\phi$. Since this wavelength is also the circumference of the electron's periodic orbit, the radius of that orbit is: $\dot{o} = 2\pi B = 2\pi\dot{v}\phi$. Its potential radiation (Rydberg) wavenumber is: $R = \frac{1}{2}\tilde{v}/\phi^2$. Some of its most important orbit formulas are stated in basic logarithms for easy checking. (See the algebraic web in Section 222.)

$C = 2\pi\phi$	$\dot{v} = rC$	$\tilde{v} = 2R\phi^L$	$\tilde{v} = 2(\tfrac{1}{2}\pi\phi)^\gamma$	$B = 2(\tfrac{1}{2}\pi)^\gamma \phi^3$	$R = (\tfrac{1}{2}\pi)^n$
7.098504	-41.75	17.802992	28.394016	21.295512	14.1970•
2.651496	9.75	14.197008	3.605984	3.605984	2.6059
9.75	-32.	32.	32.	24.901496	16.8029•

$R = 2\dot{v}\phi^L$	$B = \tilde{v}/\phi$	$B = 2R\phi$	$\dot{o} = r/\phi^L$	$\delta = 2\pi B$	$\tilde{r} = 4\pi R\phi$
-31.000000	32.000000	17.802992	-41.750000	24.901496	21.2955.
14.137008	-7.098504	7.098504	14.197008	2.651496	16.8029•
-16.802992	24.901496	24.901496	-27.552992	27.552992	3.6514•
					41.75

In Section 314, I defined a simple ratio for the orbit elements of one planet relative to another. Let R symbolize their ratio velocity in positive numbers; the larger orbit elements are R^{-1}, R^2 R^3, R^{-4}, for velocity, distance, period and attraction, respectively. The symbol 2π is added to the period of the primary orbit; it is present in all abstracted orbits by implication. The orbital velocity of a hydrogen electron in its smallest orbit is less than the speed of light by the electronic constant. Therefore, we anticipate the ratio, $1/\phi, \phi^2, 2\pi\phi^3$, $1/\phi^4$, for their values in the ultimate system of units (see Sections 215 and 1023). Its values in electron radius length-time units are redefined in the natural length units of the new international system and the ideal system in the second column. The third-column figures are gaussian values in basic logarithms.

erms and ormulas	Basic ratios	New intern. ngs system	Gaussian cgs system	Elements of electron's K orbit in hydrogen.
$= 1/\phi$	-7.098504	27.645446	27.704744	Velocity in orbit.
$= \phi^2$	14.197008	-27.552992	-27.493694	Radius of orbit.
$= 2\pi\phi^3$	23.947008	-52.546943	-52.546942	Period in orbit.
$= 1/\phi^4$	-28.394016	-6.982917	-6.923618	Attraction at orbit.

1010 Mass, Time and Length Units.
Before the ideal proportions in the preceding section can be converted into the atomic constants in general use, it is necessary to define the three international units of action—mass, time and length—with the greatest accuracy. Since a rational system of units can be worked out from any arbitrarily selected set of fundamental units, my choice of their most probable values is a matter of personal judgment based on the experimental figures which I believe must be assigned maximum weight.

In my sequence formula, the gram mass is represented by an electron's rest mass. Its most probable value, 9.108325×10^{-28} gram, was adopted from an analysis of its relations to Avogadro's number of nuclear particles in a gram mass. Its reciprocal in grams per nucleon was converted into a proton's mass and reduced to an electron's mass in grams by assuming that a proton's mass is equal to 1836.1141 electrons. This figure, which is less than that given in most physics texts, was forced upon me by the probable values of other constants. It is, however, close to the figure 1836.12 given by Cohen, Crowe and Dumond, *(FUNDAMENTAL CONSTANTS OF PHYSICS*, Interscience Publishers, 1957).

The time unit is represented by the speed of light. In my early researches, I had come to the conclusion that its old value of 299776 kilometers per second was too small, and that its latest value, 299797 km., was too large. Therefore, I adopted the speed, 299783 km., as a compromise. However, after I had developed the sequence and determined the value of the electronic constant, the figure it gave for an electron's electrostatic charge was too small. The speed of light was, therefore, revised upward to 2.997930×10^{10} centimeters per second; the same as in the book above.

The ratio value of the natural unit of length in centimeters defines the length of the centimeter, because the natural unit is an absolute constant. There are numerous wavelengths from which the ratio can be obtained, and I proceeded by assigning them different weights. Rydberg's wavenumber for an infinite mass was assigned the greatest weight, because it is generally assumed to be one of the most accurately determined values in physics. From this, I obtained the ratio: 1.0419584 centimeter, as the most probable natural length. It corresponds to $\log_2 0.059298$ and $\log_{10} 0.017850$.

The reduction formulas below are preferred experimental values checked against the final values of the atomic constants in the sequence and table, Section 407, and in the large Table of Constants, Chapter 11, page 158. Note that the energy equivalent of Rydberg's wavenumber is obtained in two ways.

Avogadro's number to proton's mass in grams. $M_0 = 1/N$. $R_M = M_P/M_0$.

$$\underset{N}{1/6.024860 \times 10^{23}} = \underset{M_0}{1.659790 \times 10^{-24}}) \times 1.007593 = \underset{R_M}{1.672393 \times 10^{-24}} \text{ gram mas}$$

Proton's to electron's mass. $m_e = M_P/R_a$. $R_m = M_P/m_0$.

$$\underset{M_P}{1.672393 \times 10^{-24}} / \underset{R_m}{1830.1141} = \underset{m_e}{9.108325 \times 10^{-28}} \text{ gram mass.}$$

Electron's mass to energy of cm. wave in emu. $h = m_c/\tilde{v}$.

$$\underset{m_0}{9.108325 \times 10^{-28}} \times \underset{c}{2.997930 \times 10^{10}} / \underset{\tilde{v}}{4.122014 \times 10^{9}} = \underset{h}{6.624461 \times 10^{-27}} \text{ erg emu.}$$

Cm. quantum to hydrogen K orbit electron's energy of motion. $E = \text{h}$

$$\underset{h}{6.624461 \times 10^{-27}} \times \underset{c}{2.997930 \times 10^{10}} \times \underset{R}{109737.32} = \underset{E}{2.179347 \times 10^{-11}} \text{ erg cgs.}$$

Speed of light to hydrogen K orbit electron's velocity. $V = c/\phi$.

$$\underset{c}{2.997930 \times 10^{10}} / \underset{\phi}{137.044809} = \underset{V}{2.1875546 \times 10^{8}} \text{ centimeters per second ve}$$

Electron's mass to its energy of motion in hydrogen K orbit. $E = \frac{1}{2}$

$$\underset{m_e}{9.108325 \times 10^{-28}} / 2 \times \underset{V}{(2.1875546 \times 10^{8})^{2}} = \underset{E}{2.179347 \times 10^{-11}} \text{ erg cgs.}$$

1011 Natural to International Units.

Using the difference between the natural length and the centimeter, we can idealize all wavelengths and wavenumbers in centimeters from their natural proportions, as defined in Section 1009. The figures below are for a rest mass electron and for a hydrogen electron in its smallest (K) orbit, circling a nucleus with a unit positive charge and an infinite mass-inertia. The unit of natural length in centimeters, symbolized by ϕ, equals $\log_2 0.059298$.

Electron constants		Natural lengths Log 2	International system in centime† Log 2 Numbers
Electron's radius wl.	r	−41.75	$\times \phi = -41.690702 = 2.817397 \times 10^{-13}$ cm.wl.
Electron's mass wn.	$\tilde{v}$	32.0	$\div \phi = 31.940702 = 4.122014 \times 10^{9}$ wn.cm.
Light second in cm.	c	34.743950	$\times \phi = 34.803245 = 2.997930 \times 10^{10}$ cm.sec
Smallest hydrogen orbit.			
De Broglie wavelength	B_w	$-24.901496 \times \phi =$	$-24.842198 = 3.324705 \times 10^{-8}$ cm.wl.
Radius of orbit	r_w	$-27.552992 \times \phi =$	$-27.493695 = 5.291431 \times 10^{-9}$ cm.
Speed in orbit, cm/sec	V_w	$27.645446 \times \phi =$	$27.704744 = 2.187555 \times 10^{8}$ cm.sec
Rydberg's wavenumber	R_w	$16.302992 \div \phi =$	$16.743695 = 1.097373 \times 10^{5}$ wn.cm.

The figures above, in conjunction with those postulated in the preceding section, makes it possible to work out the sequence of international atomic constants below. Note that powers of ten are in superscripts, and that the second sequence is in basic logarithms.

$$\underset{\substack{\text{m}_0 \\ -89.826801}}{9.108325^{-28}} \times \underset{\substack{\text{c} \\ 34.803248}}{2.997930^{10}} = \underset{\substack{ \\ -55.023553)}}{2.730612^{-17}}) \times \underset{\substack{\text{m' emu} \\ -31.940702}}{2.425998^{10}} = \underset{\substack{\tilde{v} \text{ wl.} \\ -86.964255)}}{6.624461^{-27}}) / \underset{\substack{2\pi \\ 2.65149}}{6.28318}$$

$$\text{emu} \atop 4316^{-27}) \times 2.187554^{8} = 2.306373^{19}\ )^{1/2} = 4.802471^{10}\ )/5.179876^{10} = 9.271402^{-21}$$

emu   c/4 e^{2} esu   e esu   4π𝑣̃   μ emu
4316⁻²⁷) × 2.187554⁸ = 2.306373¹⁹)½ = 4.802471¹⁰)/5.179876¹⁰ = 9.271402⁻²¹
615752)   27.704744   -61.911008)   -30.955504) 35.592197   -66.547701

1012 Electrostatic-Gravity Theory.

The force acting between two electrostatic charges is defined by the formula $F = e\dot{e}/r^2$. The gravitational force between two masses is: $F = g(m\dot{m}/r^2)$. The formulas converting an electron's charge and mass into an electro-static repulsion and gravitational attraction between two electrons at unit distance are e^2 and $m^2 g$, respectively. Therefore, the ratio of their forces in gravity units is: $e/g = e^2/m^2 g$. Note that the conventional definition of the gravity constant as the attraction between two unit masses at unit distance is the base value of the attraction of a unit mass at unit distance squared. The proper definition of gravitational attraction between two masses should, therefore, be: $F = mg \times mg$; and for equal masses: $F = (mg)^2$.

The origins of gravitational and electrostatic forces were outlined in Section 302 and will be described in greater detail in Book Two. My proof will, therefore, be confined to those numerical changes which occur when one of a system's three basic units is halved, as outlined by the table in Section 1005. The conversions below are extensions of that table to provide a background for the redefinition of a system's length, mass and time units, and thus make it possible to obtain the values of various constants, including the gravity constant and the rate at which a falling mass accelerates on the earth's surface. Since that rate is known, the new values serve as a check on my other figures.

The dyne was defined in Section 207 as that force which causes a unit mass to accelerate at the rate of one unit length in one unit of time. The erg is the energy of a two-unit mass moving with the velocity of one unit of length per unit time. Velocity is related to force and momentum, and distance traveled to energy. It will be noticed that the physical increase of a unit of force or energy produces a corresponding reduction of the numerical values of abstracted forces and energies:—i.e., they are reciprocals.

stem's Length, Mass or Time Unit Halved.
lative changes. All figures are ratios of new values in old units.

e of three basic units changed to →	Half length	Half mass	Half time
locity. One unit length in unit time. $V = 0.5$	0.5	1.0	2.0
ne. The unit of force. MV	0.5	0.5	2.0
g. The unit of energy. ½MV²	0.25	0.5	4.0
ght. Velocity in length-time units.	2.0	1.0	0.5
stracted dynes. Reciprocal of unit. $F = 2.0$	2.0	2.0	0.5
stracted ergs. Reciprocal of unit.	4.0	2.0	0.25
ss. Energy of one unit's rest mass. Mc²	4.0	0.5	0.25
ctrostatic unit. (See Section 1005).	√8̄	√2̄	0.5
ctrostatic charge squared. e^2	8.0	2.0	0.25
vity. Ratio change caused by unit × F.	4.0 × 2⟩	0.25 × 2	1.0 × 0.5
vity constant. Force times change. $g = 8.0$ ←	0.5	0.5
ctrostatic-gravity ratio. e/g	1.0	*1.0	0.5
th's gravity. Acceleration dynes. $G = 2.0$	1.0	0.5

$/g = e^2/M^2g = 2/4 \times 0.5 = 1.0$.   √8̄ = 2.8284271.   √2̄ = 1.41421356.

Gravity constant. Conversion ratios from the table above.

Half length u.   Half mass unit   Half time u

$$g = F\frac{mm}{D^L} \qquad 2 \times \frac{1 \times 1}{(.5)^L} = 8 \qquad 2 \times \frac{.5 \times .5}{(1.)^L} = .5 \qquad .5 \times \frac{1 \times 1}{(1.)^L} =$$

Earth's gravity. Conversion ratios from the gravity constant.

$$G = \frac{gM}{D^L} \qquad \frac{8 \times 1}{(2.)^L} = 2 \qquad \frac{.5 \times 2}{(1.)^L} = 1 \qquad \frac{.5 \times 1}{(1.)^L} =$$

The changes which occur in an electron's electrostatic charge were obtained from the table in Section 1005. The e/g ratio can be obtained by a comparison of charge squared with the gravity constant, in all cases where there is no change of mass; however, when such a change occurs the mass ratio must be squared. It will be noticed from the table that the e/g ratio does not change with a change of length and mass units, and that it changes in direct proportion to time. It follows that the e/g ratio for a system in which the unit of time is the time it takes a light wave to move one natural unit of length is less than its accepted value by the speed of light in natural length units. The theoretical reason for this convergence with a reduction of the unit of time is that gravity is related to momentum, and electrostatic charges to energy. Gravity is the product of a timeless deformation of space by matter, defined as a fourth dimension, whereas the two types of electrostatic forces are the products of time-related, potentially reducible rest mass energies. See Book Two for details.

In defining the changes which occur in the numerical value of the earth's gravitational force when one of its three units of action is changed, it will be noticed that the force in dynes defining the weight of a unit mass is also the increase of velocity of that mass in a free fall for each unit of time (see Section 309). Since the halving of the unit of length doubles the number of length units defining its rate of fall, the number of dynes acting upon a mass unit must also have doubled. The numerical distance to the earth's center has also doubled. A halving of the mass unit doubles the numerical value of the earth's mass, and halves the gravity constant. There is, therefore, no change in the numerical value of the forces acting upon a unit mass and its rate of fall. A halving of the time unit obviously halves its acceleration and the accelerating force acting upon a unit mass. These changes make it possible to anticipate the conversion value of the gravity constant for two systems, and thus gives a check on the values defined by the table.

1013 Gravity Constant and e/g Ratio.

The electrostatic-gravity (e/g) ratio defined by the table in the preceding section does not change when a system's length and mass units are changed: it changes in direct proportion to changes of its time (speed of light) unit. A mathematical idealization of the e/g ratio cannot be based on the speed of light in one second, because the second is an arbitrary unit of time. It must be based on a system of units in which the speed of light is a natural unit of time, or in ideal proportions to a natural length unit, wavenumber, or to a natural force or energy value.

My theory in Book Two defines gravity as originating in the statistically mean state of contained stationary periodic waves, while electrostatic charges are the reducible actions of specific waves. It follows that the time unit for an electrostatic field force is that of individual waves, whereas the gravitational field of those same waves must have a time base long enough to reduce their effects to a statistical mean state. It is, therefore, my contention that charges are related to an electron's radius wave period, and gravity to the period of a spherical wave with a wavelength of one natural unit. Because the time base of the ultimate system of units is an electron's radius period, it is my contention that there can be no gravitation in that system. However, it is nevertheless possible to postulate and define such a gravitational force. Because its electrostatic charge is unity, the e/g ratio for the ultimate system is the reciprocal of its gravity constant.

Assuming the gravity constant of the ultimate system is related to a spherical miton with Planck's energy, acting through the surface of a sphere one natural unit of length in radius, there are several factors which must be included in its formula besides the energy wavelength of an electron's rest mass in one natural length squared. There is a one-to-four difference between the wavelengths of velocity and spherical mitons, an inverse fourth power gradient of all rest masses, and a one-to-two difference between energy and momentum. These differences appear in the first formula below defining the gravity constant of the ultimate system of units. Its e/g ratio is the reciprocal of that figure, and the physical reality of both can be proved by a conversion into known experimental values. The second group of figures in basic logarithms convert its e/g ratio into that of the gaussian system in two stages. Note the simple time relations, as defined by the preceding section and Section 1023.

$$\frac{\dot{v}^2}{2\sqrt[4]{4/\pi}} \qquad \frac{(-32.)^2}{1 \times \sqrt[4]{2/1.6514961}} = -65.037126 \text{ dyne gravity in rmt.}$$

ratio.   Ultimate system's gravity constant reciprocal: 65.037126
         One natural length-time unit in electron radii: $\underline{41.750000}$
ratio.   Ideal system's time unit (1/light-second in nl.): 106.837126
         One second of time in natural length units: $\underline{34.743950}$
ratio.   Of all systems using one second as time unit: 141.581076

1014 Ideal System Sequence Units.

In this system the speed of light is idealized by making the time unit equal to the time it takes a light wave to move one natural unit of length. Its unit of mass is idealized by making it equal to that of an electron; its length unit is the natural length obtained by the idealization of observed quantum states, of wavelengths, energies and momenta. With the speed of light equal to unity, the figure defining a mass is also its rest mass energy in emu and esu. Since its wavenumber is the number of waves in one natural unit of length, the wavenumber of any defined mass is greater than its rest mass energy by $\log_2$ 32. Its units of length, mass and time are: 1.0419584 cm, 9.108325 $\times$ 10^{-28} gram, and 3.475593 $\times$ 10^{-11} second, respectively. These figures in basic logarithms are: 0.059298 cm., -89.826801 gram, and -34.743950 second.

Force is defined as F = mV, and energy as E = $\frac{1}{2}mV^2$. From the definition of the dyne and erg in Sections 207-8, we learn that one dyne of force in this system is the force needed to accelerate an electron from rest to the speed of light through one unit of length and time. Its unit of energy is the action potential of a two-electron mass moving with the speed of light, or one electron moving with a speed greater than light by the square root of two.

Since an electron's charge is the square root of its functional rest mass energy, the square root of the difference above gives us a fourth root difference between the momentum it transmits as its electrostatic charge and the transmitting energy of its rest mass. There is a great increase of wavelength when an electron resolves into the energy of a free photon. Since its rest mass energy is defined as the wavelength of that photon, it is expressed as $\log_2$ -32, whereas its true (functional) wavelength is -41.75. It is longer than that anticipated (-42.0) by the fourth root of two.

The velocities defined above are experimentally impossible because electrons approaching the speed of light have an increase of mass-inertia which becomes, theoretically, infinitely great at that velocity. However, even though the speed of light is beyond attainment, its use to idealize the proportions of the ideal system does not depend upon experiments at those velocities. They can be abstracted from lesser speeds, as defined by the table in Section 1027.

m_e	c	m'	$\dot{v}$	h	2π	$\hbar$	c/ϕ	e^2
0.0 $\times$ 0.0	= 0.0) $\times$	-32.	= -32.)	/2.651496	= -34.651496) $\times$	-7.098504	= -41.75)^h	

e	$4\pi\dot{v}$	μ	F = e^2/r^2	e/g = e^2/g	g
-20.875)/35.651496	= -56.526496	13.355984	106.837126	-148.587126	

1015 Table of Ideal System Constants.

All systems in which the time unit is equal to the time it takes a light wave to move one unit of length, the speed of light is unity, and their electrostatic and electromagnetic fields have the same numerical values. Because an electron's mass is unity in the ideal system, its numerical value is the same as that of its rest mass energy. There are, therefore, only two columns of figures; one defining the mass-energy of its constants and the other their wavenumbers.

In the table below, these two columns differ by an electron's mass wavenumber in one natural length ($\log_2$ 32). The constants of the first group are from the sequence; those of the second are formal abstractions. Note that the wavelengths, wavenumbers and radii of all systems using the same length unit are identical. We can, therefore, anticipate the results of all formal reductions to length units by noting the comparable figures of other systems. The theoretical values for the electrostatic-gravity (e/g) ratio and the gravity constant are in full accord with those obtained by experiments.

Planck's quantum. m. Electron's mass. r̃ Electron's radius wn.
Bohr magneton, hy. R Rydberg's wn. F Force on hy. K orbit.
Electrostatic unit. B de Broglie's wn. g Gravity constant.

nstants in basic logarithms.		Constants in numbers.	
Mass-energy	Wavenumbers	/ Mass-energy	Wavenumbers
-34.651496	-2.651496	ħ 3.705615 × 10^{11}	0.159549
-32.0	0.0	h 2.328306 × 10^{10}	1.0
-56.526496	-24.526496	ⱴ 9.634499 × 10^{17}	4.137956 × 10^{-8}
-20.875	11.125	e 5.199946 × 10^{7}	2.233360 × 10^{3}
0.0	32.0	m₀ 1.0	4.294967 × 10^{4}
-15.197008	16.802992	R 2.662225 × 10^{-5}	1.143417 × 10^{5}
-7.098504	24.901496	B 7.296383 × 10^{-3}	3.133987 × 10^{7}
9.75	41.75	r̃ 861.077930	3.698302 × 10^{12}
-41.75	-9.75	e² 2.703944 × 10^{-13}	1.161335 × 10^{-3}
13.355984	45.355984	F 1.048460 × 10^{4}	4.503102 × 10^{13}
-148.587126	-116.587126	g 1.865598 × 10^{45}	8.012683 × 10^{-36}

$g = \log_2 106.837126 = 1.443371 \times 10^{34}$ ratio.

1016 Formulas of the Ideal System.

There are several ways to check the constants of the ideal system of units. Its basic logarithm gives us figures that are easy to evaluate by comparison within its own frame, and with the corresponding figures of other systems. Also, we can use the conventional formulas defining the gaussian constants to obtain the constants of the ideal system. Note that the mantissas of its figures in basic logarithms can be extended beyond the six used here, and still give results that are, in theory, without error.

ectron's mass wn. Electron's mass. Electron's radius wavelength.

$$= \frac{mc}{h} \qquad \frac{0 \times 0}{-32} = 32. \qquad m_c = \frac{h\tilde{v}}{c} \qquad \frac{-32 \times 32}{0} = 0 \qquad r = \frac{e^2}{c^2 m_c} \qquad \frac{(-20.875)^2}{(0)^2 \times 0} = -41.75$$

dberg's wavenumber. Electron's charge

$$= \frac{2\pi^2 m e^4}{ch^3} \qquad \frac{1 \times (1.651496)^2 \times 0 \times (-20.875)^4}{0 \times (-32)^3} = 16.802992 \qquad e = \sqrt{\frac{hc\alpha}{2\pi}}$$

ectron's electrostatic charge. Bohr magneton. Electron's K orbit in hy.

$$= \sqrt{\frac{-32 \times 0 \times -7.098504}{2.651496}} = -20.875 \qquad \mu = \frac{he}{4\pi mc} \qquad \frac{-32 \times -20.875}{3.6514961 \times 0 \times 0} = -56.526496$$

Broglie wavelength. Electron's K orbit in hydrogen.

$$\phi = B = \frac{1}{2R\phi} \qquad -32 \times 7.098504 = -24.901496 = \frac{0}{1 \times 16.802992 \times 7.098504}$$

quated forces on hydrogen K orbit electron.

$$\frac{V^2}{r} = F = \frac{e^2}{r^2} \qquad \frac{0 \times (-7.098504)^2}{-27.552992} = 13.355984 = \frac{(-20.875)^2}{(-27.552992)^2}$$

veratio constant.

$$\frac{h}{\lambda^2} = C = \frac{F}{2mc^2(\frac{1}{2}\pi)^4} \qquad \frac{0 \times -32}{(-20.875)^2} = 9.75 = \frac{13.355984}{1 \times 0 \times (0)^2 \times (0.651496)^4}$$

avity constant.

$$= \frac{\dot{v}^2}{2L^4\sqrt{4/\pi}} \qquad \frac{(-32)^2}{1 \times 41.75 \times \sqrt[4]{2/1.6514961}} = -148.587126 \text{ dyne force}$$

Electrostatic/gravity ratio.

$$R = \frac{e}{g} = \frac{e^2}{m^2 g} \qquad \frac{(-20.875)^2}{(1)^2 \times -148.587126} = 106.837126 \text{ ratio}$$

1017 Electron Orbit Ratios.

The relative motions of two bodies circling a common center of attraction are composed of four elements in simple proportions. The figures for one differ from that of another by these ratios: $-R^1$, R^2, R^3, $-R^4$, for velocity, radius, period and attraction, respectively. In defining the elements of a single orbit, the difference between its radius and circumference, 2π, must be included in its period formula. The simple relationship above is not apparent in the elements of an orbit because these elements are defined in different ways. However, a hydrogen electron in its smallest (K) orbit does show this relationship when its four elements are in ultimate system units.

Proof that the idealized elements of this orbit are properly defined for three systems of units appears below in the form of a table of constants in basic logarithms, with conversion ratios to the simple proportions of the ultimate system by two stages. The ratio symbols are defined. Note that ϕ and L are length ratios, and that c and T are time ratios. L and T have the same value, but a reduction by L (length) increases the numerical values of its abstractions, while a reduction by T (time) reduces its abstractions; hence, L is assigned a positive, and T a negative ratio value.

Elements of a hydrogen electron's smallest K orbit; idealized.
ϕ, 0.059298. m, −86.964255. c, 34.743950. L, 41.75. T, −41.75.

		Gaussian system.	Ideal system.	Ultimate system.
V	Velocity	27.704744 ÷ϕc	−7.098504 ±LT	−7.098504	1/ϕ
b	Radius	−27.493694 ÷ϕ	−27.552992 × L	14.197008	ϕ^2
P	Period	−52.546934 × c	−17.802992 ÷ T	23.947008	2$\pi\phi^3$
F	Attraction	−6.923618 ÷ϕmc^2	13.355984 × T^{2}L	−28.394016	1/ϕ^4
E	Energy	$\frac{1}{2}$mV^2 −35.417312 ÷ϕ^4mc^2	−15.197008 ÷L^{2}T^2	−15.197008	1/2ϕ^2

1018 What Are We Defining?

Maxwell used factors derived experimentally from electrical induction and condenser phenomena when he proved, by mathematics, that the difference between an electrostatic and an electromagnetic field is equal to the speed of light. The implication of this abstract proof, when analyzed in conjunction with their different definitions, is that the electromagnetic force produced by a moving charge is less than that of the charge by its velocity less than light, and that they have the same value when the charge is moving with the speed of light.

A unit magnetic field force is defined as the product of a unit electrostatic charge moving with unit velocity—one length unit per unit time. Assuming that this magnetic field is related to the momentum of the moving charge, we find their forces equal to the speed of light as postulated above; a difference between their units equal to the speed of light. In a system of units in which the speed of light is unity (The time it takes a light wave to move one unit of length.), its emu and esu units have the same value.

A system's unit of energy is defined by a two-unit mass moving with the speed of one unit of length per unit time, with abstracted energies increasing as velocity squared: $E = \frac{1}{2}mV^2$. If a rest mass becomes a free momentum at twice the speed of light, its energy must equal the speed of light squared. In a system of units in which the speed of light is unity, the energy of its rest mass must also be unity—the same as its emu and esu units.

In Section 804, the Bohr magneton is defined by this electric current formula: $\mu = he/4\pi mc$. I obtain the same result by: $\mu = e/4\pi\tilde{v}$; the conversion from an electrostatic charge to a Bohr magneton in the sequence formula. The ratio in eu $= 4\pi\tilde{v}$ is a constant in all systems using natural length units. Since $\tilde{v}$ is the wavenumber of an electron's rest mass, it is evident that it stands for a retarding force reducing the percentage of an electron's charge which can be converted into a magnetic field in a hydrogen atom. We can also explain the ratio by noting that the wavenumber represents an electron's rest mass energy, and its charge a tendency to resolve it into something else—a radiation or a magnetic field. The forces containing its energy as a specific quantum also act in opposition to its resolution into a magnetic field.

When a system's time unit is halved, the figures defining its electrostatic charge and its Bohr magneton are also halved. The number of orbital electrons passing a given point in one unit of time, or the number of electrons passing the cross section of a conductor, is also halved (see Section 504). When the system's mass unit is halved, its charge and magneton figures increase by the square root of two. There can be no change in the number of orbital electrons, but the number of electrons passing through a conductor to produce a unit of electromagnetic force, being the reciprocal of its electromagnetic force unit, is reduced in the same ratio. A halving of the unit of length increases the charge value by the square root of two cubed, and its magneton value by that square root raised to its fifth power. The difference is caused by the halving of an electron's rest mass wavenumber in the e/μ conversion ratio. I have not investigated the relation of these changes to electric current formulas, but am confident that the charge and magneton values of the algebraic sequence are reliable.

1019 Coincidence is Not Reliable Proof.

The proper way to develop a mathematical formula is by knowing the nature of its factors, and knowing why each is included. However, this anticipates a foresight and knowledge not always present or available when needed. Where the values of physical constants are known to a fair approximation, their idealization by experimental alterations of accepted formulas and the development of new ones can be justified on the assumption that a casual coincidence of values is highly improbable. When experimental formulas give results which are in accord with their expected values to five or six figures, the probability that we are not dealing with casual coincidences can be a million to one, provided that the data on which particular results are based have not been altered to produce this accord. However, the possibility of a coincidence cannot be dismissed when the reasons for an agreement between two sets of figures are not clear.

Several years ago I discovered the formula: $e/g = (\frac{1}{2}\pi c)^4$. This gave me the ratio: $e/g = e^2/m^2 g$, to a close approximation. My investigations of a possible relationship led to the gravity formula: $g = 2\dot{v}/F$; with $\dot{v}$ an electron's mass wavelength and F the electrostatic attraction on a K orbit hydrogen electron. It was in complete accord with my new e/g formula and close to the accepted value of the gravity constant. Furthermore, it proved that the inclusion of $\frac{1}{2}\pi$ in the speed-of-light formula is an essential part of it, and not simply an addition to make its results come out right.

The implication of my formula: $e/g = (\frac{1}{2}\pi c)^4$, is that when the velocity of light is unity, as in the ideal system, the difference between the gravity constant and an electrostatic charge squared is only: $e/g = (\frac{1}{2}\pi)^4 = 6.088068$ gravities. When I checked my two new formulas against the constants of the ideal and other systems of units, both gave the same ratio values. The ratio changed as the fourth power of the difference between their time units, but did not change with changes of their mass and length units. These changes were not only incredibly large; they were completely impossible without compensating factors. My belief that the observed agreements could not be coincidental led to a search for such factors, but I finally had to reject both formulas as being contrary to facts.

The force of gravity is defined as the attraction between two gram masses, one centimeter apart. Since the rest mass energy of a gram mass equals the speed of light squared, the energy producing a gravitational attraction between two gram masses equals c^4. When the distance between these masses is one natural unit of length and the speed of light is in natural length units, their interaction energy is: $c^4 \times (\frac{1}{2}\pi)^4 = (\frac{1}{2}\pi c)^4$, the formula for the e/g ratio which I rejected above. Observation shows the true e/g ratio changes in direct proportion to time, and not to its fourth power, as defined by the speed of light. Cubing the speed of light per second in the natural length units of the new international system (Section 411) gives us the e/g ratio for any system where the speed of light is unity by the formula: $(\frac{1}{2}\pi)^4 c^3$. The result is practically identical with that from: $e/g = (4\pi\tilde{v})^3$. I am wondering if these agreements are coincidences, or relationships which I have overlooked.

1020 Ultimate System of Units.

This system is called "ultimate" because it defines numerous atomic constants with only one prime factor—the electronic constant—and the pi of geometry. It is, therefore, the simplest possible system of atomic constants. The physical reality of these constants and their proportions can be checked in various ways. Some proportions are the same for all systems of units; others deviate by quantities related to their length, mass and time units. It is possible, therefore, to obtain the accepted experimental constants of the gaussian system by using the conversion ratios appearing in the table, Section 1023.

The basic constants of the ultimate system can be obtained by noting the coincidence of values in the definition of an electron's radius. In Section 711, the formula, $r = e^2/mc^2$, defines the coincidence of an electron's charge (e) and the energy of its mass (m), at its radius wavelength (r). By postulating a unit value for all three, and by making the speed of light unity also, we obtain a simple base of reference for the electron's mass wavelength and Planck's quantum. This also gives us a series of simple constants and proportions in the definitions of an electron's elements of motion in its smallest hydrogen (K) orbit.

The simplicity of the ultimate system was made possible by using electron elements for reference. Its unit of length is the radius of an electron; its unit of mass is that of an electron; its unit of time is the time it takes a light wave to move one radius wavelength, and its unit charge is the potential energy equivalent of its rest mass. It is the energy which must be expended to reduce the mutually repelling force on the surface of a centimeter sphere to an electron's radius sphere.

The theory assumes that an electron's radius can be defined because its mass is all-electrical. Experiments prove that the value of its negative charge is the same as the positive charge of a positron or proton. This equality makes it possible to define an electron's smallest orbit in hydrogen by the sequence $-\phi, \phi^2$, $2\pi\phi^3, -\phi^4$, for its velocity, radius, period and attraction, respectively. The simplicity of the ultimate system is apparent in this sequence formula:

m_o	c	m'	$\dot{v}$	h	2π	$\hbar$	c/ϕ	e^2
$0.0 \times 0.0 = 0.0) \times 9.75 = 9.75)/2.651496 = 7.098504) \times -7.098504 = 0.0)$								$\hbar =$

e	$4\pi v$	μ	$F = e^2/r^2$	$e/g = 1/g$	g
$0.0)/-6.098504 = 6.098504$			-28.394016	65.087126	-65.087126

1021 Table of Ultimate System Constants.
The constants of this table are obtained by formal reductions of the sequence values above. We are dealing with an ultimate system because its constants are all defined by the use of one prime factor—the electronic constant—and geometrical pi. The fact that a rational system of atomic units can be developed and brought into agreement with known values on this slender foundation shows that natural phenomena are simple in origin and evolution.

The sequence above assigns the same numerical value to an electron's mass wavelength and Planck's quantum of energy; it is evident that this is the case for all systems where an electron's mass and the speed of light are both unity. This relationship becomes evident when we note that an electron's mass wavelength is observed and measured in terms of the wavelength of a free photon with the same energy, making it longer than the electron's true radius wavelength by $\log_2$ 9.75. It follows that when the wavelength of a free photon is reduced to the ultimate system's length unit—the wavelength defining the radiation energy of Planck's quantum—the energy of that wave increases in inverse proportion to their difference in wavelength. This is true because Planck's quantum of energy is the same for all wavelengths per pulsation time, regardless of shape. However, the geometry of shape determines their wavelengths (pulsation times) and, therefore, the efficiency with which a given energy can transmit a momentum when two kinds of waves are defined by the same time unit.

When an electron's mass is converted into a free photon, its radius wavelength increases to 861.077930 such lengths for the same energy. This means that the efficiency of an electron's rest mass energy as a transmitter of momenta is greater than that of a free photon's by $\log_2$ 9.75, and that we are dealing with two systems of reference units. When one system is defined in terms of the other, an error equal to the difference will appear. This error is limited to the ultimate system because it uses an electron's radius for its length and time units, whereas other systems define its radius by formal abstractions.

Because the speed of light, an electron's mass and its radius wavelength are all units of action in the ultimate system, the energy of its mass is also unity, while its energy equivalent wavenumber as a free photon is $\log_2 -9.75$. Since its energy as a free photon must be unity, like its rest mass, the energy of Planck's quantum for its fundamental wave is the reciprocal of this figure. To obtain unit values for rest mass and free photon energy, Planck's energy quantum must have the same numerical value as the electron's rest mass wavelength. Conventional formal reductions to the constants below are too large because they are free photon quantum states.

The numerical values of the mass and energy units in the first columns below, being related to free photons, are identical; their rest-mass related energies and wavenumbers are shorter by $\log_2$ 9.75. Numerical values within this second frame of reference are also identical.

h	Planck's quantum	₵	Electronic const.	F	Force on hy. K orbit
ℏ	Planck's qu./2π	R	Rydberg's wavelgt.	E	Energy to wavenumber
μ	Bohr magneton, hy.	B	de Broglie wl.	W	Wavenumber to energy

Energies quantized by their relations to forces containing free photo

		Ultimate constants in basic logarithms.			Their numerical values.	
		Defined energy	True energy		Defined energy	True energy
h	2π₵	9.75	1.	0.0	861.077930	1.0
ℏ	₵	7.098504	1/2π	-2.651496	137.044809	0.15915494
μ	½₵	6.098504	1/4π	-3.651496	68.5224045	0.07957747
E	1.	0.0	1/2π₵	-9.75	1.0	0.00116133
W	2π₵	9.75	1.	0.0	861.077930	1.0

Quantum relations of hydrogen electron in its smallest (K) orbit.

		Mass-energy	Wavenumbers		Mass-energy	Wavelength
B	1/₵	-7.098504	1/2π₵² -16.848504		7.2968835 × 10⁻³	1.1800626 ×
R	1/2₵²	-15.197008	1/4π₵³ -24.947008		2.6622254 × 10⁻⁵	3.2344291 ×
F	1/₵⁴	-28.394016	1/2π₵⁶ -38.144016		2.8349777 × 10⁻⁹	3.0373359 ×

The relative elements of any two orbits in ideal proportions can be defined by the ratios: $-R^1$, R^2, R^3, $-R^4$. The four principal numerical values, from which the elements of other orbits can be abstracted, are defined for an electron circling a proton in its smallest possible orbit below. Note that the figures follow the sequence when the period is reduced by 2π. See Section 812 for orbit sequence.

...ments of hydrogen X orbit electron.		Log 2	In numbers.
...ocity less than light.	V $1/\mathfrak{C}$	-7.098504	7.2968835×10^{-3}
...it's radius in electron radii.	D $\mathfrak{C}^2$	14.197008	1.8781280×10^{4}
...iod in el's radius wave time.	P $2\pi\mathfrak{C}^3$	23.947008	1.6172145×10^{7}
...ctrostatic attraction at orbit.	F $1/\mathfrak{C}^4$	-28.394016	2.8349777×10^{7}

There can be no observable gravitation in the ultimate system of units because gravity is a static (timeless) statistical effect of matter waves—expressed mathematically as the fourth dimension of space. Since the length and time units of this system are shorter than the wavelengths and waveperiods they define, the actions of those waves are specific within that frame of reference and cannot be reduced to a statistical mean. However, it is possible to define a gravity constant for the ultimate system by increasing the time unit to the time it takes a light wave to move one natural unit of length. Because gravity decreases as the inverse square of the distance from its source, its force at that distance is less than that of the corresponding unit charge at electron radius distance by an electron's mass wavenumber of a natural length unit squared. Its actual difference is slightly greater as shown by this formula: $g = \dot{v}^2/2\sqrt[4]{4/\pi}$. The origin of the divisor in this formula is outlined in Section 1013 and in Book Two.

The electrostatic/gravity (e/g) ratio for the ultimate system is the reciprocal of its gravity constant because its mass and charge units both have unit values. It was proved in Section 1012 that the e/g ratio changes in direct proportion to changes of a system's time unit. It follows that the difference between its observed gaussian value and that of the ultimate system is equal to the difference between the second and electron radius time. Because their gravity constants have a different relationship to one another, it is possible to check the convergence of known values on the reciprocal gravity and e/g ratios of the ultimate system, as shown by the table in Section 1023.

1022 Formulas of the Ultimate System.

The formulas of the ultimate system are grouped like those of the ideal system in Section 1016. Its constants are compared with those of four other systems in Section 1023, and its conversions to those systems are defined. The formulas below are those conventionally used, and all the figures are in basic logarithms.

...ctron's mass wn.

$$\frac{mc}{h} \quad \frac{0 \times 0}{9.75} = -9.75$$

Electron's mass.

$$m_o = \frac{h\bar{v}}{c} \quad \frac{9.75 \times -9.75}{0} = 0.$$

Electron's radius wl.

$$r = \frac{e^2}{c^2 m_o} \quad \frac{(0)^2}{(0)^2 \times 0} = 0.$$

...berg's wavenumber.

$$\frac{2\pi^2 m e^4}{ch^3} \quad \frac{1 \times (1.651496)^2 \times 0 \times (0)^4}{0 \times (9.75)^3} = -24.947008$$

Electron's charge.

$$e = \sqrt{\frac{hc\alpha}{2\pi}}$$

Electron's electrostatic charge.

$$e = -\sqrt{\frac{9.75 \times 0 \times -7.098504}{2.651496}} = 0.$$

Electron's K orbit Bohr magneton

$$\mu = \frac{he}{4\pi mc} \qquad \frac{9.75 \times 0}{3.651496 \times 0 \times 0} = 6.0?$$

De'Broglie wavelength.   Electron's hydrogen K orbit's circumference.

$$\dot{v}\phi = B = \frac{1}{2R\phi} \qquad 9.75 \times 7.098504 = 16.848504 = \frac{Q}{1 \times -24.947008 \times 7.098504}$$

Equated forces on hydrogen K orbit electron.

$$\frac{m_\circ V^2}{r} = F = \frac{e^2}{r^2} \qquad \frac{0 \times (-7.098504)}{14.197008} = -28.394016 = \frac{(0)^2}{(14.197008)^2}$$

Waveratio constant.

$$\frac{ch}{e^2} = C = \frac{FL}{2mc^2(\frac{1}{2}\pi)^4} \qquad \frac{0 \times 9.75}{(0)^2} = 9.75 = \frac{-28.394016 \times 41.75}{1 \times 0 \times (0)^2 \times (0.651496)^4}$$

Gravity constant.

$$\mathbf{g} = \frac{\dot{v}^2}{2\sqrt[4]{4/\pi}} \qquad \frac{(-32.)^2}{1 \times \sqrt[4]{2/1.6514961}} = -65.087126$$

1023 Five Systems Related and Compared.

The table contains four principal systems: The Gaussian International; the New International; the Ideal and the Ultimate; with an idealized mass system added in order to limit each conversion between two sequential systems to one factor. The first step converts centimeters to natural length units; the second reduces the gram to an electron's mass; the third reduces one second of time to the time it takes a light wave to move one natural length; and the fourth reduces the natural length and time units to the length and time units of an electron's radius. Their conversion ratios are the same, but their effects on the new constants are opposite as shown by the table.

After selecting the units of length, mass and time, the principal constants of each system are first obtained by the mathematical sequence above the table. Additional constants are then obtained through the conventional conversion formulas, as defined in Sections 412, 1016 and 1022. The figures are in basic logarithms to make it easier to check and evaluate my proof. Note that the simplicity of the ultimate system formulas and the eight numerical values at the top of the table makes its figures, theoretically, as accurate as pi. Since the ratio of a circle's circumference to its diameter has been determined for up to 15 digits, the numerical values of the ultimate system constants and its conversions to other systems can be made equally accurate.

The fundamental units of action of the five systems are defined before the sequences above the table. Their symbols are: cgs: centimeter, gram, second; ngs: natural length, gram, second; nms: natural length, electron's mass, natural time; rmt: electron's radius, mass and radius time.

FIVE SYSTEMS WITH CONVERSIONS. Ratios: $\phi = 0.059298$ $c = 34.743950$ $L = 41.75$
Idealized atomic constants.

		One gram	g	One second		One centimeter
1	G	One gram	g	One second	nl	0.059298 cm.
2	G	One gram	s	One second	nl	0.059298 cm.
3	$m_c = -89.826801$ gram	g	One second	nl	0.059298 cm.
4	$m_c = -89.826801$ gram	t	-34.743950 sec.	nl	0.059298 cm.
5	$m_c = -89.826801$ gram	t	-76.493950 sec.	rl	-41.690702 cm.

$$-89.826801 \times 34.803248 = -55.023553) \times -31.940702$$

	2π	h emu	e esu	e^2 esu	μ emu	Systems
1	$-86.964255)/2.651496 = -89.615752) \times 27.704744 = -61.911008)/35.592197 = -66.547701$					Gaussian
2	-87.082851	2.651496	27.645446	-62.088901	-66.695946	Ideal length
3	-2.743950	2.651496	27.645446	13.868950	-21.782546	Ideal mass
4	-32.0	2.651496	-34.651496	-20.875	-56.526496	Ideal time
5	9.75	2.651496	7.098504	0.0	6.098504	Ultimate

Ratios: $\phi = 0.059298$ $m_c = -89.826801$ $c = 34.743950$ $L = 41.75$

		International system. cgs.	New gaussian system. ngs.	Ideal mass system. nms.	Ideal system. nmt.	Ultimate system. rmt.
Velocity of light. Time unit	c^*	$34.803248 \div\phi$	$34.743950 \div m$	34.743950	0.0	0.0
Electron's rest mass. Unit	m_c^*	-89.826801	-89.826801	-89.826801	0.0	0.0
Electromagnetic unit; emu.	e'	$-65.758752 \div\sqrt{\phi}$	$-65.788400 \div\sqrt{m}$	$-20.875 \times\sqrt{L}$	-20.875	0
Electrostatic charge u.; esu	e^*	$-30.955504 \div\sqrt{\phi^3}$	$-31.044450 \div\sqrt{m}$	$-20.875 \times\sqrt{L}$	-20.875	0
Electron's charge squared	e^{2*}	$-61.911008 \div\phi^3$	$-62.088950 \div m$	$-41.75 \times L$	-41.75	0
Electron's radius wavelength	r	$-41.690702 \div\phi$	$27.737900 \div\sqrt{m}$	27.737900	-41.75	-1.092442
Proton's mass wavelength	$\bar{v}_p$	$-42.783144 \div\phi$	$-42.842442 \div m$	$-42.842442 \times L$	-42.842442	-1.092442
Electron's mass wavelength	$\bar{v}$	$-31.940702 \div\phi$	$-32.0 \div m$	$-32.0 \times L$	-32.0	9.75
Energy of wave units; emu.	h^*	$-86.964256 \div\phi^2$	$-87.082851 \div m$	$2.743950 \div m$	$-34.651496 \times m$	7.098504
Wave quantum energy/2π; emu.	h^*	$-89.615752 \div\phi^2$	$-89.734347 \div m$	$0.092454 \div m$	$10.842442 \times m$	10.842442
Proton's rest mass	M_p	$-78.984359 \div\phi^3$	$-78.984359 \div m$	$10.842442 \div m$	10.842442	10.842442
Gravity constant. Force unit	g	$-23.838481 \div\phi^3$	$-24.016375 \div m$	$-113.843176 \div m$	$-148.587126 \div m$	-65.087126
Ratio: electrostatic/gravity	e/g	141.581076	141.581076	141.581076	106.837126	65.087126

Elements of the smallest electron orbit in hydrogen. Infinite nuclear mass idealization.

		International cgs.	New gaussian ngs.	Ideal mass nms.	Ideal nmt.	Ultimate rmt.	
Force on electron in orbit	F	$-6.923618 \div\phi$	$-6.982917 \div\phi$	$82.843884 \div\phi^2$	$13.355984 \div\phi^2$	$-28.394016 \div L$	$1/\phi^4$
Orbit frequency in unit time	f	$52.546943 \div\phi$	$52.546942 \div\phi$	$52.546942 \div\phi$	$17.802992 \div\phi$	$-23.947008 \div L$	$1/2\phi^3$
Orbit periods in unit time	p	$-52.546942 \div\phi$	$-52.546942 \div\phi$	$-52.546942 \times\phi$	-17.802992	23.947008	$2\phi^3$
Max. radiation wavelgt.; emu.	R	$-16.743695 \div\phi$	$-16.802992 \div\phi$	-16.802992	-16.802992	$24.947008 \times L$	$4\phi^3$
Orbit momentum wavelength.	B	$-24.842198 \div\phi$	-24.901496	-24.901496	-24.901496	$16.848504 \times L$	$2\pi\phi^2$
Radius of electron's orbit	δ	$-27.493694 \div\phi$	-27.552992	-27.552992	-27.552992	$14.197008 \times L$	ϕ^2
Orbit's magnetic field; emu.	$\bar{\mu}$	$-66.547701 \div\phi$	$-66.695946 \div\sqrt{m}$	$-21.782546 \div\sqrt{m}$	$-56.526496 \times(\sqrt{L})^3$	$6.098504 \div L$	ϕ
Orbital velocity; c/ϕ	V^*	$27.704744 \div\phi$	$27.645446 \div\phi$	$27.645446 \times L$	$-7.098504 \div\phi$	$-7.098504 \div L$	ϕ
Orbital motion energy; $\frac{1}{2}mV^2$	E	$-35.417312 \div\phi$	$-35.535909 \div m$	$54.290892 \div m$	$-15.197008 \div m$	$-15.197008 \div L^2$	$1/2\phi^2$

*Figures are from the mathematical sequence.   **Ratio: $L^2 = L^3/L_T$.

1024 Selected Systems of Atomic Constants.
By changing the ideal system's length unit to an electron's radius, while retaining its time unit, there is no change of the e/g ratio, and the conversion formulas should be the same as those defining the transitions from gaussian to new international constants in the preceding table. The table following the sequence defines the constants and their equivalents of this new system, in accordance with the table in Section 1004. Those of the second table are arranged like the constants in Section 1023. The speed of light is $\log_2$ 41.75 for the electron radius system and unity for the ideal system.

$$m_o \quad c \quad m' \quad \dot{v} \quad h \quad 2\pi \quad \hbar \quad c/\text{\textcent} \quad e^2$$
$$0.0 \times 41.75 = 41.75) \times 9.75 = 51.5)/2.651496 = 48.848504) \times 34.651496 = 83.5$$

$$e \quad 4\pi\tilde{v} \quad \mu \quad F = e^2/r^2 \quad e/g \quad g$$
$$41.75)/-6.098504 = 47.848504 \quad 55.105984 \quad 106.837126 \quad -23.337126$$

Electron radius system.

	Mass	Erg emu	Erg esu	Wavenumber
$\hbar$	7.098504	48.848504	90.598504	-2.651496
h	9.75	51.50	93.25	0.0
μ	6.098504	47.848504	89.598504	-3.651496
e	-41.75	0.0	41.75	-51.50
m_o	0.0	41.75	83.50	-9.75
$\dot{v}$	-83.50	-41.75	0.0	-93.25
E	-41.75	0.0	41.75	-51.50

Conversions from the ideal system to the electron radius system.

	Ideal system	Electron radius system		Elements of smallest electron orbit in hydrogen; idealized.		
c	0.0	×L	41.75			Ideal sy.	El. rad. sy
m_o	0.0	0	0.0	F	13.355984	×L	55.10598
e'	-20.875	×$\sqrt{L}$	0.0	f	17.802992	0	17.80299
e	-20.875	×$\sqrt{L})^3$	41.75	P	-17.802992	0	-17.80299
e^4	-41.75	×L^3	83.5	R	-16.802992	×L	24.94700
r	-41.75	×L	0.0	B	-24.901496	×L	16.84850
$\dot{v}$	-32.0	×L	9.75	ô	-27.552992	×L	14.19700
h	-32.0	×L^2	51.5	μ	-56.526496×$\sqrt{L})^5$	47.84850
$\hbar$	-34.651496	×L^2	48.848504	V	-7.098504	×L	34.65149
g	-148.587126	×L^3	-23.337126	E	-15.197008	×L^2	68.30299
e/g	106.837126	0	106.837126				

The energies of the electron radius system above are large because the energy needed to accelerate an electron's mass to the speed of light across its radius-distance in one natural unit of time is extremely small. Those of the system below are also large because its electron is accelerated through one natural unit of length to the speed of light in one second, with the second in natural length units.

The idealized mass system in the preceding section appears below as a table of mass, energy and wavenumber equivalents. Its length, mass and time units are represented by an electron's rest mass wavenumber $\tilde{v} = 32.0$; its rest mass, $m_o = 0.0$; and its speed of light, c = 34.743950—one second in natural length units.

	Mass	Erg emu	Erg esu	Wavenumber
ħ	-34.651496	0.092454	34.836404	-2.651496
h	-32.0	2.743950	37.487900	0.0
μ	-56.526496	-21.782546	12.961404	-24.526496
e	-55.618950	-20.875	13.868950	-23.618950
m₀	0.0	34.743950	69.487900	32.0
Q	-69.487900	-34.743950	0.0	-37.487900
E	-34.743950	0.0	34.743950	-2.743950

In this next system, an electron's mass is made equal to an electrostatic unit of energy, divided by the speed of light squared, and the electron's rest mass wavelength squared. One Bohr magneton times 4π equals the energy of an electromagnetic unit. Its three basic units are: electron's mass, wn. $\tilde{v} = 32.0$; its rest mass, $m_0 = -64.0$; and speed of light, $c = 32.0$, for length, mass and time, respectively.

	Mass	Erg emu	Erg esu	Wavenumber
ħ	-98.651496	-66.651496	-34.651496	-2.651496
h	-96.0	-64.0	-32.0	0.0
μ	-88.526496	-56.526496	-24.526496	7.473504
e	-84.875	-52.875	-20.875	11.125
m₀	-64.0	-32.0	0.0	32.0
Q	-64.0	-32.0	0.0	32.0
E	-32.0	0.0	32.0	64.0
G	0.0	32.0	64.0	96.0

In this system the length, mass and time units were selected to cause the energy of an electron's rest mass and the energy of its electromagnetic field to have identical values. The energy of its charge in esu is the same as the electron's radius wavelength in natural length units. Its three units of action are defined by an electron's mass wavenumber $\tilde{v} = 32.0$; its rest mass by $m_0 = -89.75$; and the speed of light by $c = 24.0$.

	Mass	Erg emu	Erg esu	Wavenumber
h	-124.401496	-100.401496	-76.401496	-2.651496
h	-121.75	-97.75	-73.75	0.0
u	-101.401496	-77.401496	-53.401496	20.348504
e	-89.75	-65.75	-41.75	32.0
m	-89.75	-65.75	-41.75	32.0
Q	-48.0	-24.0	0.0	73.75
E	-24.0	0.0	24.0	97.75
G	0.0	24.0	48.0	121.75

The system below is of interest for its coincidences of values. There are only three columns because wavenumbers and energy in ergs esu have the same values. The lines for h and Q have the same values, as do the lines for m and E. The electrostatic field values are greater than the Bohr magneton by 4π. The

THE FUNDAMENTAL UNITS OF PHYSICS

basic values are: an electron's mass wavenumber $\tilde{v} = 32.0$; its rest mass $m_o = -32.0$; and its speed of light $c = 32.0$.

	Mass	Erg emu	Wavenumber Erg esu
μ	-72.526496	-40.526496	-8.526496
e	-68.875	-36.875	-4.875
h	-66.651496	-34.651496	-2.651496
h	-64.0	-32.0	0.0
Q	-64.0	-32.0	0.0
m.	-32.0	0.0	32.0
I	-32.0	0.0	32.0
G	0.0	32.0	64.0

1025 Idealizing the Electron Volt.

An electron volt whose definition in basic logarithms is simple and specific, and not too far removed from its conventional definition, is desirable for experimental and tabulating purposes. The cgs energy of the accepted electron volt is obtained by multiplying an electrostatic unit of energy in emu by 10^8, $\log_2 26.575425$. Its energy wavenumber is this energy divided by Planck's quantum in esu. It is converted into the wavenumber of a natural length unit and divided by 2048, the 11th power of two, for its ratio in ideal volts.

$$I = e' \, 10^8 \qquad 1.6019291 \times 10^{10} \times 10^8 = 1.6019291 \times 10^{12} \text{ erg esu-cgs.}$$
$$\text{Log}_2 \quad -65.758752 \quad 26.575425 \quad -39.183327$$

$$V = I/h' \qquad 1.6019291 \times 10^{12}/1.9859669 \times 10^{16} = 8066.24254 \text{ waves cm.}$$
$$\text{Log}_2 \quad -39.183327 \qquad -52.161008 \qquad 12.977681$$

$$R = \tilde{v}\phi/\tilde{v} \qquad 8066.24254 \times 1.0419584/2048.0 = 4.103852 \text{ int./ideal ra}$$
$$\text{Log}_2 \quad 12.977681 \quad 0.059298 \quad 11.0 \quad 2.036979$$

My selection of the 11th power of two—2048 waves per natural length unit—as the wavenumber of an ideal electron volt is of no theoretical significance, and it may not be the best choice. It takes 4.103852 such volts to equal one international electron volt, with 8404.68917 waves per natural length and 8066.24254 per centimeter.

1026 Observed Elements of High Velocity Electrons.

This section is accompanied by a table showing the elements of an electron moving with velocities approaching that of light. It is theoretically impossible for an electron to attain that speed, because an increasing mass inertia, ascending rapidly toward infinity near light, is an insurmountable barrier. An electron's increase of mass with speed is shown by column F in the table. It will be seen that a sixteen-million volt acceleration increases the electron's mass to 33 times its rest mass.

Since this section is intended to show the conversion of a moving

Relativity reductions. Values in international units — centimeters, grams and seconds.

A1 Ideal volts Log 2	Electron volts (V_2)	B Energy wavenumber (γ)	C Ratio of wavenumb's $R = \lambda/\gamma$	D Momentum wavenumber (λ or B)	E Velocity less light $-V = R/2$	F El's mass increase $m_1 = m_2 + I/m_0$	E1 Velocity Km's second $V = c/-V$	G Radius curve in gauss $r = \lambda/e$
26.0	16352652.	6.7950779^{10}	2.0009189	$1.3596400''$	1.0004595	33.000000	299655.32	56225.220
24.0	4088162.9	1.8320063^{10}	2.0124612	3.6368416^{10}	1.0062302	9.000000	297936.26	15246.203
22.0	1022040.7	5.4960189^{9}	2.1213203	1.1653817^{10}	1.0606602	3.000000	282647.55	4821.2738
20.0	255510.18	4.8662667^{8}	2.6532816	2.6085520^{9}	1.3416408	1.500000	223452.51	1905.7754
18.0	63877.546	1.2686123^{8}	4.3656412	2.1244375^{9}	2.1828206	1.125000	134345.02	878.51905
16.0	15969.386	32078417.	8.1862925	1.0385232^{9}	4.0931462	1.031250	73243.680	429.46069
14.0	3992.3466	8042962.1	16.093598	5.1625715^{8}	8.0467989	1.007813	37256.182	213.48792
12.0	998.08666	2012211.1	32.046856	2.5775165^{8}	16.023428	1.001953	18709.667	106.58802
10.0	249.52166	503144.35	64.023435	1.2882867^{8}	32.011717	1.000488	9365.1020	53.274544
8.0	62.380416	125791.97	128.01172	64403437.	64.005859	1.000122	4683.8368	26.634834
6.0	15.595104	31448.353	256.00586	32203437.	128.00293	1.000030	2342.0792	13.317112
4.0	3.8987760	7362.1106	512.00293	16101649.	256.00146	1.000008	1171.0597	6.6585179
2.0	0.97466940	1965.5291	1024.0015	8050812.7	512.00074	1.000002	585.53236	3.3292542
0.0	0.2436735		2048.0007	4025404.9	1024.0004	1.000000	292.76650	1.6646265

Values in basic logarithms and natural length units.

A1 Volts	Int. volts	B Energy wn.	C Ratio w-w.	D True wn.	E -Velocity	F Mass inc.	E2 % of light	B1 Volts to wn.
26.0	23.963021	36.043068	1.000662	37.043730	-0.000662	5.044394	99.954076	$1.3190445''$
24.0	21.963021	34.152003	1.000961	35.160964	-0.000961	3.169925	99.350799	3.2976114^{10}
22.0	19.963021	32.415038	1.084962	33.500000	-0.084962	1.584962	94.280904	8.2440283^{9}
20.0	17.963021	30.736966	1.423998	32.160964	-0.423998	0.584962	74.535599	2.0610071^{9}
18.0	15.963021	28.917538	2.126194	31.043732	-1.126194	0.169925	45.812285	5.1525177^{8}
16.0	13.963021	26.977974	3.033210	30.011184	-2.033210	0.044394	24.431084	1.2881294^{8}
14.0	11.963021	24.994397	4.008415	29.002812	-3.008415	0.011229	12.427302	32203236.
12.0	9.963021	22.993593	5.002111	28.000704	-4.002111	0.002815	6.240862	8050808.9
10.0	7.963021	20.999648	6.000528	27.000176	-5.000528	0.000704	3.123856	2012702.2
8.0	5.963021	18.999912	7.000132	26.000044	-6.000132	0.000176	1.562357	503175.56
6.0	3.963021	16.999978	8.000033	25.000011	-7.000033	0.000044	0.781232	125793.89
4.0	1.963021	14.999995	9.000008	24.000003	-8.000008	0.000011	0.390623	31448.472
2.0	-0.036979	12.999999	10.000002	23.000001	-9.000002	0.000003	0.195312	7362.1181
0.0	-2.036979	11.0	11.0	22.0	-10.0	0.0	0.097656	1965.5295

Table in the succeding section continue the sequence above.

electron's observed international values into simple ideal proportions in natural length units, the sequence defining its acceleration energy is in ideal electron volts. These are converted into international electron volts, as shown by columns A and A1. Multiplying the values of this last column by the wavenumber of one electron volt gives us the electron's energy of motion in waves per centimeter in column B1. These figures are greater than those in column B because the latter's are reduced by the relativity effect of increasing mass-inertia with increased speed. Multiplying the figures in column B1 by 1.0419584 gives us wavenumbers in natural length units. These are in ideal proportions in powers of two, as defined by the table in Section 1027.

After obtaining the electron's energy of motion wavenumber in centimeters in column B1, we turn to Section 810 for the relativity reduction formulas. The second formula gives us the increase of mass due to motion, with the electron's rest mass assigned unit value. This is the electron's energy of motion added to its rest mass energy, with the sum divided by its rest mass energy. The increase is shown in column F.

Column B is the electron's relativity energy of motion wavenumber; C is the ratio difference between it and the electron's true, de Broglie momentum wavenumber (Column D). Multiplying B by C, therefore, gives us D. The difference between the electron's velocity and the speed of light is equal to one half of the ratio C. Its values in E, used as the divisor of the speed of light, gives us the electron's velocity in kilometers per second (Column E1), and its velocity in percent of the speed of light (Column E2). The electron's recurve in a magnetic field of one gauss is obtained by dividing its de Broglie wavenumber in D by its electrostatic charge wavenumber 2.418203×10^6 waves per centimeter.

Multiplying the two columns of wavenumbers, B and D, by 1.0419584, gives us their values in natural length units. When these and the unchanged figures of four other columns are converted into powers of two, the seven columns of basic logarithms below appear. Note that the increase of an electron's mass-inertia by motion is infinitesimal below one ideal electron volt, and that five significant figures become simple number values at low velocities.

1027 Idealized Elements of Electron Motions.

The table in Section 1026 clearly shows that the elements of moving electrons can be expressed in simple numbers in powers of two for low velocities when their accelerating forces in natural length units are idealized. By eliminating the observed increase of mass at high velocities, the idealization can be continued to twice the speed of light, as shown by the accompanying table. It answers the theoretical question of what would happen if such an elimination was possible: The electron would dissolve into a free momentum when the accelerating energy equalled its rest mass energy. The coincidence of energy and momentum wavenumbers at twice the speed of light is obviously significant. It is the theoretical velocity of a free momentum.

The increase of an electron's mass-inertia with increasing velocity was included to show its negligible values at low velocities. It is my belief that no actual increase of mass occurs; that the observed increase of inertia is the opposition of the velocity photon with which it integrates against a change of speed and direction, and that the electron's rest mass is functionally stationary within the configuration of directional forces, thus reducing speed to less than that of light.

The electron volt wavenumber is idealized as $\log_2 11$, or 2048 waves in one natural length unit, as defined in Section 1025. The simplicity of the table as a whole supports my definition of the natural length unit and my contention that nature's mathematics is in powers of two.

IDEALIZED ELEMENTS OF A MOVING ELECTRON.
Note: Effects of velocity increase of mass are excluded.

(V_e) A Electron volts in ideal u.	(γ) B Energy wave number	(R) C Ratio $\gamma-\lambda=w$. numbers	(λ) D Momen- tum w. number	(V) E Veloci- ty less light	(m_γ) F Vel. increase of mass added to rest mass u.
22	33	0	33	+1	1.584962
20	31	1	32	0	0.584962
18	29	2	31	-1	0.169925
16	27	3	30	-2	0.044394
14	25	4	29	-3	0.011229
12	23	5	28	-4	0.002815
10	21	6	27	-5	0.000704
8	19	7	26	-6	0.000176
6	17	8	25	-7	0.000044
4	15	9	24	-8	0.000011
2	13	10	23	-9	0.000003
0	11	11	22	-10	0.0
-2	9	12	21	-11	
-4	7	13	20	-12	
-6	5	14	19	-13	
-8	3	15	18	-14	
-10	1	16	17	-15	
-12	-1	17	16	-16	
-14	-3	18	15	-17	
-16	-5	19	14	-18	
-18	-7	20	13	-19	
-20	-9	21	12	-20	
-22	-11	22	11	-21	

Any system using the natural length unit will find the four center columns above measurably accurate for low velocity electron speeds. Other columns, such as one defining an electron's energy of motion, one its momentum, one its radius curve in a gauss field, etc., can be added to those above; it will be noticed however, that their defined values depend upon the mass and time units selected for this system. The increase of mass-inertia in the last column reduces the electron's speed below that shown in the table. Its true values for high velocities are defined in the preceding table.

1028 Testing the Ideal Velocity Table.
The table in the preceding section, defining an electron's ideal proportion elements of motion at various velocities, can be tested for reliability by using it to obtain known results. It will be used to define the elements of one international electron volt and the energy wavenumber of one statcoulomb. All principal reductions are in basic logarithms.

Since one international electron volt equals $\log_2$ 2.036979 ideal proportion volts, its other elements must have values above the two-volt line in the table. The mantissa for B is the same as for A. For D it is halved; the reciprocal of D gives us those for C and E. By adding their characteristics, we obtain their basic log values below. The two wavenumbers are then divided by the natural length unit in centimeters for their centimeter values. The figures equivalent to the $\log_2$ numbers can be compared with those in Sections 703 and 1025.

A Volts	B Energy	C Ratio	D Momentum	E Velocity
2.036979	13.036979	9.9815105	23.0184895	-8.9815105
	0.059298		0.0592980	
	12.977681		22.9591915	
4.103852	8066.24254	1010.95987	8154647.09	c/505.47994

The reciprocal of D gives us 1.226294×10^{-7} as the electron's de Broglie wavelength. Its velocity of 5.930858×10^7 centimeters per second is obtained by dividing the speed of light by the velocity ratio. All these values are in accord with observations.

One erg is defined as the energy of a two-gram mass moving with a speed of one centimeter per second. It follows that its energy wavenumber must be abstracted from the table by postulating an electron speed of one centimeter per second: the reciprocal of the velocity of light in centimeters per second. Notice that we are now dealing with a ratio less than the speed of light which must have the same value for all length units. It is used to obtain the other values from the table. The energy wavenumber thus obtained is multiplied by the number of electrons in a two gram mass for the wavenumber of one statcoulomb, after its conversion into a centimeter value. The final figure can be checked against Fig. 25W in the large square table of physical constants. (Chapter 11, page 159).

From that table we also obtain the number of electrons in a two-gram mass by dividing the latter's wavenumber by that of an electron as defined by this formula (in powers of two).

$1.0 \times 121.767503/31.940702 = 90.826801$ electrons.

Since my table does not include the low velocity of one centimeter per second, the ideal proportion values which would appear in a continuation of the table are defined above those used in the reduction. The electron's velocity reduction ratio, the reciprocal of the speed of light as defined by Fig. 2W in the large square table of constants, is -34.803248, and the wavenumber of one statcoulomb in Fig. 25W is 52.161008 in powers of two.

A	B	C	D	E
Volts	Energy	Ratio	Momentum	Velocity
-48.	-37.	35.	-2.	-34.
-49.606496	-38.606496	35.803248	-2.803248	-34.803248
	0.059298			

90.826801 × -38.665794 = 52.161007 **waves per statcoulomb centimeter.**

1029 Special-Purpose Systems.

Systems of fundamental units can easily be worked out by the mathematical sequence in Sections 217 and 1005, especially when the reductions are performed by logarithms. From my examples it will be noticed that, while the mass and time units can be changed at will, the unit of length is a constant. It is invariable, in the sense that a rational system of units cannot be developed by the use of an arbitrary unit without reductions to natural lengths in sensitive formulas. This is also true for the length unit of the ultimate system. It is evident that an electron's charge to mass, and through that mass to the gravity constant, is a transcendental, unchangeable proportion which must appear in all acceptable systems. The radius of an electron's idealized orbit in hydrogen is fixed by its quantized velocity and its relation to the electron's mass and the electrostatic attraction between electron and proton.

I have worked out about 50 systems of units for various purposes by posing a problem in which two factors are either identical or in specific proportions. Some systems can be worked out by inserting the anticipated results in the mathematical sequence, with the remaining constants obtained by reversing some of the reductions; while in other systems the wanted relationship can be obtained by experiment. Only the most important systems are included in this book.

1030 Unsolved Problems.

A theoretical definition of the gravity constant is the most important problem to be solved. Elementary logic tells us that there is a great difference between tapping the fundamental energies of a mass and its reactions to its environment as an inert body, but the problem of how to define this difference remains.

Until a short time ago I did not believe it possible to work out a theoretical definition of the rest masses of protons and neutrons. The neutron's mass is still an unsolved problem, but I found a formula for the proton's. A proton's mass wavenumber can be obtained by the formula: $P = 6\tilde{v}\pi^5$. $6\pi^5$ is equal to 1836.11809 electrons (Section 815). The combination of figures is given a tentative explanation by the theory of saturation in Book Two.

Another problem which may come up is where to apply the small difference between the ratio of a circle's circumference to its radius and one-fourth of that ratio raised to its fourth power. The inverse fourth-power gradient of rest mass waves obviously relate the quartering to the difference between free and bound waves, and the increase to the saturation of rest mass waves within specific photon radii. Note that a ratio is obtained by division and a difference by subtraction.

	2π	$(\tfrac{1}{2}\pi)^4$	Ratio	Difference
Number	6.28318531	$\div\ 6.08806824$	$= 1.03204909$	0.19511707
Log 2	2.651496	2.605984	0.045512	-2.357588

My theory assumes that energy waves are periodic pulsations, stationary in their configuration spaces, transmitting directional forces. The momenta of these forces are transmitted with twice the speed of light, but cannot escape from their carriers. Free photons, combining energy and momentum, move through a configuration space with the speed of light. The difference between energy and momentum in stationary patterns produces the difference noted above. The subject is discussed in Book Two.

It is my belief the problems of theoretical physics can be solved through logical analyses of facts already known, rather than through discoveries of new truths by experiments. I cannot conceive of anyone discovering the working of a watch by using a sledge hammer on it and counting the pieces as they fly. I do not believe that the building of bigger and better cyclotrons and linear accelerators can bring us closer to the solution of fundamental problems in atomic physics. Something may be accomplished, but we can accomplish much more through realistic re-evaluations of known facts by making theory conform to the probable limitations and possibilities of nature.

1031 Conclusions.

In this chapter I have presented proof of various postulates. I have proved there is a definable unit of length in nature, slightly longer than one centimeter; I have proved the mathematical sequence of atomic units is valid for any system of units we choose; I have proved the specific numerical value of the electronic and waveratio constants and the constants of the ultimate system of units; thus showing the fundamental simplicity of their origin. I consider this proof conclusive because it brings fact and theory into accord.

I am aware that many scientists will not consider it so, since all physical phenomena contain obvious logical implications that they have, so far, refused to treat as possibilities, for reasons I believe are superficial and irrelevant. My proof may well be among those they believe (and hope) can be safely ignored.

Sixty years ago theoretical physicists abandoned beliefs and principles of research that were, until then, considered the very essence of physical science. Being unable to explain local relativity within a realistic ether mechanical frame, they accepted the postulate of general relativity as having been proved. In doing so they had to abandon the universally accepted principles of research which, until then, had acted as a restraining influence on irresponsible conclusions. Their acceptance of general relativity caused them to abandon mechanics, causality, continuity, understanding, and the logical implications of facts as transcendental principles of research in theoretical physics. Their rejection of classical philosophy in the name of realism became a new philosophy rejecting reality in the name of expediency.

This new philosophy replaced the principles of experience we all live by with legislated postulates: A mathematics without comprehensible relations to experience; experiments with arbitrary limitations on permissible deductions; facts whose interpretations are not related to the transcendental truths of nature, but to the perceptions of man and the limitations of his tools and, finally, the absurd postulate that what cannot be observed does not exist.

Chapter 11

TABLE OF PHYSICAL CONSTANTS

The heterogenous values in this table give the reader a cross-check on the accuracy of those appearing in the preceding formulas. They show that my figures have not been doctored to obtain anticipated results. Those who question the validity of the premises on which they were developed will notice that my figures are within the margins of probable error of those values in use. Note that only one figure out of eight is an accepted constant, the other seven are, mostly, worthless equivalents.

TABLE OF PHYSICAL CONSTANTS

This square table contains 882 figures arranged in 42 lines and 21 columns. About 180 of its most significant values have been underlined. Over half of these are within the margin of probable error of the physical constants in books on physics; the remainder are unit values, legislated ratios, figures from mathematical formulas, or values of theoretical significance. All the phenomena defined are potentially reducible to energy. The columns have the same rate of change from line to line, and the lines change at the same rate from column to column. The interlocking definitions of the table thus makes the values of all abstracted figures specific, once the principal difference between two columns or two lines have been determined.

The question of which of the heterogeneous phenomena in the table are functionally related, related by formula, or unrelated theoretical equivalents, is left for the reader to decide. It must be emphasized that many of the definitions are not related in fact, but can be related through redefinitions of terms. The nature of electrostatic and gravitational fields, for example, precludes an assignment of mass to their field values. We can do so only by redefining them as pure energy which can, potentially, reappear in various forms: as mass, motions, heat, etc. Neutral energy is not convertible into electromagnetic field values, so we postulate a redefinition of its cgs value into its convertible electrostatic (esu) value equivalent. Note that all the figures are energy equivalents.

TABLE   151

The purpose of this table is, primarily, to bring out the fundamental identity of multiple terms. I use it also as a cross-check on the formal values appearing in the preceding sections. Not all its equivalents are useless fillers. I have, for example, used an electron's charge wavenumber, Fig. 19U, for the purpose of defining an electron's radius curve in a gauss field (Sections 810 and 1026-G). In Section 1028 I use the wavenumber of a statcoulomb (Fig. 25W).

The figures of the table are useful for the purpose of bringing out those simple relationships between phenomena which are often hidden behind the complexities of formal reductions. They can also be used for the purpose of satisfying our interest in certain relative proportions. For example: Eddington once commented on the number of fundamental particles in our universe. The figure he gave is close to the one in 42E, with the latter thus serving as a check on the origin of his figure and the rationale of his reasonings. He divided the probable mass of the universe by the mass of a statom.

While all the positive logarithm figures in columns V and W are in the proportions defined above their columns and in section 108, their negative values are not because the mantissas of log 10 numbers are always positive while those of log 2 numbers are negative. (See Section 113.)

Some of the astronomical constants are of questionable value. We know very little about the sun's magnetic field as a constant, since it is highly variable on the sun's surface and varies with the sunspot cycle, but the question is raised so that a comparison can be made. My figure for the quantity of free energy within the sun is problematic, and the figures for the galaxy's mass and the universe's mass are to be treated as approximations. However, the figures for the earth's mass and the sun's mass, and the sun's radiation loss per second, are reasonably accurate.

PHYSICAL CONSTANTS.

And their equivalents in the international units of physics.

Col-umn	Sym-bol	Read superscripts as powers of ten.	Gram mass. Weight and inertia $M = Q/c^2$ — A	Erg energy cgs, emu Abcoulombs Electromagnetic u. $E = Q/c$ — B	Erg energy cgs, esu Statcoulomb Electrostatic unit $Q = Mc^2$ — C
1	$\mathcal{F}$	Frequency quantum unit. (h/2πc)	1.173080^{-45}	3.516812^{-38}	1.054316^{-27}
2R	f	Frequency quantum unit. (h/c)	7.370680^{-48}	2.209678^{-37}	6.624461^{-27}
3	$\hbar$	Reduction of cm. wave photon. (h/2π)	3.516812^{-38}	1.054316^{-27}	3.160765^{-17}
4N	C_p	Calorie. Physical. (Heat per mole)	7.728243^{-38}	2.316873^{-27}	6.945823^{-17}
5M	C_c	Calorie. Chemical. (Heat per mole)	7.730368^{-38}	2.317510^{-27}	6.947733^{-17}
6P	T	Temperature. (Degree C. per mole)	1.535793^{-37}	4.604200^{-27}	1.380307^{-16}
7	h^T	Idealized wave unit. (1.041984 cm.)	2.120697^{-37}	6.357702^{-27}	1.905994^{-16}
8T	h	Centimeter wavelength photon.(Planck)	2.209678^{-37}	6.624461^{-27}	1.985967^{-16}
9	μ_D	Deuteron magneton.(Hy. isotope two)	1.442619^{-34}	4.324871^{-24}	1.296566^{-13}
10	μ_o	Nuclear magneton unit	1.684319^{-34}	5.049470^{-24}	1.513796^{-13}
11	μ_N	Neutron magneton	3.259157^{-34}	9.770724^{-24}	2.929195^{-13}
12	V^T	Idealized electron volt. (Theory)	4.343188^{-34}	1.302057^{-23}	3.903477^{-13}
13	μ_P	Proton magneton	4.698576^{-34}	1.408600^{-23}	4.222884^{-13}
14H	V	Electron volt.(International unit)	1.782380^{-33}	5.343451^{-23}	1.601929^{-12}
15	χ_R	Red light photon.(Wavenumber 14000)	3.093550^{-33}	9.274245^{-23}	2.780354^{-12}
16	χ_V	Violet light ph. (Wavenumber 24000)	5.303228^{-33}	1.589871^{-22}	4.766321^{-12}
17	R	Rydberg's wavenumber for inf. mass	2.424842^{-32}	7.269505^{-22}	2.179347^{-11}

No.	Sym.	Description			
18	μ	Hy. K orbit electron magneton.(Bohr)	3.092601^{-31}	9.271402^{-21}	2.779502^{-10}
19G	e	Electron's electrostatic charge	5.343451^{-31}	1.601929^{-20}	4.802471^{-10}
20S	Å	Angstrom wavelength photon. (10^{-8} cm.)	2.209678^{-29}	6.624461^{-19}	1.985967^{-9}
21F	m_0	Electron's rest mass.	9.108325^{-28}	2.730612^{-17}	8.186184^{-7}
22E	M_0	Statom. Nucleon.(Isotope $O^{16}/16$)	1.659790^{-24}	4.975933^{-14}	1.491750^{-3}
23	M_P	Proton's rest mass	1.672392^{-24}	5.013715^{-14}	1.503077^{-3}
24	M_N	Neutron's rest mass	1.674698^{-24}	5.020627^{-14}	1.505149^{-3}
25C	Q	Statcoulomb.(Electrostatic unit)	1.112646^{-21}	3.335635^{-11}	1.0
26	G	Gram-centimeter gravity acceleration	1.091133^{-18}	3.271140^{-8}	980.6650
27K	W	Joule.(Meter-kg.-sec. & watt-second)	1.112646^{-14}	3.335635^{-4}	1.0000007
28L	C	Calorie.(Heat capacity per gram mole)	4.656158^{-14}	1.395884^{-3}	4.1847617
29	KM	Kilogram-meter gravity acceleration	1.091133^{-13}	3.271140^{-3}	9.8066507
30	H	Horsepower. (English-American unit)	8.189075^{-12}	0.2455027	7.3600009
31	BTU	British thermal unit. (252 calories)	1.173352^{-11}	0.3517627	1.05456010
32B	E	Abcoulomb. (Electromagnetic unit)	3.335635^{-11}	1.0	2.99793010
33J	KWH	Kilowatt-hour. (Electrical quantity)	4.005526^{-8}	1200.829	3.60000013
34A	g	Gram mass. ($E = mc^2$)	1.0	2.99793010	8.98758420
35D	gm	Dyne-centimeter radius sp. gravity	1.500760^{7}	4.499174^{17}	1.348821^{28}
36	$S\mu$	Sun's magnetic field. (An estimate)	7.878×10^{6}	2.362×10^{17}	7.080×10^{27}
37	S_R	Sun's radiation loss per second	4.228×10^{12}	1.268×10^{23}	3.800×10^{33}
38	E_M	Earth's mass	5.984×10^{27}	1.794×10^{38}	5.378×10^{48}
39	S_E	Sun's free energy within its mass	7.010×10^{37}	2.101×10^{38}	6.300×10^{48}
40	S_M	Sun's mass	1.980×10^{33}	5.936×10^{43}	1.780×10^{54}
41	G_M	Our galaxy's mass. (An estimate)	1.000×10^{45}	2.998×10^{55}	8.988×10^{65}
42	U_M	The universe's mass	1.000×10^{55}	2.998×10^{65}	8.988×10^{75}

PHYSICAL CONSTANTS.

	Dyne force Gravity on cm. radius sphere $F = gm$	Statom mass unit (Physical) $M_0 = O^{16}/16$	Electron's mass unit m_0	Electrostatic charge unit, esu e	Electron volt unit V	Kilowatt-hour unit (Electric current) KWH
	D	E	F	G	H	J
1 $\mathfrak{F}$	7.816574^{-56}	7.067644^{-25}	1.287921^{-21}	2.195361^{-18}	6.581538^{-16}	2.928655^{-41}
2R f	4.911298^{-55}	4.440731^{-24}	8.092245^{-21}	1.379386^{-17}	4.135302^{-15}	1.840128^{-40}
3 h	2.343354^{-45}	2.118830^{-14}	3.861096^{-11}	6.581538^{-8}	1.973099^{-5}	8.779902^{-31}
4N C_r	5.149552^{-45}	4.656158^{-14}	8.484812^{-11}	1.446302^{-7}	4.335912^{-5}	1.929395^{-30}
5M C_c	5.150968^{-45}	4.657438^{-14}	8.487145^{-11}	1.446700^{-7}	4.337104^{-5}	1.929926^{-30}
6P h_T	1.023344^{-44}	9.252938^{-14}	1.686142^{-10}	2.874160^{-7}	8.616530^{-5}	3.834186^{-30}
7 h'_T	1.413082^{-44}	1.277690^{-13}	2.328306^{-10}	3.968778^{-7}	1.189812^{-4}	5.294429^{-30}
8T h	1.472373^{-44}	1.331300^{-13}	2.425998^{-10}	4.135302^{-7}	1.239735^{-4}	5.516575^{-30}
9 μ_D	9.612589^{-42}	8.691578^{-11}	1.583847^{-7}	2.699789^{-4}	0.0809378	3.601572^{-27}
10 μ_0	1.122310^{-41}	1.014778^{-10}	1.849208^{-7}	3.152118^{-4}	0.0944983	4.204988^{-27}
11 μ_T^N	2.171671^{-41}	1.963596^{-10}	3.578217^{-7}	6.099349^{-4}	0.1828542	8.136652^{-27}
12 ∇_T	2.893992^{-41}	2.616610^{-10}	4.768372^{-7}	8.128058^{-4}	0.2436735	1.084299^{-26}
13 μ_P	3.130797^{-40}	2.830826^{-9}	5.158551^{-6}	8.793149^{-4}	0.2636124	1.173023^{-26}
14H V	1.187652^{-40}	1.073859^{-9}	1.956869^{-6}	3.335635^{-3}	1.0	4.449803^{-26}
15 γ_R	2.061322^{-40}	1.863820^{-9}	3.396398^{-6}	5.789423^{-3}	1.735628	7.723205^{-26}
16 γ_N	3.533695^{-40}	3.195120^{-9}	5.822396^{-6}	9.924725^{-3}	2.975363	1.323978^{-25}
17 R	1.615742^{-39}	1.460933^{-8}	2.662226^{-5}	0.0453797	13.604515	6.053741^{-24}

#	Symbol						
18	μ	2.060690^{-38}	1.863249^{-7}	3.395357^{-4}	0.5787648	173.5096	7.720838^{-24}
19G	e	3.560496^{-38}	3.219354^{-7}	5.866557^{-4}	1.0	299.7930	1.334020^{-23}
20S	A	1.472373^{-36}	1.331300^{-5}	0.0242600	41.35302	12397.35	5.516575^{-22}
21F	m_0	6.069141^{-35}	5.487638^{-4}	1.0	1704.577	511020.4	2.273940^{-20}
22E	M_0	1.105966^{-31}	1.0	1822.2775	3.106213^{6}	9.312209^{8}	4.143750^{-17}
23	M_P	1.114364^{-31}	1.007593	1836.1141	3.129799^{6}	9.382917^{8}	4.175213^{-17}
24	M_N	1.115900^{-31}	1.008982	1838.6452	3.134113^{6}	9.395851^{8}	4.180969^{-17}
25C	Q	7.413884^{-29}	670.3537	1.221576^{6}	2.082261^{12}	6.242474^{11}	2.777778^{-14}
26	G	7.270536^{-26}	6.573924^{5}	1.197951^{9}	2.042001^{12}	6.121775^{14}	2.724069^{-11}
27K	W	7.413884^{-27}	6.703537^{9}	1.221570^{13}	2.082261^{16}	6.242474^{18}	2.777778^{-7}
28L	C	3.102533^{-31}	2.805270^{10}	5.111980^{13}	8.713766^{16}	2.612326^{19}	1.162434^{-7}
29	KM	7.270536^{-24}	6.573924^{10}	1.197951^{14}	2.042001^{17}	6.121775^{19}	2.724069^{-6}
30	H	5.456618^{-19}	4.933803^{12}	8.990758^{15}	1.532544^{19}	4.594461^{21}	2.044444^{-4}
31	BTU	7.818384^{-19}	7.069280^{12}	1.288219^{16}	2.195869^{19}	6.583062^{21}	2.929333^{-4}
32B	E	2.222630^{-18}	2.009673^{13}	3.662183^{16}	6.242474^{19}	1.871450^{22}	8.327583^{-4}
33J	KWH	2.668998^{-15}	2.413273^{16}	4.397653^{19}	7.496141^{22}	2.247290^{25}	1.0
34A	g	6.663290^{-8}	6.024860^{23}	1.097897^{27}	1.871450^{30}	5.610476^{32}	2.496551^{7}
35D	gm	1.0	9.041869^{30}	1.647680^{34}	2.808597^{37}	8.419978^{34}	3.746724^{14}
36	S_μ	0.525	4.75×10^{30}	8.65×10^{33}	1.47×10^{37}	4.42×10^{39}	1.97×10^{14}
37	S_R	2.82×10^{5}	2.55×10^{36}	4.64×10^{39}	7.91×10^{42}	2.37×10^{45}	1.06×10^{20}
38	E_M	3.22×10^{20}	3.61×10^{51}	6.57×10^{54}	1.12×10^{58}	3.36×10^{60}	1.49×10^{35}
39	S_E	4.67×10^{20}	4.22×10^{51}	7.70×10^{54}	1.31×10^{58}	3.93×10^{60}	1.75×10^{35}
40	S_M	1.32×10^{26}	1.19×10^{57}	2.17×10^{60}	3.71×10^{63}	1.11×10^{66}	4.94×10^{40}
41	G_M	6.66×10^{38}	6.02×10^{68}	1.10×10^{72}	1.87×10^{75}	5.61×10^{77}	2.50×10^{52}
42	U_M	6.66×10^{48}	6.02×10^{78}	1.10×10^{82}	1.87×10^{85}	5.61×10^{87}	2.50×10^{62}

PHYSICAL CONSTANTS.

	Joules Watt-second $W_c = Mc^2 \times 10^7$ K	Calories Gram-mole heat capacity. C = CN L	Calories Statom-mole heat degree centigrade. (Chemical) M	Calories Statom-mole heat degree centigrade. (Physical) C N	Temperature K, absolute per degree centigrade. K P	Wave period in second Q
1 𝔎	1.054316^{-34}	2.519417^{-35}	1.517496^{-11}	1.517913^{-11}	7.638269^{-12}	6.283185
2R f	6.624461^{-34}	1.582996^{-34}	9.534708^{-11}	9.537330^{-11}	4.799266^{-11}	1.0
3 λh	3.160765^{-24}	7.553034^{-25}	0.4549347	0.4550598	0.2289900	2.095841^{-10}
4N Cp	6.945823^{-24}	1.659790^{-24}	0.9997251	1.0	0.5032086	9.537330^{-11}
5M Cc	6.947733^{-24}	1.660246^{-24}	1.0	1.000275	0.5033469	9.534708^{-11}
6P T	1.380307^{-23}	3.298413^{-24}	1.986701	1.987247	1.0	4.799266^{-11}
7 h'	1.905994^{-23}	4.554607^{-24}	2.743333	2.744087	1.380848	3.475593^{-11}
8T h	1.985967^{-23}	4.745711^{-24}	2.858439	2.859225	1.438786	3.335635^{-11}
9 λD	1.296566^{-20}	3.098303^{-21}	1866.171	1866.684	939.3316	5.109235^{-14}
10 λD0	1.513796^{-20}	3.617400^{-21}	2178.834	2179.433	1096.709	4.376060^{-14}
11 λV	2.929195^{-20}	6.999670^{-21}	4216.044	4217.203	2122.133	2.261530^{-14}
12 V	3.903477^{-20}	9.327836^{-21}	5618.346	5619.891	2827.977	1.697067^{-14}
13 λP	4.222884^{-20}	1.009110^{-20}	6078.075	6079.747	3059.381	1.568705^{-14}
14H V	1.601929^{-19}	3.828006^{-20}	23056.86	23063.20	11605.60	4.135302^{-15}
15 λR	2.780354^{-15}	6.643996^{-19}	40018.14	40029.15	20143.01	2.382596^{-15}
16 λχ	4.766321^{-15}	1.138971^{-14}	68602.53	68621.39	34530.87	1.389848^{-15}
17 R	2.179347^{-14}	5.207817^{-14}	313677.4	313763.7	157888.6	3.039654^{-16}

#		A	B	C	D	E	F
18	μ	2.779502^{-17}	6.641960^{-18}	4.0005886	4.0016886	2.0136846	2.383327^{-17}
19G	μ	4.802471^{-17}	1.147609^{-17}	6.912285^{6}	6.914186^{6}	3.479278^{6}	1.379386^{-17}
20S	$\triangle$	1.985967^{-15}	4.745711^{-16}	2.858439^{8}	2.859225^{8}	1.438786^{8}	3.335635^{-19}
21F	m_0	8.186184^{-10}	1.956189^{-11}	1.178253^{10}	1.178576^{10}	5.930698^{9}	8.092245^{-11}
22E	M_0	1.491750^{-10}	3.564719^{-11}	2.147103^{13}	2.147693^{13}	1.080738^{13}	4.440731^{-24}
23	M_P	1.503077^{-10}	3.591786^{-11}	2.163406^{13}	2.164001^{13}	1.088944^{13}	4.407267^{-24}
24	M_N	1.505149^{-10}	3.596738^{-11}	2.166388^{13}	2.166984^{13}	1.090445^{13}	4.401200^{-24}
25C	Q	1.000000^{-7}	2.389623^{-8}	1.439318^{16}	1.439714^{16}	7.244765^{15}	6.624461^{-27}
26	G	9.806650^{-5}	2.343419^{-5}	1.411489^{19}	1.411877^{19}	7.104688^{18}	6.755070^{-30}
27K	W	1.0	0.2389623	1.439318^{23}	1.439714^{23}	7.244765^{20}	6.624461^{-34}
28L	C	4.184761	1.0	6.023204^{23}	6.024860^{23}	3.031761^{23}	1.582838^{-34}
29	KM	9.806650	2.343419	1.411489^{24}	1.411877^{24}	7.104688^{23}	6.755070^{-35}
30	H	736.0000	175.8762	1.059338^{26}	1.059630^{26}	5.332147^{25}	9.000626^{-37}
31	BTU	1054.560	252.0000	1.517847^{26}	1.518265^{26}	7.640038^{25}	6.281731^{-37}
32B	E	2997.930	716.3921	4.314976^{26}	4.316162^{26}	2.171930^{26}	2.209678^{-37}
33J	KWH	3.600000^{6}	860264.1	5.181546^{34}	5.182971^{34}	2.608115^{29}	1.840128^{-40}
34A	g	8.987584^{13}	2.147693^{13}	1.293600^{37}	1.293955^{37}	6.511294^{36}	7.370680^{-48}
35D	gm	1.348821^{21}	3.223173^{20}	1.941383^{44}	1.941916^{44}	9.771890^{43}	4.911298^{-55}
36	S_μ	7.08×10^{20}	1.69×10^{26}	1.02×10^{44}	1.02×10^{44}	5.13×10^{43}	9.36×10^{-55}
37	S_R	3.80×10^{26}	9.08×10^{35}	5.47×10^{44}	5.47×10^{44}	2.75×10^{44}	1.74×10^{-60}
38	E_M	5.38×10^{41}	1.29×10^{41}	7.74×10^{64}	7.74×10^{64}	3.90×10^{64}	1.23×10^{-75}
39	S_E	6.30×10^{41}	1.51×10^{41}	9.10×10^{64}	9.10×10^{64}	4.56×10^{64}	1.05×10^{-75}
40	S_M	1.80×10^{47}	4.25×10^{46}	2.56×10^{70}	2.56×10^{70}	1.29×10^{70}	3.72×10^{-81}
41	G_K	8.99×10^{53}	2.15×10^{58}	1.29×10^{82}	1.29×10^{82}	6.51×10^{81}	7.37×10^{-93}
42	U_M	8.99×10^{68}	2.15×10^{68}	1.29×10^{92}	1.29×10^{92}	6.51×10^{91}	7.37×10^{-103}

PHYSICAL CONSTANTS.

	Frequency Waves per second $F = 1/P = vc$ — R	Angstrom wavelength $A = 10^{-8}$ cm. — S	Centimeter wavelength $\gamma = 1/\hat{v}$ — T	Wavenumber in one centimeter $\tilde{v} = 1/\gamma$ — U	Common logarithms Wavenumbers Log 10. $2 \times \gamma 3.21928$ — V	Basic logarithms Wavenumbers Log 2. $10 \times /.30103$ — W
1 ϞϞ	0.1591549	1.883655^{19}	1.883655^{11}	5.308828^{-12}	-12.724998	-37.454744
2R f	1.0	2.997930^{18}	2.997930^{10}	3.335635^{-11}	-11.523178	-34.803248
3 ₁h	4.771354^{9}	$\underline{6.283185^{8}}$	$\underline{6.283185}$	0.1591550	-1.201820	-2.651496
4N Cp	1.048512^{10}	2.859225^{8}	2.859225	0.3497452	-1.543752	-1.515624
5M Cc	1.048800^{10}	2.858439^{8}	2.858439	0.3498413	-1.543871	-1.515227
6P T	2.083652^{10}	1.438786^{8}	1.438786	0.6950302	-1.842004	-0.524852
7 hT	2.877207^{10}	1.041958^{8}	1.041958	0.9597312	-1.982150	-0.059298
8T h	2.997930^{10}	1.000000^{8}	1.0	1.0	0.0	0.0
9 μD	1.957240^{13}	153171.3	1.531713^{-3}	652.8638	2.814823	9.350638
10 μo	2.285161^{13}	131191.2	1.311912^{-3}	762.2462	2.882095	9.574113
11 μN	4.421786^{13}	67799.08	6.779908^{-4}	1474.946	3.168776	10.526447
12 V	5.892520^{13}	50876.88	5.087688^{-4}	1965.530	3.293480	10.940702
13 μp	6.374684^{13}	47028.68	4.702868^{-4}	2126.362	3.327637	11.054171
14H V	2.418203^{14}	$\underline{12397.35}$	$\underline{1.239735^{-4}}$	8066.2425	3.906671	12.977681
15 γR	4.197102^{14}	7142.857	7.142857^{-5}	14000.00	4.146128	13.773140
16 γv	7.195032^{14}	4166.667	4.166667^{-5}	24000.00	4.380211	14.550747
17 R	3.289848^{15}	911.2670	9.112670^{-6}	109737.32	5.040355	16.743695

18 μ	4.195816^{16}	71.45047	7.145047^{-7}	1.395571^{6}	6.145995	20.416553
19G e	7.249603^{16}	41.35302	4.135302^{-7}	2.418203^{6}	6.383493	21.205504
20B A	2.997930^{18}	1.0	1.000000^{-8}	1.000000^{8}	8.000000	26.575425
21F m_0	1.235751^{20}	0.0242600	2.425998^{-10}	4.122014^{9}	9.615110	31.940702
22E M_0	2.251881^{23}	1.331300^{-5}	1.331300^{-13}	7.511454^{12}	12.875724	42.772229
23 M_P	2.268980^{23}	1.321268^{-5}	1.321268^{-13}	7.568488^{12}	12.879009	42.783142
24 M_N	2.272108^{23}	1.319449^{-5}	1.319449^{-13}	7.578922^{12}	12.879608	42.785130
25C Q	1.509557^{26}	1.985967^{-8}	1.985967^{-16}	5.035331^{15}	15.702028	52.161008
26 G	1.480370^{29}	2.025123^{-11}	2.025123^{-19}	4.937972^{18}	18.693549	62.098625
27K W	1.509557^{33}	1.985967^{-15}	1.985967^{-23}	5.035331^{22}	22.702028	75.414505
28L C	6.317135^{33}	4.745237^{-16}	4.745237^{-24}	2.107166^{23}	23.323699	77.479650
29 KM	1.480370^{34}	2.025123^{-16}	2.025123^{-24}	4.937972^{23}	23.693549	78.708265
30 H	1.111034^{36}	2.698325^{-18}	2.698325^{-26}	3.706003^{25}	25.568906	84.938066
31 BTU	1.591918^{36}	1.883219^{-18}	1.883219^{-26}	5.310057^{25}	25.725100	85.456930
32B E	4.525546^{36}	6.624461^{-19}	6.624461^{-27}	1.509557^{26}	26.178850	86.964255
33J KWH	5.434405^{39}	5.516575^{-23}	5.516575^{-30}	1.812719^{29}	29.258331	97.194070
34A g	1.356727^{47}	2.209678^{-29}	2.209678^{-37}	4.525463^{36}	36.655671	121.767503
35D gm	2.036122^{54}	1.472373^{-36}	1.472373^{-44}	6.791758^{43}	43.831983	145.606693
36 S_μ	1.07×10^{54}	2.81×10^{-36}	2.81×10^{-44}	3.57×10^{43}	43.552	144.677
37 S_R	5.74×10^{59}	5.23×10^{-42}	5.23×10^{-50}	1.91×10^{49}	49.281	163.711
38 E_M	8.12×10^{74}	3.69×10^{-57}	3.69×10^{-65}	2.71×10^{64}	64.433	214.040
39 S_E	9.51×10^{74}	3.15×10^{-57}	3.15×10^{-65}	3.17×10^{64}	64.501	214.269
40 S_M	2.69×10^{80}	1.12×10^{-61}	1.12×10^{-70}	8.96×10^{69}	69.952	232.177
41 G_H	1.36×10^{92}	2.21×10^{-74}	2.21×10^{-82}	4.53×10^{81}	81.656	271.254
42 U_M	1.36×10^{102}	2.21×10^{-84}	2.21×10^{-92}	4.53×10^{91}	91.656	304.474

Book Two

The Logic of Theoretical Physics

BY

EIGIL RASMUSSEN

DORRANCE & COMPANY
Philadelphia

CONTENTS

Page

PREFACE

A meaningful theory of atomic physics must be based on an acceptable philosophy of possible truths—an intuitive perception of physical reality as the mind evaluates various possibilities. The observed phenomena are like separate bricks which cannot become a useful edifice until they are blueprinted by a philosophy, cemented by logical associations and proved by mathematics and experiments. Since proof is the subject of my first book, this one deals primarily with the logical and philosophical implications of facts.

The theory outlined on the following pages is based on the "classical" conception of physical reality. It assumes that all phenomena in nature are the logical products of physically real causes, and that the first product of an incomprehensible first cause is a physically real medium with action potentials—a universal ether with the properties of a perfect gas.

I reject the postulates of modern physics because scientific realism anticipates logical continuities of observations into the unknown. I reject its "mind-oriented" postulates and its use of the natural limitations of mathematics for the purpose of limiting our logical explorations of physical phenomena in depth. My theory defines the observed local relativity motions and rejects the theory of general relativity. It defines the fourth dimension as a product of three-dimensional dynamics and rejects the variable time dimension.

In support of my theory, the reader will find numerous logical explanations of problems that are usually ignored by science. The most important of these is my solution of the problem of containment. Gravity and the two kinds of electricity are explained.

Los Angeles, January 1970   Eigil Rasmussen

PROLOGUE

I love to wander along the narrow winding paths of a forest in the twilight. With the coming of darkness, colors fade and shapes become indistinct; the moss on the trees, the broken branches and rotten wood cease to draw attention and divert the mind from the silent symbols of an ever-present will to life and, through them, to the oneness of life in its countless forms.

In the semi-darkness of a fragmentary truth, the mind conjures an illusion of completeness, a purity of colors, a symmetry of shapes, and a host of unrevealed possibilities, as outlines merge imperceptibly with one's desire into an ideal of perfection.

In the light of day, the illusions flee as the imperfections stand out to challenge the eye and mind. The truth-seeker finds his attention drawn to a multitude of small truths, which separately are of little moment, and finds them submerging those basic truths which alone can give the lesser ones a profound meaning.

My preference for the twilight zone in the field of ideas is frustrated by a desire to peer behind the veil of hidden truths, and an awareness of the need for light, for facts and yet more facts, if the scaffolding of my conception is to become the framework for a realistic appraisal of observed phenomena.

As I wander among the trees, my mind's eye sees a mighty world come into being, pass through its appointed cycle, and disappear: birth and death; growth and decay; eternity. An illimitable void; mighty shapeless forces contesting; order out of chaos; a universe of galaxies; a galaxy of stars; a sun with planets among the stars; the earth; a faint stirring of life on its surface; a constant struggle; birth and unfolding; death and destruction; evolution; an integration of life forms; increasingly complex survival potentials; viruses, bacteria, protoplasms, worms, fishes, reptiles, mammals and, finally, man; a climax–disintegration; chaos out of order; a void, with an immense time passing; the end, and then the beginning of a new cycle–eternity.

Los Angeles,   Eigil Rasmussen
March, 1948.

Chapter 1

FUNDAMENTAL POSTULATES

The first cause is beyond understanding, but retroactive reasoning leads to simple causes. Local relativity is accepted, and general relativity and variable time are rejected. Phenomena are all comprehensibly logical. The ether's properties are those of a perfect gas, with conclusions differing from those of classical theory. Variations of density, velocity and direction of motion exist everywhere in space. Long waves with great energy contains, compacts and induces motions of short waves with little energy. The universe is an immense spherical wave in its contracting stages, with the constantly increasing density near its center acting as a container of periodic waves. Contained stationary waves become matter. Stage one-to-two is a transition from potential to maximum convergent contraction, and an increase to maximum matter. We are from two- to six-billion years past Stage two. Matter is disintegrating toward its disappearance at Stage three, perhaps forty- to fifty-billion years from now.

1-1 Introduction.

The first cause of all physical phenomena is beyond our understanding. We do not know whether the ether of space, the appearance of matter and the evolution of life are the creations of a supreme being, or the products of complex physical causal forces. We are not wholly blind, however, because there are observable continuities which make it possible to anticipate events and, by retroactive reasoning, to draw reasonable conclusions regarding their causes. There are facts of physics which make it possible to anticipate some of the limitations and potentialities of its first abstractions.

Theoretical physicists must be not only mathematicians but also logicians and philosophers, because they are constantly dealing with problems in the twilight zone between the known, the unknown, and that which will forever remain beyond our understanding. They advance by discovering physical relations and proportions that can be expressed by figures and checked by experiments. They must be able to give reasons for their concepts that are logically probable and comprehensible in the light of facts, or give acceptable reasons why that is not possible. Because most physicists are good mathematicians, poor logicians and worse philosophers, their reasons for adopting certain practices and preferences are often puerile, even though their results are true and are to be taken into consideration in the development of a rational and comprehensible theory. Theoretical physics is possible because it rests on a broad foundation of mathematical, experimental, observational and logically comprehensible relations and proportions.

My researches started with a rejection of relativity, because I considered its fundamental postulates contrary to reason and beyond proof by experiment and observation. I accept local relativity, as observed by Michelson and others, for reasons defined elsewhere, and reject the general relativity postulated by Einstein. The former can be proved and can be given a rational explanation; the latter is an unprovable abstraction which leads to illogical conclusions. Einstein's relativity of perception is a mind-related postulate, which introduces the supernatural by implication. It has caused physicists to reject the very foundation of observational physics—the principles of logic, causality and mechanics—which served classical science as a restraining influence on mathematical explorations beyond facts. I accept Einstein's theory of the fourth dimension, with qualifications, because it can exist as a deformation—a static stress—of three-dimensional space.

Minkowsky's theory of variable time is rejected because it postulates impossible properties. The irrationality of modern science is evident in the assumed reversibility of time (because mathematical formulas are reversible), and by its indifference to the nature of time. Time is a product of the finite velocity with which force is transmitted through space between separate points. It can, therefore, be defined by abstractions from repetitious phenomena and psychological continuity. Time, however, cannot be a variable dimension because it is nothing, by itself.

Since all our observations and experiments are in three dimensions and ordinary time, the sanest and safest approach to the problems of physics is to assume, a priori, that all phenomena in nature are physically real within that frame. We must not go beyond its limitations until the mechanical implications of physical reality have been explored and found wanting. We must investigate all the logical and mathematical possibilities of physical reality before we turn to extra-physical concepts and pure mathematics for proof. And we must treat the abandonment of a physical reality in three dimensions as a last resort, because the purpose of all science is comprehension, and comprehension is rooted in experience.

It is my contention that an acceptable theory of atomic physics must be based on the assumption that all phenomena in nature are physically real, and that they have comprehensible origins because they act logically within the principles of simple mechanics. These root causes are discovered by reducing the phenomena to their elements—the simplest properties which they have in common. The logical implications of these properties are explored as dynamic possibilities within the physical framework. They are then reintegrated into a recreation of known physical phenomena through logical deductions and mathematical proportions.

My theory is based on the following postulates:

A. Our physical world is a functionally integrated whole, with its phenomena interacting throughout the immensities of space within the principles of simple mechanics and known laws of physics. It is, therefore, potentially comprehensible in all parts and functions.

B. In theory, anything short of the whole is incomplete, because the implication of each factor in a phenomenon, however simple, goes beyond its momentary limits to embrace, by association and conversion, the whole field of fundamental physical knowledge.

C. Understanding is essential to science. In physics it anticipates the interactions of factors according to the classical definition of logic, causality and mechanics. And it assumes, *a priori*, the continuity of observed and accepted physical laws, structures and relations where their presence cannot be ascertained.

D. Prudent investigators limit their explorations in physics to provable relations and proportions, to phenomena that appear true in the light of observations, experiments and mathematics, or become acceptable as logical deductions from such facts.

E. The implications of known phenomena and accepted postulates must be explored to their limits, because their unexplored logical implications are not invalidated by neglect or indifference. They either support or reject a theory, or prove the investigator an incompetent logician.

F. All research in physics is based on the assumption that causes are simpler than their products. It is, therefore, assumed that all physical phenomena converge on a common first cause—an ether—whose nature is limited by that convergence to the simplest properties in the light of facts.

G. Physical realities imply a physically real first cause. However, it seems improbable there can be two or more first causes, or that the single first cause can have complex properties. It is assumed that the ether's properties are the simplest possible, and that the first structures abstracted from it produced the world we know, and are now sustaining it, by their ability to act, interact and differentiate.

H. The existence of structures with functional continuities in time implies tendencies to integrate and preserve, and an ability to act and react in their support. We postulate a continuous action, transmitted through space as an interaction between the functional forces of physical phenomena.

I. The simplest kind of force is that produced by a wave. It is assumed the ether's properties are limited to those essential to the periodic pulsations and transmission of waves. The classical theory of the ether is, therefore, accepted provisionally as the first definable cause of natural phenomena: the product of an unknown and incomprehensible first cause.

J. The postulate of ultimate simplicity makes the ether the only physical reality in space, with its potentialities for action appearing as periodic waves. All known physical phenomena, such as masses, quantum states, electricity and magnetism, have come into being as different dynamic possibilities of ether waves.

K. First conclusions derived from apparently valid postulates should be accepted as working hypotheses until contrary proof is presented.

Postulate (P): The ether has the properties of a perfect gas. Conclusion (C): Unchanging static stresses are impossible. P: Waves are locally reversing dynamic deviations from the mean ether. C: Density differences and ether motions are transition states of periodic waves. P: Waves disperse. C: Matter and photon waves are contained. P: The area of a wave's increasing density acts as a containing force on shorter waves. C: All waves are contained by an immensely long wave in its contracting stages. P: Momenta are transmitted through the ether. C: Momenta cannot pass through each other without interaction. P: Everything is ether. C: Momenta can pass through matter as easily as through empty space. P: Momenta are directed forces; energy is periodically reversing momenta. C: Wave momenta are contained by the contracting ether; energies are self-contained. They can disperse by induction, but not by expansion.

1-2 The Ether.

My theory of the ether is the classical theory which assumes that its properties are those of a perfect gas. This assumption leads to the conclusion that it is composed of moving and constantly colliding particles of infinitesimal size in comparison with the configurations of forces they bring into being. It is assumed that they have mass-momenta because they make their presence known by their ability to transmit forces and momenta through space. It is obviously impossible however, to know their nature and discover their origin beyond the implications of observable phenomena. We do not know if there is such a thing as a fine and gross ether with phenomenal implications, but it appears highly improbable to me. My theory assumes that the ether is the same everywhere throughout infinite space.

The ether was originally conceived as a medium for the transmission of waves. Obviously, the acceptance of electromagnetic waves caused science to accept that which made wave motions possible—the ether of space. Einstein admitted its existence, but argued that motions must be relative because no experiment has ever shown a physical motion through the presumably stationary ether. It must have properties, therefore, which are peculiar and self-contradictory when analyzed in terms of the simple ether postulated by classical science.

The ether's properties and its distribution as a universal medium throughout the immensities of space lead to the conclusion that it is stationary, while experiments appear to show that it is moving with matter. Since physical bodies can move through the ether without observable loss of energy, it is argued that the ether must be extremely tenuous. However, this is contradicted by the observation that the transverse wave motions of photons can exist only in a medium with the properties of a rigid solid. Einstein argued that we must not let these contradictions stand in the way of scientific progress, and physicists accepted his relativity theory as a more realistic approach to the resolution of their problems.

It is my contention that most scientists cannot perceive the problems of physics as a whole, but frequently draw wrong conclusions by ignoring significant aspects of those they attempt to solve. In bringing out the contradictions above, they postulate a difference between particles and waves, even though it is logically improbable that nature permits the existence of both. It is the rule of theoretical physics that its fundamental phenomena must be the simplest possible, and that we must not assume the existence of two types of units if one will serve the purpose of both. Since ether waves are the simplest conceivable form of action in nature, it is assumed that all fundamental particles and phenomena are composed of waves, and that their properties, therefore, can be reduced to the action potentials of waves. That this is so has been proved by the conversion of matter into the energy of free waves, by interaction conversions, and by many other phenomena.

Returning to the subject of ether motion, it will be noticed that if everything in space is a form of ether waves, a mass does not move through the ether but is transmitted through it. That means it can pass through the ether without loss of energy.

A concentration of matter waves in the fundamental particles imply their containment in some way, because it is common knowledge that uncontained waves disperse. The only form that such containing forces can take within the framework of my theory is as a continuous contraction of the ether, with wave expansions producing local containing reactions by space. This theory not only explains the transverse nature of light waves, but also the concentration of such waves in free photons, the inverse relationship between wavelength and energy, and many other phenomena.

Although the center of a light photon moves through the ether with an immense velocity, it is obviously stationary relative to its configuration space, as defined by the forces producing and supporting that motion. In this same sense, a moving mass is always stationary relative to its configuration space, even though it is moving relative to the ether. Assuming that the configuration space accompanying the earth's motion through the ether acts with equal force on all waves and electromagnetic fields on its surface, the stationary state thus produced cannot be distinguished from an earth which is stationary in the ether. This type of relativity is, however, a local phenomenon with a descending gradient of power with distance; while Einstein's general theory of relativity is presumed valid for any distance, however great. His theory, therefore, leads to assumptions which are contrary to experience and common sense.

We do not know what the ether is beyond its observable effects, and we do not know how far it extends into space, short of infinity. Reason tells us that its minimum area must be immensely greater than the size of our universe, which appears immense by our measures. Astronomers postulate an age of not less than six billion years, and we must assume the physical extension of the universe into space in all directions is far greater than that.

Even though my ether theory is the same as that of classical science, our conceptions of its potentialities are not the same. To classical scientists the ether is a superficial addition to the particle theory of matter, giving waves something to wave in; in contrast to my theory where it is everything, because it defines those particles in terms of waves. My theory of a contracting ether gives us a wave-containing force whose interactions with waves take the form of a new dimension in physics. Like the proverbial bird "Phoenix" which, after it had been consumed by flames, was resurrected from its ashes, my contraction theory resurrects the classical ether by exploring implications ignored by classical science.

1-3 Variations.

A variation in the ether is any convertible difference in its density, momentum and directions of motion, defined by mathematical gradients of powers in space and time. These three types of action and potential action are the only dynamic possibilities of an ether with the properties of a perfect gas in a world in which it is the only physical reality. The ether is in constant change, with the three states resolving into each other according to the laws of dynamics.

My assumption that all physical phenomena are patterns of ether waves is based on their reductions to a common first cause, and my belief that this cause must be the simplest possible. It leads to the conclusion that the fundamental particles of matter are the products of contained waves because, as indivisible particles, they cannot evolve the specific masses, charges and other properties associated with electrons, positrons, protons and neutrons. It is argued that their observed interactions in the form of attractions, repulsions and a transference of energy cannot occur unless they have a common nature at the point of interaction. Also, the resolution of fundamental particles, or a part of their masses, into free photon waves implies a common nature as waves, because ether waves are the simplest form of action in nature.

Reason tells us that static stresses in an ether with the properties of a perfect gas are physically impossible. Waves are continually converting the potential states of high and low densities into divergent and convergent ether motions; the momenta of opposite motions, in turn, resolve into reversals of the potential states where they separate or converge. This postulated functional equality of opposites for periodic waves must be qualified by noting that momenta are directional increases of the velocities of local ether particles. The energy of local periodic waves can, therefore, be described as a slight increase of the ether's temperature at that point. It causes a corresponding reduction of the ether's density and a tendency to equalize it by a dispersal of the waves. It accentuates the containing forces produced by the contracting ether.

Because the ether is the same in matter as in empty space, a momentum can pass through both with equal ease. However, there are functional interferences in matter, related to containment, which may inhibit or prevent its passage. The action potentials of momenta can be defined by these postulates: "All momenta move from their origins to infinity in space with unchanging directions and powers," and "Because momenta are ether motions, two momenta cannot occupy the same space at the same time. Opposite equal momenta resolve into momentary potential states at the point of interaction, and then into a reversal of their directions of motion." Note that the first postulate assumes a transmission, and the second a reflection during an interaction. Since both are true as abstract principles of continuity, we must use both interpretations when evaluating the interrelations between phenomena. In actual practice the continuity of a momentum is submerged by complex interactions and containing forces.

The ether transmits momenta with twice the speed with which it transmits the periodic pulsations of moving (free photon) waves. In an area of increasing density, momenta are reflected back upon their origin by local contractions and converted into contained periodic wave patterns. Interactions between waves cause them to separate into center-acting stationary patterns and patterns moving with the speed of light. These two types of wave patterns can then unite and produce all the observed intermediate velocities of matter. Center-acting stationary patterns can take the form of spherical periodic pulsations, or patterns in which two half-waves revolve and change their plane of motion, thus producing a statistical sphericity in minimum time. These are the wave patterns of electrons and positrons, respectively.

Reason tells us that it must be almost infinitely improbable than an ether, apparently extending to infinity in all directions, can have the same density and motion everywhere, with the exception of light waves, as postulated by the classical ether theory. On the contrary, it seems highly probable that differences of density and motions are present everywhere in space, and that they resolve into a multitude of wavelengths with periodicities ranging from countless billions of years to infinitesimal fractions of a second. The interactions of uncontained waves with the ether to overcome its local opposition to change produce single waves whose momenta are proportional to wavelengths. (Note that the energy of a contained wave pattern is inversely related to wavelength.) The momenta of high-energy long-wavelength waves act upon low-energy waves with a deflective acceleration where their momenta overlap, and as a containing force in areas of increasing density. These interactions cause low energy waves to cluster and resolve into stationary and moving patterns, or disintegrate such patterns into dispersing waves.

My theory postulates the presence of variations everywhere in the ether. For the purpose of analysis we will assume that the longest waves in space are in a state of chaos—that they are single waves without specific shapes and wavelengths, and that they are constantly changing in response to casual interactions. Low-energy waves in their areas of convergent momenta and increasing densities are contained and are made to cluster and integrate into stationary and moving wave patterns.

We can now postulate three stages in the evolution of our universe. The first of these is the PRIMITIVE FIELD composed of casual waves of immense length and periods. The second is the SUPER-UNIVERSE composed of integrated wave patterns in areas of increasing densities. The third is OUR UNIVERSE. It is assumed to be the central wave of a spherical wave pattern in the super-universe.

1-4 The Universe.

For reasons which will be discussed elsewhere in this section, I believe our universe is the central wave of a spherically pulsating wave pattern, with matter evolving in the central area of that wave from variations which happen to be present during its contracting stages. The potential quantity of matter in an area depends upon the ether's local rate of contraction, and its actual quantity upon the energy of local variations. Concentrations of energy are, in turn, determined by local rates of contraction and a tendency of waves to cluster and integrate into matter with time.

The first condition for the evolution of matter in space is, therefore, that waves must be present in areas of increasing density, and that the increase must be of long duration in time. Since wavelengths and wavetimes are functionally proportional, it follows that the duration of our universe in years must be associated with an area of increasing density of roughly the same size in light years. We know from observation that both are immense and must be counted by the billions of years and light years.

We have no way of defining the density of the ether by experiment or observation. It cannot be defined from the motions of matter because matter does not move through the ether, but is transmitted through it as locally contained wave patterns. It cannot be defined by noting the behavior of transverse waves, because contained motions produce transverse waves at any density. With no acceptable criterion of the ether's permissible density, we cannot set a time limit to its increase. An increase through billions of years is mathematically acceptable if the size of our universe is correspondingly large.

Mathematically, a uniform contraction of the ether as a whole can be produced by a constant reduction of its size without a change of shape. This postulate is highly improbable because it does not agree with the apparent size and age of our universe, as observed and evaluated by astronomers, and because it postulates an improbable continuity of contraction in space and time.

A more satisfactory solution is obtained by postulating a spherically contracting wave of such immense size that the increasing densities at its center do not deviate perceptibly from a uniform rate in all directions for masses with energies less than that of a star or galaxy, even though the wave as a whole transits from decreasing densities along its radius to a maximum increase at its center. Because the theoretical periodicity of this wave produces progressive dynamic changes in space and time during its contraction, we anticipate the appearance of physical motions by the galaxies in response. They integrate and converge, while the rate of increase is increasing to a maximum during the first-quarter wave period, and disintegrate and diverge during the second quarter as the increase is accompanied by a descending rate which becomes zero at maximum density at the end of the half-cycle. No matter can exist during its third- and fourth-quarter divergent decreasing density cycles.

My belief that our universe is an electron in the super-universe is based on the following propositions. Electrons have the spherical pulsation patterns needed to produce the expected uniform increase of density at their centers. Because their wave patterns abstract containing forces from the local increase of density in the super-universe and transfer them to their centers, the contracting forces in that area are always immensely greater than the intrusive forces tending to destroy their spherical shapes. The rate at which the super-universe is contracting locally must be infinitesimal compared with that of our universe, and the energies of the waves intruding casually into our universe from the super-universe must also be infinitesimal, in comparison with the forces acting upon them to contain and convert them into matter in the central area of our universe. The tendency of these intrusions to expand and disperse produces marginal deformations of our universe's natural dynamic progression, and the universe reacts with containing forces which reduce their dispersals and its deformation to a minimum.

The dynamic progression of our universe's spherical pulsation pattern can be defined by four stages. Stage one is the potential momentum of a low-density center which transits into a high-density sphere at half-wave distance, and an alternation of low and high densities beyond. They are periodic waves, supported by the central wave and pulsating in consonance with it. The resolutions of these potential states into ether motions bring us to Stage two: a maximum convergent momentum in the central area and a consequent maximum increase of density for that area. This stage should also produce a potential maximum of matter in our universe, with a probable delay in its appearance, because integration-evolution acts through time in partial independence of its initiating cause. A decreasing rate of increasing density between Stages two and three produces a corresponding reduction of matter through its resolutions into radiant energy. At Stage three all matter will have been disintegrated into free energy. The high-density center at Stage three resolves into a divergent momentum at Stage four, and a reversal of densities as Stage one is repeated. A new cycle of convergent motion will then bring a new universe into being. At the present moment we are probably from two to six billion years past Stage two.

The age of our universe has been estimated from various phenomena—from the expansion of our universe; the disintegration of stars by radiation; the disintegration of galaxies at the edge of our universe; the organization of double stars and star clusters; the evolution and organization of the galaxies and the solar system; the age of the earth from the evolution of life to its present forms and from the age of its oldest rocks. These last estimates are obviously minimum ages, since the universe is probably not less than ten times older than the earth. We have reasons to believe the earth is not less than two billion years old, and may be as old as six billion years. The age of the universe has been estimated as about 87.6 billion years, but it can well be anything between 50 and 1000 billion years old. The size of the visible universe, being its area of increasing density, is obviously much smaller, but I do not believe that the two-to-six billion light years radius suggested by some is large enough.

The assumption that our universe is the central area of a spherical pulsation pattern in its contracting stages—an electron in the super-universe—leads to the following conclusions: A universe of matter comes into being and then disappears during the contracting stages of each wave period. The periodic convergence of its spherical wave on its point-center produces a reaction from that center which tends to create a perfect spherical shape and an ideal dynamic progression in space and time. The super-universe is filled with countless waves interacting and overlapping everywhere. Those present in our universe at the time of its contraction tend to deform its ideal shape and its natural dynamic progression, and the universe reacts with containing forces which first convert their momenta into periodic energy waves, and then cause these waves to integrate into matter waves. It will be noticed that all deviations from the primary field's natural dynamic progression are local variations which resolve into periodic pulsations and physical motions.

We are dealing here with two distinctly different phenomena whose interactions cannot be separated in practice: a contracting ether whose dynamic progression appears locally as a continuous and unchangeable advance in space and time, and local deviations from this continuity which resolve into periodic waves and physical motions. We define the powers, periods, motions and shapes of these waves by idealizing their configuration field—the contracting ether. However, the tendency of waves to expand and disperse produces local containing reactions by the contracting ether, thus causing them to evolve specific shapes and quantum states in confinement. These shapes and states become the fundamental particles of matter, with the center of each particle expanding its wave momenta along a steep gradient against the local contractions of the ether until the particle is, in theory, abstracting containing forces from the universe as a whole.

We can now outline the evolution of galaxies of matter from Stage one to the present. At Stage one we find numerous, casually moving momenta and momenta related to external wave patterns, all with wavelengths too long to be observable within the universe's natural pulsation time. Their momenta, relative to those of the contracting ether, are infinitesimal, even though they are immense to us. As the universe advances toward Stage two, the ascending increase of densities in its central area contains these momenta and causes them to transit into periodic waves with constantly decreasing wavelengths. There is a corresponding compacting of the waves into galaxies of casually moving waves. The compacting pressure of overlaying waves is transmitted to the galactic centers as concentrations which tend to reduce casual intrusions by local escapes into structures in those areas. The electrons and protons which came into being at the centers of the galaxies at that time united into immense clouds of hydrogen gases during the first periods of our universe's evolution. The gravitational attractions of local concentrations caused these clouds to separate into stars and star clusters. The heat and compacting pressures at the centers of these stars caused the formation of complex nucleas from atoms stripped of their electrons in those areas, and the elements and their isotopes came into being and are still being created.

Just as the integration of casually moving waves into structure is greatest at the centers of the stars, because it is here the availability of energy and the tendency to escape into structure is greatest, so also the tendency to disintegrate those structures which are functionally unstable is greatest in those areas. It is my belief that the evolution and disintegration of matter occur simultaneously at the centers of the stars, and that the dominance of growth or disintegration in particular stars is the product of a bias based on its natural stability at its center and the natural progression of the contracting ether. The dissolution of matter when the forces containing it are decreasing is an imperative, but its momentary form is a local disintegration of its weakest structures, such as radioactive atoms.

Chapter 2

CONTAINED WAVE REACTIONS

Momenta are ether motions, transmitted with twice the speed of light. All physical phenomena are momenta and potential momenta. Energy is stationary, periodically inverting wave momenta, and running waves with stationary transverse states. All waves and their expansion momenta are contained by local contractions of the ether, and the wave momenta react with a fourth-dimensional displacement of the contracting ether's natural dynamic progression. Any point in an area of increasing density is a center of local contraction. Its rate and force gradient is defined. Spherically contained waves evolve center-acting, center-supported properties. Converging field reactions define their wavelengths. Stationary patterns are contained by permanent static stress fields. The contracting ether can therefore interact with countless point centers. Time cannot be a variable dimension. Contained waves initiate, and converging field forces react. These forces have no observable existence until activated. A fundamental unit of length and time is anticipated and defined. Wave and force gradients are defined. Their relations to the natural unit of length and time define quantum states. New length units redefine gradients.

2-1 Force, Momentum and Energy.

All physical phenomena in space are either momenta or potential momenta. A momentum is a directed motion of the ether transmitted through it with twice the velocity of light. A force is the blocking of one momentum by another. Energy is a stationary pattern of periodically inverting momenta, alternating with potential momentum states.

The only way in which an ether with the properties of a perfect gas can manifest its presence is through the momenta of transmitted ether motions, and through the appearance of potential momenta when opposite moving momenta block each other's motions. This potential appears as high-ether density momentum equivalents which resolve at once into a continuation of the original momenta; a reaction which can also be interpreted as the mutual reflection of opposite equal momenta.

A momentum is always a transmission in the direction of the ether's motion, because the increasing density of the contracting ether can then contain it as a moving wave pattern. Note than an expanding, decreasing density attracts and accentuates the motion of a contracting ether, thus causing it to converge on the origin of a negative momentum and resolve into an increase of density and then into the periodic waves of a stationary energy pattern. The difference between these two types of reactions gives us a clue to the origin of the two kinds of electrostatic charge.

Energy is contained and self-contained momenta. It is a stationary wave pattern of periodically inverting momentum and potential momentum states, with the latter defined as alternating high and low densities. The alternations of opposite motions and densities and their periodic inversions are such that the mean of each wave period, and the areal mean of each wave, is the same as the mean density of the ether and the mean stationary state of local configuration space—the configuration of directional forces accompanying the stationary states of moving bodies. Energy waves can, therefore, move through the ether without an interaction with its contraction beyond that produced by each wave period, and a momentum can pass as easily through the energy waves of matter as through empty space, provided such interactions are reducible to a statistical zero state.

The periodic waves of a contained wave pattern are stationary in their own local configuration spaces, but are moving relative to other patterns when they combine with a directional momentum. The waves transmit this momentum through the (otherwise impenetrable) contracting ether and are displaced by the momentum in its direction of motion. While the waves of functionally stationary patterns are displaced by their momenta as a whole, the waves of velocity patterns and free photons are transmitted by induction-expansion in the direction of their momenta (like the transverse pulsations and directional motions of sea waves). We can define the difference by stating that the first (mass-related) kind of waves are always stationary and the second kind are always moving with the speed of light, as defined by their local configuration spaces. The waves of a moving mass combined both types of wave motions in a proportion defined by its velocity.

A free photon moves through a configuration space with the speed of light, because it combines the stationary energy of periodic waves with a momentum transmitted with twice that speed in equal proportion. We can also define a free photon's velocity by stating that one half of its momentum, being transverse and periodically potential; is in a potential state, and that its photon's velocity is therefore halved. Note that all photons are stationary in their own configuration spaces.

The momentum of a free photon is a directional ether motion which cannot pass through the contracting ether without interaction. By integrating the two kinds of motion, we obtain a recurve of the contracting ether, with the combined momentum passing through the photon's center and resolving into a potential state at its apex of motion. A free momentum cannot pass through the contracting ether by itself, because its theoretically infinite time relations cause its containing forces to build up toward infinite powers; however, it can be transmitted through the contracting ether by periodic waves (like sound waves carried by a radio transmitter). Periodic waves can expand through the contracting ether by induction, but they cannot move and cannot evolve a gradient to space without an implementing momentum and a containing, converging field reaction. The tendency of all waves to expand and disperse appears as a pattern's expansion momentum proportional to its photon's energy, with the converging field's reaction producing its natural wavelength.

A momentum expanding in all directions from a stationary point-center is associated with a reduction of the ether's density proportional to the local rate of expansion. It can be defined for a spherical pulsation pattern as an expansion momentum which is slightly greater than that converging on its center, because a part of its momentum continues outward in support of the pattern's expansion as a whole. The less-than-mean ether density at its center, increasing toward its natural value with distance, acts as a containing force which converts the two momenta to equality, thus producing a stable pattern which does not expand as anticipated by theory. This reduction of density at a stationary wave pattern's center can also be defined as a temperature effect. The energy of local periodic waves increases the velocity of local ether particles in the direction of their motions, and the ether expands and reduces its local densities in proportion. This temperature effect appears as a static stress field which increases the forces containing the rest-mass energies of fundamental particles greatly. However, it does not appear with the waves of free photons.

The momentum of a moving mass is defined as mass times velocity ($F = mV$), or force multiplied by time ($F = FT$). Its energy is one half of its mass times its velocity squared ($E = \frac{1}{2}mV^2$). The potential states of energy gives us its half-mass value, while the increase of stationary energy waves to carry the momentum of its velocity pattern gives us an increase of energy with an increase of velocity equal to momentum squared.

My postulate, that all physical phenomena originated as momenta and potential momenta in the ether, is based on my ether theory and the reduction of phenomena to their first causes. It is argued that all actions and their consequent changes are initiated and brought to their observed conclusions by combinations of forces.

We know that objects of apparent permanence and stability are composed of molecules and atoms in rapid motion. Atoms are composed of electrons circling positive nuclei of protons and neutrons, also moving. The permanence of these structures is caused by attractions which keep them from separating, and repelling forces which keep them from merging. In all these cases we are dealing with force of some kind. Indeed, it is inconceivable that anything can occur without an implementing force. According to Einstein, the rest mass energy of any physical body is equal to its mass in grams times the speed of light squared ($E = mc^2$). When this energy is released it appears as free photons of waves.

Since a wave motion is the simplest form of action in the ether, the conversion of matter into waves must mean that the fundamental particles of matter are all composed of waves, contained by the contracting ether.

2-2 Contracting Ether Momenta.

If all matter is composed of waves, it is evident that such waves will disperse by expansion and induction if they are not contained by a counter-force. It is theoretically possible for waves to repel each other by interference, but it is inconceivable that they can produce the attractions observed in atoms and molecules. Their functional relations to the energies of matter show that attractions must originate in space as a reaction to those energies, and that the containing forces must be equivalent to those of their causes. We bring these observations into accord with the theories of modern physics by noting that the functional deformation of the ether's natural dynamic progression by matter can be interpreted as the fourth dimension.

The limited possibilities of a universal ether with the properties of a perfect gas limit the dynamic possibilities of containment to the local convergent forces associated with a constantly increasing density of the ether. For the purpose of this analysis, it is assumed that its local increase is uniform and continuous in space and time, and that its rate of change appears the same for immense distances into space, due to the size of the universe.

The physical ether motions causing the increasing ether densities are negligible in comparison with the forces they bring into being. Although we are dealing with the products of ether motions, these motions are too small to produce observable physical motions by themselves, whereas the forces abstracted from them by waves blocking their natural dynamic progression can accelerate matter to great velocities. The term "ether motion" is used because it is easy to visualize, but the reader must keep in mind that we are dealing with a configuration space in which transmitted forces and phenomena interact to produce observable physical motions from the energies and momenta abstracted from infinitesimal ether motions.

A comparison with the compression of a gas leads to the conclusion that increasing ether density is accompanied by an increase of the speed of light, as its contraction momenta transit into an increase of its base velocity. Because the sizes of quantum states and, therefore, of atoms and molecules, are determined by the speed of light, there is a constant swelling of matter proportional to that increase which should make the speed of light unchanged with time. Our ignorance of the ether's density makes us equally ignorant of the rate at which the speed of light is increasing. The swelling of matter acting against a contracting ether should produce an apparent increase in its rate of contraction.

A uniform increase of the ether's density over large areas means that any casually selected point is a local center of convergent ether momenta. The momentum in any direction obviously increases in direct proportion to distance, and the forces passing through the surface of a sphere, being proportional to its cubic content, increase as the cube of the distance. This ratio defines the potential increase of its containing forces with distance from the center of an expanding wave pattern. Since the expansion momentum of an expanding wave pattern decreases with distance, its expansion will be contained at the distance where their opposite momenta are equal and reflect each other back upon their origins. This distance defines the photon radii of wave patterns.

A converging field momentum not only increases with distance from zero power at a point, it also increases in direct proportion to the time through which it reacts to the momentum of a single wave expanding from that point. This reaction time can be reduced by reducing its wavelength through subdivision. A single wave photon can increase its energy and wavelength up to the point where converging field reactions cause it to reduce wavelength by resolving into a pattern of waves. The maximum wavelength of a free photon's plane wave defines the natural unit of length, a unit which can be confirmed by various phenomena. Since its energy can be defined by relating it to Planck's quantum, it can be used to obtain the rate at which the converging field forces pass through the surface of any sphere per unit time.

Observation shows that the natural unit of length is equal to 1.0419584 centimeter, and that a free photon with this wavelength has an energy, in new international units, of 6.101685×10^{-27} erg emu, and 1.755581×10^{-16} erg esu per second. The wavelength and photon radius of a spherical wave with this energy is one fourth of that above. Four cubed gives us 64 as the contraction momentum passing through the surface of a sphere, one natural unit in radius, relative to that acting on a plane wave. The latter's energy per second times this figure gives us 1.123572×10^{-14} dynes per second. A year of 3.1558×10^{7} seconds gives us 3.545768×10^{-7} dynes per sidereal year. The reciprocal of this figure shows that it takes 2.82 million years for one dyne of force to pass through the surface of a sphere, one natural unit in radius. The cube root of the reciprocal of dynes per second, (8.9×10^{13}), is 44648. A sphere of this radius in natural lengths, or 446.48 natural meters, will have one dyne of force passing through its surface each second.

Although this infinitesimal force makes my postulate, that the ether has been contracting at a rate which makes it possible for billions of years, seem more plausible, it poses another, equally incredible. We wonder how it is possible to abstract from a contraction of the ether those immense force containing the energies of matter in stars and galaxies. My answer is that each fundamental particle of matter surrounds itself with a static stress field abstracted from the containing forces of the universe as a whole. After each abstraction the contracting ether resumes its original flow pattern through the static fields. The static stress fields remain because they are displacements of the universe's natural dynamic progression in time, and a deformation of its shape in space. However, neither of these displacements can be observed locally. The subject will be discussed in detail in the next section.

2-3 Contained Waves.

Waves have properties and tendencies which become the properties and tendencies of matter when they are contained by the contracting ether. It is in the nature of waves to disperse by expansion, induction and motion, and thus to fill all available space in their medium. In doing so they tend to adopt the shape of their container, and/or to move in such a way as to produce a statistical distribution which leaves no part of a container of limited size untouched. When periodic waves with different wavelengths are contained in common, they tend to reduce casual interferences by an integration of motions and wavelengths through an exchange of energy. The expansion of waves appears as a tendency to increase wavelengths through an absorption of energy, and to resolve energy in excess of a natural periodicity into running waves. Expansion by induction appears as a tendency of stationary waves to reduce their gradients by enlarging their active areas without changing the location of loops and nodes.

The converging field forces containing stationary patterns of periodic waves are zero at their center and increase with equal power in all directions; they appear, therefore, as a spherical barrier of increasing power with distance. The natural shape of such a wave pattern is a sphere with natural gradients to space. It may appear as spherical pulsations or as plane waves with a statistical spherical distribution in time. These are the wave structures of electrons and positrons, respectively.

Converging field momenta cannot initiate an action, but react with an equalizing power to all actions initiated by waves. When the energy of a wave pattern is increased, its photon increases in size until the converging field reaction to its expansion pressure is equal to the increase. The increased converging field force is transmitted through the pattern to its center as a compacting pressure which reduces its wavelength. A pattern's natural wavelength is, therefore, inversely proportional to its energy. This is a well-known fact of physics which science accepts without knowing its cause, because wavelengths are normally expected to increase with an increase of energy, as they do in natural phenomena dealing with single waves.

The waves of a pattern contained by the contracting ether are partly self-contained. A wave is self-contained when the positive and negative densities and motions of its periodic pulsations are equal in space and time. If we take two subsequent waves of a pattern with an energy gradient descending toward zero with distance, it is evident that the farthest wave will have the least energy. The difference in energy between the two waves is contained by the reaction momentum of the contracting ether, or rather by the static stress field equivalent to that momentum, while their equal energies are self-contained. Since self-contained energies cannot produce a charge potential, the electrostatic charge of an electron or positron is equal to the square root of its effective mass, as defined by its radius wavelength.

Another type of self-containment takes the form of a local reduction of ether density proportional to the concentration of energy in the fundamental particles of matter. Since we are dealing here with the forces which also inhibit the converging field's natural dynamic progression, there is no way to distinguish between them. It is argued that an expansion momentum which can inhibit a contracting ether's natural dynamic progression will produce the displacement equivalent of contraction in an ether of unchanging density. However, there is a vital difference between them, because a contracting ether causes the concentrations of energy and the quantum states of matter, whereas energy acting as the cause of containment will disperse in response to the natural tendencies of waves because there is no functional incentive to concentrate.

The theory of displacement is based on the assumption that the energy of periodic wave motions represents an increase of the ether's local temperature above that defined by its mean particle motions at that moment. There is, therefore, a directional reduction of the ether's density, proportional to the local concentrations of energy. It can be compared with the expansion of a gas when its local temperature is raised, due to the increased velocities of its molecules.

The reduction of ether density at the wave center of a fundamental particle is a form of self-containment which follows it everywhere. It takes the form of a static stress field which acts in conjunction with the contracting ether to contain the waves of matter under all conditions. It cannot prevent the dissolution of matter waves in the absence of a contracting ether, but it does extend the time through which it occurs, thus acting as a stabilizing force by giving the contracting ether time to re-establish its dominance. I believe it increases the containing forces, because it interacts with both contained and self-contained waves.

We can now outline the interaction between an evolving wave pattern and the contracting ether. The pattern exerts an expansion pressure which can also be defined as a momentum transmitted through its wave pattern from its center to an interaction with the contracting ether momentum. Since an interaction between opposite, equal momenta can be treated as a mutual reflection and as a transmission, the effects of both will be noted. A mutual blocking reflection returns the wave momentum to its center through the pattern, while the convergent momentum is reflected back upon its origin as an expanding displacement of the universe's dynamic progression in space and time. Being a pure momentum, it is transmitted with twice the speed of light. When the interaction is treated as a continuation of the original motions, we find the wave pattern extending its periodic motions into space toward infinity, while the converging field forces are transmitted to the wave center by its pattern, and then expand from the center to a resolution into the increasing densities of the ether around it.

The contained expansion pressure of a wave pattern is transferred to the contracting ether as a displacement of its natural dynamic progression in space and time. This displacement expands through the whole universe as a theoretical motion of it as a whole. It remains a permanent static stress field in space, proportional to the wave energy producing it. If we define time by the natural dynamic progression of the universe, the retardation of this advance by matter becomes a local displacement of advancing time, with the static stresses becoming a permanent force containing the energies of matter, as the converging field resumes its natural advance as if the stress fields were not there. It can, therefore, interact with the countless particles of matter in an area and resolve into static stresses without losing its ability to ineract with new centers. It is possible for an immense number of fundamental particles with great energy potentials to exist in a small area, because each particle is contained by a static stress field acting in conjunction with the converging field without being dependent on it. However, the converging field forces act constantly to define their quantum states by replenishing lost energies.

2-4 Is Time Variable?

Time is nothing by itself and cannot, therefore, be a variable dimension, as postulated by modern science. Theory defines it as the transmission interval between two separate points in a space which cannot transmit a force with infinite velocity. For its practical definition we rely on the intervals of experimentally verifiable periodic phenomena, such as periodic wave motions, the earth's rotation period, the time it takes a light wave to move a specific distance and return, and the periodic motions of clock pendulums.

We can also use the natural dynamic progression of the universe as time-keeper, with the increasing density of the ether as a local measure of its advance. Since the expansion pressures of matter waves produce local momentary reductions of that continuity, there are matter-related displacements of local times, proportional to the static stress fields produced by matter.

2-5 Waves Initiate and Convergence Reacts.

The converging field cannot initiate an action, but reacts to actions initiated by the expansion pressures of waves supported by a center. Its reactions cannot exceed its initiating cause, but its containing momenta become equal to the expansion momenta of that cause under all conditions, because its powers increase with distance and time toward infinity, whereas those of a wave pattern are finite and decrease with distance. It will appear, on first sight, that an attraction cannot come into being under a condition of complete equality, but further analyses show that attraction is the product of different tendencies. Wave repulsions are specific and avoidable, whereas the reactions by space are continuous in time and distributed in space and, therefore, cannot be avoided.

The difference can be compared with a continuous stream of air being blown through a whistle, with its hollow center acting as the organizer of the sound waves emanating from it.

The center of a wave pattern acts in conjunction with the containing forces of the contracting ether as the organizer of its periodic waves. The contracting ether reacts to the expansion pressures of these waves as a continuous convergent force because its blocking and inversion of their expansion momenta occur in depth. However, as this force comes close to the wave center, it resolves into its periodic wave pattern as a functional part of that pattern.

Let us assume two wave patterns are potentially able to integrate their waves in a way which reduces the deformation of the contracting ether. This potentiality appears as a tendency to accentuate that reduction by a physical approach, with the approach implemented by a periodic avoidance of periodic repulsion waves. Since the containing reactions by space are not in the form of periodic waves, there is no way to avoid their convergent forces. However, if the waves of two patterns produce destructive interferences with their fundamental wave structures, the tendency to separate becomes dominant, and they will seek out the repulsive forces to implement that tendency.

Electrostatic charges are abnormal states in which energy or momentum is dominant. Similar charges repel because the dominant state is accentuated beyond its normal quantum value, and opposite charges attract because a merger of energy and momentum in their fields reduces their dominant states toward the inactive state of neutral space. Note that an electrostatic attraction has a different origin from that produced by interacting waves.

The potential forces of the converging field increases in all directions from a wave center at an equal rate. It tends, therefore, to contain all waves within a given area as a physical or statistical spherical distribution, and all deviations from that shape are potentially reducible. The tendency of contained waves to expand and disperse, being neutralized by the contracting ether, resolves into a spherical distribution with an integration of wave structure around a point center. It is a point because the waves must have a support against their containing forces. All attractions and repulsions can be defined as a tendency of contained waves to evolve maximum integrations around point centers, and a tendency of the contracting ether to reduce all deformations of its natural sphericity and dynamic progression to a minimum.

Converging field forces have no observable existence until they are activated by the expansion momenta of periodic waves. The energy gradient of a wave pattern is defined by the descending force of its expansion momentum as it interacts with the relative increase of its containing converging field momentum. Since this reaction cannot exceed its immediate cause, there is a theoretical residue of that expansion which, in theory, continues the wave pattern's expansion to infinity in space. However, the combination of contained and self-contained energy gradients confines nearly all its wave energy to a small area near the fundamental wave of a stationary wave pattern. Since the energy of a wave pattern can exceed the potential forces of its local converging field within an area which can be defined from its mass-momentum gradient, the transition distance where it becomes less than the converging field potential can be obtained. It defines the pattern's photon radius.

2-6 Nature's Unit of Length and Energy.
That a fundamental unit of length and energy exists in nature can be proved by the implications of observations and experiments. I note that specific relationships in nature imply the presence of a specific first cause. Planck's constant, defined as the energy of a centimeter wave, can be used to obtain the energy of a free photon by multiplying it by the photon's wavenumber in one centimeter. Since any system of units using an arbitrary unit of length will give us the right proportions, the existence of a natural unit of length is implied but not defined. We must, therefore, turn to the quantized energies and wavelengths of electrons, positrons, protons and neutrons for proportions which can be simplified to give us the natural unit of length and energy. In Book One this unit was obtained by idealizing an electron's mass, radius and hydrogen orbits.

It is to be assumed that every observable relationship in nature is implemented by a definable cause or causes. Where that relationship is specific, as in the energy-wavelength-quantum relations above, we must assume their causes are specific and in natural geometrical proportions. Obviously, the interrelations, processes and proportions that nature uses to define its phenomena must be simpler than those used by physicists, because their centimeter, gram and second are arbitrary units of action that may require complex formulas for the expected results. The true unit of length and energy in nature can, therefore, be discovered by developing new and simpler formulas, and by bringing out the simple proportions used by nature.

The existence of a natural unit of length and energy can also be anticipated by my theory. The expansion momentum of a periodic wave decreases with distance by dispersal and self-containment and, where the latter can be disregarded, its total value through the surface of an enlarging sphere cannot exceed that of its origin. However, the converging field momentum opposing its expansion increases from zero at the wave center to the cube of the distance times the wave's pulsation time. A wave's momentum is dominant near its center, but as it expands it containing forces increase rapidly toward an equality of power with distance. Since two oppositely directed momenta cannot pass through each other without interaction, it follows that their forces must equalize at a definable distance from the wave center. Since both are reflected back upon their origins by the interaction, the point of equality defines the photon radius of a single wave photon.

If we start from zero and gradually increase a wave's energy, its wavelength increases with its photon radius toward a natural maximum size. Beyond it, an increase of energy causes the wave to sub-divide into an increasing number of waves with shorter wavelengths, thus reducing the action time of its containing force per unit pulse in inverse proportion to energy. It follows that there is a maximum wavelength for a single wave photon, and that its energy can be obtained from Planck's quantum. Note that the reduction of containing forces, with the reduction of wavelength accompanying an increase of energy, does not change the containing forces per unit time, as defined by a system of units. The longest wavelength possible for the plane-polarized wave of a free photon moving through space with the speed of light defines the natural unit of length. In Book One I prove that the natural unit of length equals 1.0419584 centimeter. Its energy is 6.357702×10^{-27} erg emu, and 1.905994×10^{-16} erg esu in gaussian units. Since the speed of light is the only measure of time in nature, we find that one pulsation period of a wave with that wavelength, or the time it takes light to move one natural unit of length, equals 3.475593×10^{-11} second. This unit is used in defining the atomic constants of the ideal system of units. My contention, that nature defines its constants and relations with the outmost simplicity, is brought out by the ultimate system of units. Its unit of length is abstracted from the natural unit.

2-7 Momentum and Energy Gradients.

One of the great problems of physics is how to relate the quantized masses and quantum states of matter to the geometry of space. To solve this problem we must start with their relations to the natural unit of length through the interrelated gradients of contained momenta and self-contained energies. It must be assumed these gradients are inversely related to those of their container.

Logic tells us that observable quantities of wave energy with continuities in time must be concentrations with gradients to zero in space. A center-supported wave pattern acting against the containing forces of a contracting ether evolves such concentrations. Since its photon radius defines their point of equal power, a first conclusion is that the tendencies of waves dominate within that radius and those of the converging field beyond. Since the force potential of the contracting ether is proportional to the cube of the distance, the momentum gradient of a contained wave pattern must decrease as the inverse cube of the distance from its center beyond its photon radius.

We have strong reasons to believe that this inverse cube gradient of the contained wave momenta is continued with the photon radius of a spherical wave pattern to its center. If this is true, the gradient must be implemented by a building up of wave-containing forces by local wave-induced reductions of the ether's density, thus creating a static stress field with a maximum power at the pattern's center. It is as if the converging field reactions to the wave pattern's expansion pressure at a distance become transferred to its center through a compacting of its functional waves, with a consequent reduction of its fundamental wavelength. This local concentration of energy is accompanied by the building up of a static stress field with local containing powers beyond the potentials of local ether contraction momenta.

The converging field momentum passing through the surface of a sphere is equal to its cubic content—the cube of the distance. It follows that its linear contraction momentum is directly proportional to distance; an assumption in obvious accord with the mathematics of my contracting ether postulate. An expanding momentum, supported by a wave center, will decrease in power in inverse proportion to the containing contraction momenta reflecting it back upon its origin in depth. My theory of the development of a spherical wave pattern's natural quantum states lead to the conclusion that its expansion pressure (its blocked potential momentum) decreases as the inverse cube of the distance. Because the energy which can be contained by a specific momentum is greater by one power, its energy gradient is equal to the fourth power of the distance. The surface area of an enlarging sphere increases as the square of the distance. It follows that the linear momentum and energy of a spherical wave pattern decreases as the inverse fifth and sixth powers of the distance, respectively.

These steep linear gradients are for rest masses whose powers cannot be altered by interferences with their wave patterns. All energy changes of such patterns must occur by transmissions through their centers. The action potential of a fundamental particle's wave pattern is limited to the repulsive forces which appear when the fundamental waves of two particles come into contact, since a further approach would destroy their natural shapes and quantum states. The neutral energy of a particle is normally stable and changes only under exceptional circumstances. The electrostatic charge potential acting through the center of a particle's rest mass is equal to the square root of its charge mass. Its action potential to space decreases as the inverse square of the distance.

The inverse square law of electrostatic and gravitational forces is a linear action potential, related to the dispersal ratio of an unchanging force acting through the surface of an expanding sphere. Since all the energy of a fundamental particle of matter appears to be concentrated near its center, its displacement of the ether in the form of a containing static stress field must also be maximum in that area. A static stress field is a timeless displacement of the ether which expands from its source in all directions with twice the speed of light. As a stable configuration extending toward infinity in space, its total action potential through the surface of a sphere is the same at all distances, and its linear potential, therefore, decreases as the inverse square of the distance.

The inverse square law of the linear action potential between two particles can also be obtained from the converging field forces. Since the linear momentum of a contracting ether increases in direct proportion to distance, the linear energy it can contain increases as the square of the distance. It follows that the linear momentum and energy of interaction between two particles decrease as the inverse distance and distance squared for momentum and energy, respectively. The difference between the energy gradient of a rest mass and that of energy liberated by such a mass is due to the fact that the potential momentum of the contracting ether does not become an effective force until it is brought into being by the actions of wave momenta.

An analysis of the origin of wave gradients can be made by comparing the distribution of forces when a hollow sphere contains waves filling its space by random motions and the waves of a spherical wave pattern, acting always by motions to and from its supporting center. In the first case, the distribution of energy is statistically the same everywhere within the sphere; in the second, there is a functional maximum at the center, with each spherical wave of the pattern having the same energy. It follows that the linear energy of such a pattern decreases as the inverse square of the distance from its center.

In developing my theories, it is necessary to use facts as a guideline to the solution of problems by logical deductions within the accepted framework. The concentration of wave energy in dynamically stable fundamental particles is one such fact which I believe justifies the following conclusions. The concentration of energy at the center of a spherical pulsation pattern produces an ether displacement in the form of a wave-containing static stress field. It causes an accumulating increase of the concentration of energy and static stress field to a natural maximum. There is a consequent increase of mass gradient, accompanied by a reduction of the momentum transmitted through the surface of a sphere, one natural unit of length in radius. The converging field forces acting to contain the energy within that sphere can, therefore, contain additional energy, and will cause energy to be absorbed from the casual waves of space until a natural balance is attained. The contracting ether momenta, therefore, act as the organizer of center-acting waves and determine the maximum energy which can be contained by a stationary wave pattern; it determines the energy of its natural quantum state.

When we say that a center-acting force or energy decreases as the inverse square, cube or fourth power of the distance from its supporting center, this statement can be expressed mathematically, using any units of length, provided that we use the proper combination of factors. For an understanding of nature's way, however, it is necessary to use its units of measurement. The natural unit of length is an obvious factor in the definition of quantum states, and the mathematics of gradients tells us that the energy which can be contained by the contraction momentum passing through the surface of a sphere with that radius increases when the momentum gradient of its wave pattern becomes steeper. In nature, a stationary pattern's wavelength is also the length unit it uses to define its momentum and energy gradients to space. My best example of this relationship is the ultimate system of units in Book One.

A spherical wave pattern with a momentum decreasing in power with distance as the inverse cube gives us the following sequence: 1, 1/8, 1/27, 1/64, 1/25, 1/216, and so on. Its inverse fourth power energy gradient is: 1, 1/16, 1/81, 1/256, 1/625, 1/1296, and so on, for the sequence of waves. By halving the wavelength and unit of length, the expansion pressure decreases to one eight at unit distance. The energy which can be contained by a building up of its contained momentum to its original value is sixteen times greater. Observation shows that the effective energy at the wave center is greater than the transmitted momentum by the momentum squared. In defining this relationship, it is also necessary to take into consideration the natural ratio difference between energy and momentum as defined by their velocity formulas: $E = \frac{1}{2}MV^2$, and $F = MV$.

Chapter 3

THE FUNDAMENTAL PARTICLES

A theory of physical phenomena must be comprehensible and consistent. The possibilities of ether dynamics are sharply limited. Atomic physics is idealized by a web of fundamental constants. In nature their base ratios are as one-to-two. Natural length-time unit gives us a free photon's longest wavelength. Spherical, radial and velocity waves are fundamental. Their longest wavelengths are in the ratio: 1, 2 and 4, respectively. Spherical patterns give us negative electrons; radial patterns give us positive protons; and velocity patterns give us free photons and physical motions. The second quantum wavenumber of a spherical wave is obtained by raising its photon radius to one natural length. Its third quantum is this ratio raised to its fourth power—an electron's rest mass wavenumber. Its true (radius) wavenumber is the ratio raised to its fifth power. Its negative charge at unit distance is the square root of its radius wavelength. A stationary wave pattern's mass combines contained and self-contained properties. A positron's revolving, precessing radial waves define its positive charge. Its mass is the same as that of an electron. Its different gradients give us different photon radii. A proton is a positron with its unsaturated interspaces filled with neutral waves. Its rest mass is defined. A neutron is a proton circled by electron equivalent spherical waves.

3-1 Theory, Philosophy and Reality.

A theory of physics must not only be in accord with facts, it must also be comprehensibly logical by a provable consistency of relations and proportions within its accepted frame of reference. Where several solutions appear possible, it serves as a guide by eliminating those which are not in accord with its interpretations of facts and which exceed the limitations imposed by an impartial and indifferent nature. The solution of any problem in theoretical physics must be approached and evaluated in the perspective of total knowledge, as interpreted by a combination of facts, logic and philosophy.

A scientist enters the realm of philosophy when he selects, out of various possibilities, a particular interpretation of facts. When modern science states: "Science is not interested in philosophy or the nature of physical reality," its interpretations of permissible conclusions is a philosophy which can be criticised as such, in the light of their transcendental purpose. Its disinterest in the nature of physical reality is used by modern science to justify its rejection of logical implications that do not support its theories. It accepts waves and rejects the medium which makes them possible. It accepts general relativity and, by doing so, it rejects the scaffolding of logic, causality and mechanics, and the axioms of experience upon which science has been building for centuries. It is replaced by a mind-oriented philosophy that is closer to religion than to science.

In the development of my ether theory, with matter appearing as the logical product of its dynamic possibilities, I must work within a sharply restricted frame of reference; so restricted that the reader may well wonder how it is possible to bring the numerous facts of atomic physics within its compass. When such doubts entered my own mind, a conviction that general relativity, variable time, and other mind-oriented interpretations of physical facts cannot be accepted as final solutions kept me searching for comprehensible alternatives. I am convinced that the classical ether theory gives us the only acceptable rational foundation for physical interpretation of physical phenomena.

However, even if I should fail to solve all the problems posed by the contracting ether theory, my rejection of the theory of modern science does not depend on the success of my theory. Our differences go beyond the question of which theory gives the best mathematical interpretation of physical phenomena to the philosophy of the meaning and purpose of science. I hold that natural truths transcend our tools and knowledge and cannot be legislated; that we must seek out the nature of physical reality because it is the alpha and omega of all the physical sciences; that a realistic blending of mathematics, logic and measurements is essential to the solution of problems in physics, and that the implications of accepted phenomena do not disappear by being ignored. I question the isolation of phenomena in modern science by ignoring implications beyond those under immediate investigation, and I question the judgment of its scientists when they make a few marginal problems serve as the criterion of the truth or falsity of a whole science, while ignoring a multitude of significant questions. The old adage that ignorance is no crime is not true when used to prove the unprovable or deny the undeniable.

In developing my theory of quantum states I postulate an integration of contained waves, with the shape and action potential of the container determining their wavelength-energy relations. A wave nature of the fundamental particles of matter is postulated, because it is the only dynamic possibility in the ether; because we know from experiments that wave energy can be converted into matter, and matter into free photon waves; and because wave patterns can evolve particle properties with functional and potential extensions into space, while hard particles cannot evolve wave properties, quantum states and action gradients into space by natural extension.

The contracting ether produces several quantum-related phenomena. It causes interfering casual waves to integrate into center-acting stationary wave patterns by reacting in depth to their expansion (momentum) pressures. The integrations continue until natural quantum maximas (the rest masses of fundamental particles) have been attained. This process also replenishes the energy lost by a fundamental particle, through absorptions from the local field of casual waves. A stationary wave pattern's energy is quantized by a functional equality of expansion pressure and containing reaction momentum at one natural unit of length, both acting through the surface of a sphere of that radius. It is also defined as a saturation of converging field forces within that sphere. There are three types of center-acting waves, defined as spherical, radial and velocity wave patterns. The functional efficiency of their containing forces decreases with increasing concentration on a plane and along an axis in the ratio: four, two and one, and their wavelengths increase in inverse ratio. Spherical and radial wave patterns are functionally stationary, and velocity patterns can be free photons or the bound photons of moving stationary particles and masses. Note that a mass can be stationary in its local configuration space and yet be moving visually or relative to the ether. Velocity patterns are always moving with the speed of light, relative to the local configuration space, as free photons or as the bound photons of moving masses. In the latter case they produce the local configuration space relation to which the masses are functionally stationary.

3-2 Atomic Physics Idealized.

A vitally important fact of theoretical physics is that all fundamental quantum states, proportions and gradients are formally interrelated, in the sense that different combinations of constants can be used to obtain other constants, thus giving us a closed web of numerous atomic constants. The web includes related arithmetical and geometrical factors and excludes all constants which cannot be obtained by reductions within the web. The significance of the web is that relations and proportions are fixed by algebraic formulas, and that the atomic constants can be brought into a more rational relationship by changing the length, mass and time units used to define their numerical values within the web.

By idealizing the constants of the web, I discovered the natural unit of length and the simplicity of the ultimate system of units. In that system an electron's rest mass, charge and wavelength radius all have unit values, and the conversion of its mass into the energy of a free photon increases its wavelength by $\log_2$ 9.75, or 861.07793 in figures. It is the same figure as the energy of Planck's quantum for that system. These identities are obviously of immense theoretical importance.

In mathematics all numerical values are multiples and divisions of the unit one. When one figure is obtained by raising the value of another to a higher power, the difference between them decreases with a reduction of the base value until they coincide at unity. The first elementary difference above unity is two raised by their difference in powers, with the result halved. When it is squared, cubed and raised to its fourth power, their ratio values are one-to-two, one-to-four and one-to-eight, respectively.

In atomic physics the convergence on unity noted above is of great importance, because we expect its constants to originate from a common unit or a simple one-to-two or one-to-four ratio at their base. This postulate is based on the assumption that nature cannot define the specific numerical values of its constants and their relations without an origin as a simple ratio difference; a difference which, in turn, has its origin in the relation between two or more elementary factors. Among them I note the difference between momentum and energy, and the difference between spherical, radial and velocity waves. They combine with geometrical differences and pi in various ways to define the constants as they appear in nature.

It is theoretically possible for nature to define a base difference of two and, by combining two such differences, it can also define four; but it cannot define three or five, because they are irrational numbers. This postulate must be qualified by noting that these irrational numbers can appear by addition and as geometrical differences. The theoretical implication of the algebraic web is that all base ratios are in ideal simple proportions, and that these idealizations include their gradients and powers. When we define a specific ratio as being its base ratio squared, cubed or raised to its fourth power, we do not expect to qualify the result by adding or subtracting a quantity of unknown origin to obtain the observed ratio or constant. It is evident, however, that when we combine different phenomena there may be known factors which cause deviations from ideal proportions; among them I note the difference between Rydberg's wavelength for an infinite mass and its observed wavelength.

3-3 Natural Lengths to Waveratio Constant.

When an electron and a positron unite, their rest masses resolve into two oppositely moving free photons. The wavelengths of these photons are longer than an electron's radius wavelength by 861.07793 such waves, or 9.75 in basic logarithms. This is also the difference, in the ultimate system of units, between an electron's period in its smallest hydrogen orbit and the orbit's radius, and the difference between the reciprocal of its orbital energy and radiation wavelength. In all systems of units, a halving of the difference between the orbit's radius and its radiation (Rydberg) wavelength gives us the waveratio constant.

A theoretical definition of the waveratio constant starts out by noting the difference between waves supporting an axis moving through space with the speed of light, stationary plane (running, revolving) waves, and stationary spherical waves. The first are the plane waves of velocity patterns and free photons; the second, the plane waves of positrons; and the third, the spherical waves of electrons. All three types are distributed symmetrically around supporting point-centers. It is obvious that converging field forces react with maximum efficiency to spherical waves, and that their power to contain is least for waves whose energies are concentrated in directional expansion axes. Since wavelengths are inversely related to their container's efficiency, it is assumed that spherical, radial and velocity wavelengths are in the ratio one, two and four for the equal energies of their single wave photons. They are defined also as Planck's quantum for the longest, structurally organized wavelengths possible. Note that longer wavelengths, such as radio waves, are disorganized transmissions, comparable to the transmission of sound waves.

A velocity pattern's longest wavelength defines also the photon radius of a spherical wave pattern's second quantum state, and the natural unit of length of 1.0419584 centimeter. The one-to-four difference in wavelength between spherical and velocity waves in their first quantum states is used to obtain the waveratio constant of their second and third quantum states. A first conclusion is that the wavelength of a spherical wave pattern with Planck's quantum of energy equals 0.2604896 centimeter.

This wavelength is the natural unit of length for stationary wave patterns, just as four such units equal the natural unit of length defining the wavelengths and energies of free photons. The doubling of a stationary wave pattern's energy halves its wavelength and increases its photon radius by the fourth root of two. Since one half of this energy is statistically in a potential energy state, its corresponding momentum is unity. This halving of rest-mass energy can be compared with the halving of a moving body's mass in the definition of its energy of motion, $E = \frac{1}{2}MV^2$, while its momentum is $F = MV$. The definition makes energy and momentum values identical at twice unity. Note that a doubling of Planck's quantum of energy for a spherical wave pattern doubles its wavenumber in its own length units, and that its wavenumber is eight in the longer natural length units.

It is assumed that electrons and positrons attain their natural quantum states because stationary wave patterns with less energy tend to absorb energy from casual ground field waves in their environments, until the photon radius of one natural unit of length has been attained. Note that the contracting ether momentum passing through the surface of a sphere is equal to distance cubed, and that the energy it can contain is equal to its fourth power. It follows that a natural length unit sphere, four stationary radius units in size, can contain energy equal to four raised to its fourth power. This gives us 256 waves as the wavenumber in the smaller length unit, and 1024 in the larger.

We know from observation, however, that this last figure is too large by the fourth root of two, because the expected ratio is 861.077930 waves. A first conclusion is that the corresponding increase of wavelength or photon radius is caused by the difference between energy and momentum units; a difference which, in turn, is the product of the potential energy states of periodic waves, as contrasted with the continuity of free momenta. This difference appears also as a momentum velocity twice the maximum attainable by energy.

The momentum and energy of a moving mass is defined by $F = MV$, and $E = \frac{1}{2}MV^2$, respectively. Note that its energy at higher velocities is equal to momentum squared, and that a unit of energy, defined as a unit mass moving one unit of length in unit time, is obtained by $E = \frac{1}{2} \times (\sqrt{2})^2 = 1.0$. The unit of energy for an energy gradient equal to its fourth power is, therefore, $E = \frac{1}{2} \times (\sqrt[4]{2})^4 = 1.0$. By taking this root as the reduction factor in the conversion of a spherical unit wave photon to the saturation energy of a sphere four times larger, we get the waveratio constant from this formula:

Figures $\quad (4)^4 \times 4/\sqrt[4]{2} = 256 \times 4/1.18920711 = 861.077930$ waves

Log 2 $\quad (2)^4 \times 2/0.25 = 9.75$

The waveratio above was calculated from the difference in size of spherical and velocity waves, when both have the energy of Planck's quantum. The ratio is, however, valid for all spherical waves, whatever their lengths, because the local forces containing the fundamental wave of a pattern act also upon the energies expanding radially from its center to define its second quantum state. When an electron resolves into the energy of a free photon, the energy of that photon and, therefore, its reciprocal wavelength in electron radii, is equal to the waveratio constant above. It follows that the energy of Planck's quantum is equal to the waveratio constant for the ultimate system of units, and that the electron's mass wavenumber is equal to the energy of Planck's quantum in the ideal system of units.

3-4 Three Fundamental Wave Types.

The first condition for the evolution of integrated wave patterns in nature is that they must be center-supported against their containing reactions originating in the contracting ether. There are only three types of waves that conform to this condition. They are spherical, radial and velocity waves, with mathematical relations to spheres, planes and axes, respectively. The first is a stationary spherical pulsation with a potential energy point-center. The second is a stationary pattern of two dynamically balanced half-waves revolving around a common kinetic point-center. Their containing reactions cause them to change their plane of rotation in such a way as to produce a statistical sphericity in minimum time. The third is a pattern of transverse waves with a directional flow (momentum) axis moving with the speed of light. It can combine with a stationary pattern as its velocity pattern of physical motion. In this union, both retain their original dynamic states; the velocity pattern's waves continue to move with the speed of light, and its directional momentum acts constantly upon the stationary pattern as a displacement which appears as its physical motion, with both photons moving with a speed which leaves their centers stationary in the local configuration space, even though they may be moving relative to their transmitting ether.

My theory of ideal proportions leads to the conclusion that efficiency of the forces containing spherical, radial and velocity patterns are as 1, 1/2, and 1/4, and the wavelengths and photon radii of their first quantum single wave photons are in the ratio of 1, 2, and 4, respectively. Their gradients of energy to space decreases as the inverse fourth power, inverse cube and inverse square of the distance from their centers.

3-5 Momentum, Energy and Charge.

Periodic energy waves are always stationary in their local configuration space and will, therefore, move in response to a momentum with a velocity which preserves that state. It follows that the periodic waves of free photons are transverse, because that is the direction in which the stationary state can exist in a pattern moving with the speed of light. Periodic waves resolve into momenta, or their static stress equivalents, in proportion to their energy gradients to space, a gradient which, in turn, is determined by their containing converging field reactions and a local, containing ether displacement originating in those reactions.

Momenta are always transmitted with twice the speed of light through the ether, but cannot expand from a center against the contracting ether momenta converging on that center, without resolutions into periodic energy waves and a consequent reduction of velocity. While the gradients of contained waves cause them to act as carriers of momenta from stationary centers and through space, the momenta, in turn, make it possible for energy to be transmitted through the ether with speeds ranging from stationary to the velocity of light.

The separation of energy and momentum states at the centers of stationary wave patterns, and a potential union of them in space as free photons, appears as an attraction between opposite electrostatic charges. The point-center of an integrating wave pattern can organize as a potential or momentum center, but not as both. Since a spherical wave pattern can liberate only potential energy, it can expand into space by induction, but lacks the momentum which converts it into a radiation. A radial wave pattern can liberate momenta, but lacks the energy to convert it into a radiation. However, the union of a spherical wave pattern's energy with the momentum of a radial pattern makes a radiation possible, and the tendency to liberate this energy appears as an electrostatic attraction.

3-6 The First Quantum State.

When the energy of a periodic wave is gradually increased from zero, its wavelength and photon radius increase in proportion at a different rate. At first its wavelength is longer than its photon radius, but the converging field forces acting through time on each wave-pulse reduce its increase relative to the photon radius until they have the same value. Beyond this point the photon radius continues to increase, but the wave subdivides into a pattern of shorter wavelengths, thus reducing the time during which the converging field can act on individual pulsations. An increase of energy above that for the maximum wavelength causes the wavelength to decrease in inverse proportion to energy.

The first quantum state defines the longest possible wavelengths of the three fundamental patterns. They are single wave photons with identical energies, defined as Planck's energy quantum for those wavelengths. I call them spherical, radial and velocity mitons, in accordance with their shapes and functions, but they are also known as longitudinal and transverse waves. The latter are divided into a revolving pattern with a stationary center and a pattern of running waves moving with the speed of light.

The efficiency of wave-containing converging field forces obviously decreases when the distribution of wave momenta deviates from that of a sphere. My theory of ideal proportions postulates a relative efficiency ratio for spherical, radial and velocity mitons of 1, 1/2 and 1/4, respectively. Since wavelengths increase in inverse proportions, their relative sizes and photon radii are in the ratio of 1, 2, and 4, respectively. The physical sizes corresponding to this ratio are 0.2604896, 0.5209792 and 1.0419584 centimeters, respectively. The three types of mitons have identical energies, defined as Planck's quantum for those wavelengths. Their energies decrease from center to space as the inverse fourth, third and second power of the distance, as defined by their respective length units.

The postulated idealizations above are based on a combination of theory and observation. By making those assumptions it is possible to give a theoretical definition of an electron's rest mass and radius wavelengths. Besides the identities and simple proportions implied by the accepted idealizations of theoretical physics, their presence can also be observed in various phonemena. I note the one-to-two velocity ratio of bound and free momenta; the half mass value of energy to momentum of a moving mass, and their simple gradient of power with increasing speed; the half-spin value of an orbital electron to its energy of motion; and the geometrical differences where pi is doubled or halved, and the one-to-four difference in area between a circle and the surface of a sphere. Note also that electrons and positrons have the same mass and charge value, even though their charges have opposite signs.

3-7 The Second Quantum State.

The second quantum state is defined by the energy which a spherical wave pattern must absorb in order to increase its photon radius by four, from that of a spherical miton's to a velocity miton's radius. It is a theoretical saturation of converging field forces through the surface of a sphere, 1.0419584 centimeter in radius, by the expansion pressure (momentum) of a spherical wave pattern's energy. The radius is the wavelength of a velocity miton. It is also the maximum distance a single wave can expand from a stationary wave center as a directional axis, without subdividing into multiple waves. It defines the difference between the potential containment and absorption of intruding casual waves, and their escape or expulsion by the pattern.

The wave energy which may be absorbed by a spherical or radial stationary wave pattern to produce and support their natural quantum states exists in nature as low-energy casual photons; probably as single-wave free photons. The forces containing the waves of matter act also upon these ground field waves, causing them to become concentrated in matter, with maximum concentrations at the centers of galaxies and the centers of stars. They are the residue of an original chaos; a concentration of casual wave energies in galatic clusters before matter came into being at their centers.

The converging field momentum passing through the surface of a sphere is equal to its radius cubed, and the energy it can contain is that radius raised to its fourth power. The energy which can be contained by a sphere, one natural unit in radius, is the fourth power of that radius in spherical miton radii. The fourth power of four (4^4 = 256.) gives us 256 as the wavenumber and the energy of its second quantum state. Since we are dealing with energy, it is the same for both length units; however, when we redefine it in terms of wavenumbers we get 256 in spherical miton radii and 1024 in natural length units. Observation shows that these figures must be divided by the fourth root of two for their true wavenumbers, probably due to the difference between energy and momentum as outlined in section 3-3. When the two wavenumbers are divided by 1.18920711, we get 215.26948 and 861.07793, respectively.

The energy and wavelengths of the second quantum state are valid for all waves contained as stationary wave patterns, because the local forces containing the fundamental waves of such patterns act also to contain the forces expanding from their centers as radial axes. The unit of length to be used to define the gradients and powers of the second quantum state is, therefore, the wavelength of the pattern in question.

3-8 The Third Quantum Electron.

An electron is a stationary spherical wave pattern in its third quantum state. Its point-center is a periodically reversing potential energy state supporting its wave pattern against the contracting ether momenta converging on it; and against the static stress field originating at the center as an energy-induced displacement of the ether in the form of a reduction of its local density, and as a blocking of its local contraction momentum. An electron's rest mass energy and potential momentum decrease as the inverse fourth and third power of the distance, respectively. Their linear gradients therefore decrease as the inverse sixth and fifth powers, respectively, of the distance, with the unit of distance defined by its wavelength. The electron's potential energy center defines its negative electrostatic charge, because it is the only point at which a stationary wave pattern can absorb and liberate energy.

The great concentrations of energy near an electron's center, as defined by its behavior as a particle and by the gradients postulated above, originated as an integration bias of the converging field forces. Their spherical convergence on the center of inertia of all waves and wave clusters causes the waves to integrate around point-centers. This means there must be a concentration of energy at their centers, because a spherical central wave must have enough energy to equate the total energy of its farthest wave when its wave pattern is not contained, and it must exceed it where the converging field forces produce a descending gradient of wave energy with distance. The concentration of energy causes a reduction of the ether's density at the wave center and a consequent increase of its containing forces in the form of a static stress field. It is followed by an increase of energy at the center with the increased steepness of its gradient to space, and a local increase of the static stress field until a natural balance between them is attained.

An electron's rest mass energy is equal to the energy of its second quantum state, in mitons, raised to the fourth power. Since a miton's energy is the same as Planck's quantum for a single-wave free photon in all systems in which the speed of light is unity, the number of mitons defined above is also the wavenumber, in one natural unit of length, of a free photon with an electron's rest mass energy. In the ultimate system of units their identical values are the reciprocal of an electron's second quantum waveratio constant.

The simple conversions which give us an electron's rest mass energy in wavenumbers from the fundamental one-to-four wave ratio, through its second quantum energy to its third quantum energy-wavenumber in one natural length unit, are defined below.

Quantum   1   2   3
Numbers $(4)^4 = 256)^4 = 4.29496730 \times 10^9$ wavenumber nl.

Log 2 $(2)^4 = 8)^4 = 32.$ wn. nl.

An electron's radius wavelength (its true wavelength) is equal to the reciprocal of its rest mass wavenumber times the second quantum waveratio constant. It can also be defined as being equal to the reciprocal of its second quantum energy raised to its fifth power times the base ratio, divided by the fourth root of two. Both conversions appear below.

er $(256)^4 \times 861.07793 = 3.6983016 \times 10^{14}$ wn.   Recip. $2.7039439 \times 10^{-15}$ nl.

2     $(8)^4 \times 9.75 = 41.75$ wn. nl. $2.8173971 \times 10^{-13}$ cm.

er $(256)^5 \times 4/1.18920711 = 3.6983016 \times 10^{14}$ wavenumber in nl.

2     $(8)^5 \times 2/0.25 = 41.75$ wn. nl.

The physical reality of an electron's radius wavelength can be proved by its functional relations to the constants of the ultimate and ideal systems of units. In the ideal system its action potential at the distance of one natural unit is equal to the square root of its radius wavelength, as defined below.

$e = \sqrt{2.7039439 \times 10^{-13}} = 5.1999462 \times 10^{-7}$.   Log 2 $e = \sqrt{-41.75} = -20.875$

An electron's quantized rest mass is defined by a functional integration of its energy, momentum and wavelength, and an equivalence of contained and containing momenta at the surface of a sphere of specific size. We can approach this problem by analyzing their relations in the velocity pattern of an electron being accelerated to twice the speed of light; a theoretical increase defined in Book One. The energy and momentum formulas for a moving mass are

$E = \frac{1}{2}MV^2$ and $F = MV$, respectively. Because the unit of velocity in nature is the speed of light, the free photon wavenumbers defining its energy of motion are longer than the momentum-related wavenumbers observed as the electron's velocity pattern. There is a convergence of energy and momentum wavenumbers with increasing velocity which leads to a theoretical identity at twice the speed of light, when the electron's rest mass and the mass of its velocity pattern have the same values. This apparent increase of an electron's mass reduces its observed velocity to less than light under all conditions of motion (see Book One). The (de Broglie) wavelength of its velocity pattern is obtained by dividing Planck's quantum of energy by mass times velocity: $B = h/MV$. Note that MV is the formula for momentum, and that it is directly proportional to the electron's velocity wavenumber. An increase of its energy of motion by four doubles its velocity and momentum and halves its velocity wavelength.

A free photon moves with the speed of light, even though its momentum is transmitted by its transverse energy waves with twice that speed, because the energy is a mass equivalent with the same value as its momentum inhibiting the photon's motion. Although this energy is not a rest mass, it appears as an increase of a stationary wave pattern's mass when the photon unites with it to become its velocity pattern of physical motion. The energy-momentum of a free photon, divided by Planck's quantum, gives us its wavelength in natural length units: $\dot{v} = h/E$.

An electron's rest mass is all-electric. Since it contains no inhibiting neutral mass, we expect its rest mass energy to transmit a momentum through its stationary center equal to that energy—like the energy of a free photon. Since the radius of a velocity miton is four times longer that that of a spherical miton, the latter transmits four momentum units through its center in equal time for equal energies. When a spherical miton's energy is increased by 256, it produces a photon radius equal to that of a velocity miton's—one natural unit of length. Its momentum, however, is still four times greater than its energy, and its wavelength is four times shorter. The momentum for that pattern is, therefore, 1024 base units, divided by the functional difference between the energy and momentum of a stationary wave pattern: the fourth root of two. The final figure for its transmitted momentum and radius wavenumber is 861.07793.

It will be noticed that if the energy of this pattern is converted into that of a free photon, the difference in wavelength is still four. Since the observed difference is the same as the last figure above, it is evident there is an increase of the functional efficiency of a stationary wave pattern's energy, due to a reduction of wavelength with an increase of its energy, until the difference between its energy and transmitted momentum is equal to 861.07793. The increase is effected by the compacting of a stationary wave pattern's energy, with a consequent reduction of wavelength, due to its building up of a containing, static stress-field from the converging field's containing forces. There is a corresponding increase of momentum transmitted through its center per unit time relative to its transmitting energy. In the ideal system of units this time unit is the time it takes a light wave to move one natural length. The observed increase of energy is 256 raised to its fourth power.

Nature defines a quantum state through two length units—the natural unit of length and its wavelength—and its gradient of energy from center to space. Since gradients are related to wavelengths, it is evident that different wavelengths with identical gradients have different action potentials at the distance of one natural unit of length. A reduction of wavelength is accompanied by an increased concentration of energy corresponding to the preservation of its gradient. My theory of an electron's rest mass energy and radius wavelength postulates a total momentum gradient (the force passing through the surface of a sphere) equal to the inverse cube of the distance from its center in radius wavelength units. Its dispersal as the inverse square of the distance implies a linear momentum gradient equal to the inverse fifth power of the distance. Since its total energy decreases as the inverse fourth power, the electron's linear energy gradient must decrease as the inverse sixth power of the distance. Note that these gradients define the electron's rest mass; not its charge gradient. Its electrostatic charge is the potential force which can be released in any direction by its center from the forces containing its fundamental wave; its force decreases, therefore, as the inverse square of the distance.

A possibility which must not be overlooked is that the anticipated wavelength equal to one fourth of the electron's rest mass wavelength (the wavelength it would have as a free photon with an electron's energy) is the unit of length within which its second quantum wavelength evolves by local integration. The facts are clear, and the logic of an electron's evolution to its natural quantum states is roughly known, but the specifics of its transformation from a first, through a second, to a third quantum state is still in question.

The converging field forces interact with evolving, center-supported integrations of periodic waves, and in doing so define the natural quantum states of the fundamental particles of matter. The products of these interactions appear as a compacting of the wave pattern and a displacement of the local ether by the expansion pressure of its periodic waves. This displacement takes the form of a static stress field equivalent of converging field forces through which the converging field resumes its natural dynamic progression. In this way it can build up a high concentration of energy and a static stress field with a containing gradient whose value is determined by the natural gradient of the energy it contains. It has no direct relationship to the local converging field forces, since it is immensely greater near the electron's center, decreasing with distance, even though its continued existence is determined by its interactions with the converging field forces at great distances from its cause as it expands to become a displacement of the whole universe.

My theory of an electron's rest mass energy would be in accord with facts if we postulate an increase of containing forces equal to the energy of its second quantum state raised to its fourth power, for energy, and to its fifth power for a first approximation to the reciprocal of its radius wavelength.

3-9 The Third Quantum Positron.

A positron is a stationary radial wave pattern in its third quantum state. Its point center transmits the wave momenta of two dynamically balanced plane-polarized half-waves, 180 degrees apart, circling it on a plane. They respond to the converging field reactions on that plane with a tendency to escape by precessing and changing the plane of rotation, thus evolving a statistical sphericity in minimum time. (The same tendency causes atomic electrons to produce a spherical cloud effect.) The changes of plane cause the evolution of secondary waves with longer wavelengths. Their sole function is to carry the energy which produces those changes.

There is a physical similarity and a functional difference between velocity and radial waves. Both have moving plane waves organized to support their motions, but the center of a velocity pattern moves with the speed of light, while that of a radial wave pattern is stationary. The containing reactions of the former recurve around its moving pattern to become its momentum of motion, while those of the latter converge on the plane of their causative waves as a containing force reducing their wavelengths. The inertia of the revolving waves opposes their tendency to escape the containing reactions by changing their plane of rotation into areas where they are absent. This tendency is implemented by the evolution of secondary waves acting in consonance with the primary wave to produce a statistical sphericity in minimum time.

The equal masses of electrons and positrons, and the identical values of their negative and positive electrostatic charges, must be implemented by physical and functional identities of their quantizing causes. A first conclusion is, therefore, that the second quantum radius, defined as the distance an axial wave can expand without subdividing into a pattern of two or more waves, is the same for both radial and spherical wave patterns; and that the saturation energy within a sphere of that radius is the same for physically and statistically distributed waves. It is assumed the permissible action time is long enough to produce such a distribution of radial waves within the sphere.

In nature, the speed of light is a constant. The radius of an enlarging sphere, therefore, gives us a time unit whose length increases at the same rate as the radius. Beginning with zero, an enlarging length-time unit defines, first, two opposite divergent and convergent axes which resolve into two dynamically balanced waves, revolving around a common center of inertia. The increasing time unit next defines the wave energy as a distribution on a precessing plane, with extensions of descending powers to zero at the poles (like the lines of force of a magnetic field). As the precession and change of the plane of revolution become increasingly statistical with a longer time unit, the energy transits from a statistical distribution on a plane to an apparent uniform distribution within a sphere. Three different time values, therefore, give us an axis, a plane and a sphere; and three different definitions of a radial wave pattern's energy gradient and action potential. They decrease as the inverse square, cube and fourth power of the distance from the supporting wave center, respectively.

These three different definitions give us three photon radii for equal energies, and a functional increase of gradient with time and distance as the radial wave pattern's energy and momentum transit from local paired axes through their rotation on a plane to a statistical spherical distribution. It is evident that my attempt to give a comprehensible logical description of a radial wave pattern's dynamic processes is difficult and questionable, because it must deal with a complex of interrelations which are opposite to those of an electron in those aspects dealing with its opposite electrostatic charge, but must nevertheless result in identical quantum states. An explanation will be made to give the reader a background for criticism, but it may contain serious errors.

The inverse square gradient of an expanding axis can be ignored, because rotation limits its range to less than a single wave by depriving it of support from the wave center. Its maximum expansion before the contracting ether, or the static stress field, reflects it back upon the center as a converging axis, and defines the pattern's primary wavelength. It is to be contrasted with the wavelength defined along a circle whose radius is equal to the wave's mean energy as it orbits the center. Note that a radial wave motion is center-supported and that its orbiting wave, defining its dynamic transitions of state along a circle, is not. The primary wave's pulsation period is determined by the speed of light, whereas its orbiting equivalent exceeds it by 2π—the ratio of a circle's circumference to its radius.

The inverse cube gradient of a radial wave pattern's energy and momentum, acting on a plane, is primary because it has a functional continuity in time. An invariable plane of rotation with an electron's energy would extend far beyond its natural quantum radius; however, as its plane of rotation changes toward a statistical sphericity with the evolution of precessionary waves, the increasing efficiency of its containing forces reduces its photon radius in proportion.

The wave-containing converging field forces are 100 percent effective against all center-supported periodic pulsations in longitude, when its effectiveness is defined at half-wave distance. The functional efficiency of a radial wave pattern's containing forces is, therefore, at its maximum potential on its plane of revolution, decreasing to zero at its poles. Its tendency to escape these reactions by changing its plane of revolution brings into being a group of secondary radial waves whose sole functions are to produce those changes with maximum effectiveness. The interactions of these secondary waves with the contracting ether increase its functional efficiency, by their interactions with it as waves and by their displacements of the plane of rotation of the primary pattern toward a statistical sphericity. Enough such waves with different energies and wavelengths cause the efficiency ratio of a radial wave pattern to increase until it cannot be distinguished from that of a spherical pattern. Note that all radial waves acting from a common center have essential functions, and that they interact to produce the quantized positive electrostatic charge of a positron.

A spherical distribution of a radial wave pattern's contained and containing momenta brings us to the question of whether its rest mass energy is completely contained or partly self-contained. In the first case its concentration on the precessing wave planes along an inverse cube gradient brings the photon radius of a positron's quantum states beyond those of an electron's; in the second case, the containing reactions cause the evolution of self-contained energy with an inverse fourth-power gradient, thus producing the same energy-momentum relations and photon radii as those of an electron.

The first postulate is based on the energy-momentum equivalence of a free photon. It is assumed that the functional half-value of a radial wave pattern's containing forces anticipates its expansion beyond the radius, defining a saturated second quantum state, in order to produce a functional saturation of the converging field forces within that radius. Since we are dealing with a momentum pattern, it is possible that its velocity of transmission with twice the speed of light is a factor in the definition of a radial wave pattern's second quantum photon radius. This radius is obtained by taking the cube root of an electron's or positron's second quantum energy. The result is to be compared with 4 spherical miton radii (smr) in one natural length.

Figure $\sqrt[3]{256}$ = 6.34960421 spherical miton radii.
Log 2 $\sqrt[3]{8}$ = 2.66666667

The second postulate is based on the assumption that the saturation of converging field forces within a sphere, one natural unit in radius, defines the energy and momentum it can contain. It is assumed the inverse cube gradient of a radial pattern's momentum can be defined by a statistical sphericity identical in power with that of a spherical wave, and that its containing reactions cause self-contained energy with an inverse fourth power gradient to evolve within that radius. The nature of that energy is in question, although it is evident that a part of it takes the form of a transverse momentum supporting the revolutions of the radial waves—like the magnetic field of an orbiting charge.

There is some question about a positron's wavelength. A first conclusion is that, since its rest mass energy is the same as that of an electron, its wavelength should also be about the same. My theory postulates a wavelength twice that of an electron's, or longer. I do not know if a positron's true wavelength has ever been measured but, from the observed radii of atomic nuclei a proton's radius is only one half that of an electron. It is possible, therefore, that the conversion of a positron into a proton is accompanied by a four-to-one reduction of wavelength. This difference may account for the bonding forces which cause a positron to increase its mass by an absorption of neutral waves, thus transiting from an unstable to the stable quantum mass of a proton.

I noted in a previous section that all center-acting wave patterns have a concentration of energy at their centers, since they must support a quantity of energy at that point, which cannot be less than its total energy acting through the surface of a sphere of any radius. Their concentrations must be far greater when the converging field reacts in depth to their expansion momenta with a containing force, thus producing a gradient of descending power from center to space. These concentrations of energy appear as local increases of the ether's mean temperature, with a consequent expansion-reduction of its density proportional to that energy. The displacements act as a wave-containing static stress field with a gradient of descending power from center to space, corresponding to that of the energy it contains.

The evolution of a radial wave pattern from free energy to its observed natural quantum states is based on the assumption that contained casual waves will integrate—that they escape into structure—and that the spherical symmetry of the contracting ether and its containing reactions to their expansion pressures cause them to integrate around point centers as center-supported dynamic actions. These conditions eliminate all but spherical and radial waves, and the different dynamics of these waves make it impossible for both to evolve around the same center.

The static stress field which evolves with a concentration of energy around a positron's point-center acts as a containing force which increases the concentration and, therefore, its own local power, since it is proportional to the local energy. This compounding of effects initiated by an original concentration increases the energy which can be contained by the contracting ether, by that energy raised to its fourth power. It is evident, however, that the positron's waves are no longer contained by the contracting ether, but by a static stress field, as noted previously. The tendency of this static stress field to equalize the density of the ether by dispersal takes the form of a force containing the positron's waves, and as a tendency to evolve a spherical symmetry of its gradient from center to space around those waves. It is comparable to the symmetry of the converging field forces which brought it into being.

A positron's rest mass energy is defined as the energy which can be contained by a static stress field, when the energy contained by the contracting ether as its second quantum state is raised to its fourth power. The two states are the same as those of an electron.

3-10 The Fourth Quantum Proton.

A proton is a stationary radial wave pattern in its fourth quantum state. It is a positron with neutral waves added to the interspaces of its charge pattern. It has, therefore, a positron's electrostatic charge and an increase of mass equal to about 1836.1141 electrons. The fractions are not final, since they were obtained by experiments, as defined in Book One, and not by the theory of ideal proportions. A positron is dynamically unstable, but when the neutral energy above is added to its mass it become a stable proton.

Only a few hours after I had written the comments above, I discovered that a proton's mass wavenumber can be defined by: PM = $(4^4\pi)^4$ 6π. When it is divided by an electron's mass wavenumber, we get 1836.11809 electrons. It will be noticed that six digits of this figure are the same as those above, as defined by me in Section 1010, Book One. The formula is simple, but the only factor which can be recognized as being present in the electron and positron formulas is the second quantum mass wavenumber 4^4 = 256.

In the past, the absence of pi as a factor in formulas in which it might be present has made me wonder if my judgment had been warped by a preference for simple ideal proportions. However, in the formula above it appears twice. The first reduction, $\tilde{v} = 4^4\pi$, gives us 804.2477184 as the wavenumber of a proton's second quantum state. Its wavelength is longer than that of an electron's by 1.07066257. A first conclusion is that the wavenumber above is that of the positron's second quantum primary waves, and that the remainder is related to the energy of its secondary precession waves. By assuming that its primary and secondary waves combine to define its electrostatic charge, the theory is in good accord with facts. When the second quantum wavenumber is redefined as energy and raised to its fourth power, we get the energy-wavenumber $4.18368858 \times 10^{11}$. This figure is obviously a product of the increase due to the static stress field.

Since the figure is greater than a positron's mass by 97.4090904, and gives us a wavelength longer than that of an electron by 8.8398108 electron radii, it is obviously not related to either. I believe it is the energy of a proton's primary wave, increased from that of a positron's by an increase of containing forces due to the integration of neutral waves into its functional pattern. When it is increased by 6π = 18.84955592, we get the wavenumber of a proton's rest mass. Note that 6π is related to the conversion of the volume of a sphere to the area of its surface. It may be a spherical distribution of neutral and secondary radial waves, acting in support of the primary pattern's constant change of its plane of rotation.

My arguments and conclusions above may be specious, since the same results can be obtained by the formulas PM = $6\pi^5$ and $6\tilde{v}\pi^5$ for a proton's mass in electrons and wavenumbers respectively. The figure 6 is obtained by doubling the momentum-related surface area of a unit radius sphere to the energy-related volume defining its mass. The reciprocal of its linear mass gradient gives us the fifth power accent of pi in the two formulas and the sequence below.

Area to ½ volume R = 2a/v		Proton in electrons R = P_M/E_M	Electron. Mass wavenumber $E_M\tilde{v}$	Proton. Mass wavenumber $P_M\tilde{v}$
6.000000 × (3.14159265)^5	π^5	= 1836.11810) ×	4.2949673 × 10^7	= 7.8860671 × 10^4
2.584963	1.6514961	10.842442	32.0	42.842442

My theory of the evolution of matter and electrostatic charges is not in accord with the ancient theory of virtues. That theory assumed that matter is composed of particles with specific masses, some of which have imbedded in their surfaces something which impart to them the virtue of a positive or negative action potential. It provides the atmosphere in which the present assumption of science, that the charges on protons and electrons are reversible, can flourish. It assumes that somewhere in space there are areas of negative matter, areas in which positrons are stable, electrons unstable, and protons with negative charges form the nuclei of atoms.

Many scientists will claim that they are simply suspending judgment on the origin and relations of matter and charges; however, if this is so, their acceptance of the theory of reversibility of electrostatic charges loses its reason for existence. The fact that we have two kinds of charges means that there must be something producing that difference, something which makes the above postulate untenable as a principle of physics.

While a spherical wave pattern fills all available space with its waves, a radial wave pattern contains unsaturated areas near its center, due to its transition gradients to space and the use of a time unit short enough to eliminate its statistical sphericity. We know that its charge as a positron is the same as that of a proton, that a positron's is normally unstable and a proton's stable, and that its positive value is the same as the negative value of an electron. Obviously, a proton's charge pattern is primary, and fixed by the forces containing a positron's and electron's patterns. Its rest mass must, therefore, be composed of neutral waves evolving in a positron's unsaturated areas, and acting in consonance with the shape and motions of its charge pattern. Its evolution to a natural quantum maximum must occur within this frame, because center-supported waves cannot be neutral. Neutral stationary waves can have no common center of support and reference beyond the loose bonding which appears in all clusters, due to local momentary integrations. Without a radial organizer of its neutral wave structure, the waves would disperse and disappear into the casual, low-energy waves of the ground field. Because the neutral waves of a proton's rest mass are functionally related to its charge pattern, the energy they represent combines with those of the pattern to reduce its wavelength. Assuming that their forces are not center-acting, except for those binding them to the proton, it is evident that the rest-mass energy of a proton can build up to a high value before the bonding forces of that mass attain a natural quantum state.

There is a fundamental similarity between the wave structure of a free photon and the moving waves of a stationary radial pattern. If the identity of a free photon's energy and momentum can be applied to a radial pattern's wave structure, the statistical spherical distribution of a positron's rest mass energy should have an inverse cube gradient to space. To equate an electron's second quantum rest mass energy, its photon radius must be larger than one natural unit of length by the cube root of two. In spherical miton radii the difference is as 4.0 to 6.34960421. It may be possible to account for a positron's greater radius by noting that a free momentum is transmitted with twice the speed of light.

The inverse cube gradient of a positron's rest mass means that there is a tendency to attain saturation within its natural photon radius by filling the interspaces within its pattern with neutral waves, thus raising its mass gradient to the inverse fourth power of the distance from its center. In the transition to a proton's rest mass, the saturation energy of its pattern's second quantum state should equal its photon radius raised to its fourth power. The static stress field which evolves from the concentration of energy increases this result to its fourth power for a proton's rest mass. The second set of figures below are in basic logarithms.

2Q en.	2Q radius	2QP en. wn.	4QP mass wn.	error	Proton m.
$\sqrt[3]{256}$=6.3496042)^4	=1625.4987)^4	= 6.9814636×10^{14})	× 1.129572	= 7.886067 ×
8	2.6666667	10.666667	42.6666667	0.176875	42.842442

The first result is too small, but is close enough to show a possibly meaningful realtionship. An even closer result is obtained by doubling an electron's radius wavenumber and redefining the result as a proton's mass wavenumber. The doubling is justified by a conversion of energy to momentum, and the conversion is justified by the difference between the momentum transmitted by an electron's rest mass energy and that transmitted by a positron's.

	Electron's true mass wavenumber	Proton's provis. mass wavenumber	error	Proton's tru mass wavenum
Figures	2×3.6983016×10^{12}	=7.3966031×10^{14})	× 1.0661742	= 7.886067 ×10
Log 2	1 41.750000	42.750000	0.092442	42.842442

It is one thing to define a proton's wave structure by formula, and quite another to describe it in detail by deductive reasoning. The latter must, of necessity, be based on logical probabilities which may be highly questionable. We cannot simply increase the energy-momentum of a positron's fundamental structure, because that will also increase its charge, and we know that this increase does not occur. It seems probable, therefore, that a proton's neutral waves are center-related but not center-acting. My first postulate is based on this assumption.

The modern theory of wave mechanics, first suggested by Schrodinger, postulates periodic pulsations of various shapes for the quantum transitions of orbital electrons in the atoms. It is to be assumed that a similar relationship exists between a proton's primary plane of rotation and its neutral wave patterns. It seems probable that their pulsations are transverse to the proton's center, and that they act in consonance with its moving primary plane and its precession waves. It is impossible to describe the numerous different shapes and periods which can develop within this frame of reference. Whatever their shapes, they are functional, they are integrated, and they are interacting with the center in a way which binds them to it with sufficient force to make a dynamically stable pattern of rest-mass waves.

There are two other possibilities which, although they seem less probable, should be considered. The first of these is a spherical pulsation to and from the proton's center, with its negative charge combining with an increase of the positive charge to produce a neutral state. It cannot be a principal cause because such short waves would be destroyed by the primary radial waves; however, it is possible that it can exist as relatively long spherical waves because the center should then behave like a spherical point. The second possibility is based on the assumption there can be two kinds of radial waves; a half wave with a kinetic center and a full wave with a potential center. I am highly sceptical of this postulate and am simply suggesting it as a possibility which should be explored. It appears to me that it would give us a positive electrostatic charge, even though its central state is potential energy.

My theory of the evolution of matter assumes that it originated from the integration of a multitude of casually moving ground field waves contained in common by the contracting ether. After a local maximum integration into matter, there remains a residue of electrostatically neutral ground field waves within and around the fundamental particles of matter—like the atmosphere surrounding a planet. A first conclusion is, therefore, that the conversion of a positron into a proton is effected by the absorption-integration of clustering neutral ground field waves into the interspaces within its photon radius. Because its charge cannot be increased, the interactions of ground field waves with its charge pattern appears as an integration into its dynamic processes without an increase of that charge. While I assume the process to be gradual, it may be an abrupt transition when sufficient energy is available. However, it is evident that marginal gains and loses due to environmental changes are gradual.

3-11 The Fifth Quantum Neutron.

A neutron is a radial wave pattern in its fifth quantum state. It is a proton with its electrostatic charge extinguished beyond its point-center by the addition of an electron-equivalent negative charge. Its mass is equal to about 1838.6452 electrons and is, therefore, greater than that of a proton by about 2.5311 electrons. This gives it a mass wavenumber equal to 7.896921×10^{12} waves in one natural unit of length. Its log two value is 42.8443.

A neutron is electrostatically neutral. It is dynamically stable in atomic nuclei with the proper proportion of protons—positive charges—and it is unstable in free space. There it resolves into a proton and a high-velocity electron within a period of time, estimated at about 18 minutes on the average. It will be noticed that the relationship between a proton's charge and quantized mass is also present in atomic nuclei as a proportion between their number of protons and neutrons.

The center of a wave pattern acts as the organizer of its functional structure. It is the only part of the pattern which can absorb and liberate energy, and it does so to preserve its natural quantum states and functions against destructive intrusions. Its opposition to destructive interferences with its functional processes includes its interactions with opposite charges, when they pass beyond marginal interferences and intrude into its vital dynamic processes. The difference is between an intrusion which can be resolved into a statistical mean and one which cannot. There is an attraction between opposite charges when distance makes their mutual intrusions marginal, but when they come too close together, one of them or both will be destroyed.

When an electron comes too close to the positive nucleus of an atom, it may be destroyed by nuclear forces. The destruction continues until the residue of dispersed low-energy spherical pulsations behave statistically as a marginal intrusion. They may then unite with a proton as an electron equivalent negative cloud of orbiting spherical pulsations. Since their pulsations are immensely longer than those of an electron, their orbits are defined by the motions of their point centers. They are probably highly eccentric, like those of comets circling the sun.

There is a tendency of orbiting bodies to approach the attracting center by increasing their velocities to the maximum attainable for their masses. An increase of mass reduces that velocity because it requires a greater energy for its attainment. If this is so, the infinitesimal energies of the electron equivalents should be associated with orbital velocities near that of light, and their energies of motion should increase their apparent rest-mass energies by a large value. The increase of a proton's mass by 2.5311 electrons when it is transformed into a neutron can be explained by this theory. According to my table of electron velocities in Book One, their velocities should average between 85 and 90 per cent of light.

The tendency of electron fragments to reassemble into an electron increases with a reduction of the rest-mass energy of each fragment. It prevents their reductions beyond a minimum energy and serves as the incentive which causes a neutron to resolve into a proton and an electron in free space.

In my theory of the proton I noted that ground field waves tend to cluster around the fundamental particles of matter because the forces containing their waves also act to contain and integrate casual waves in their vicinity. Obviously, a proton's capture and integration of neutral waves into its rest mass can be extended to include the capture and integration of casually moving negative ground field waves, provided the circumstances are such as to favor this reaction. Other factors, such as the availability of such waves and a requirement that the transformation of a proton into a neutron must be completed each time, probably decide whether the conversion occurs or not.

My theory of a neutron as a proton circled by an electron-equivalent number of spherical pulsations, moving close to its center and not far beyond the radius of its primary wave, produces a statistical cloud effect similar to that produced by a hydrogen electron in an s quantum state. When this theory is compared with the conventional assumption that a neutron is simply a mass without an electrostatic charge, the difference between them can be tested by noting their implications and comparing them with the facts of physics.

Observation shows that electrons, positrons, protons and neutrons all have electromagnetic (spin) fields related to their charges and masses. Electrons and positrons have the same spin field values, while that of a proton is less by its mass ratio to a fair approximation. A neutron's spin field is less than that of a proton's by about one third. This ratio is in reasonable agreement with my assumption that the proton preserves its spin field as a neutron, and that its value is reduced by its orbiting electron equivalents. In contrast, conventional theory does not postulate a spin field for a neutral particle. Another proof of my theory is that a neutron in free space reverts to a proton with the expulsion of a high-velocity electron. It makes sense if the electron equivalent is distributed, as postulated by me. However, if the center is neutral, and all other factors are even, a reversal of charges by the expulsion of a positron would be just as probable as that actually observed.

Chapter 4

ORGANIZATION. ELECTRICITY.

Organizers are the products of a tendency of contained waves to escape into center-supported structures. An organizer can be the point-center of a spherical or radial wave pattern. Its reaction time is zero because it is one-dimensional. Organization is an energy equivalent. Waves exert a static expansion pressure which displace their containing ether contractions. The converging field resumes its motions through these static stress fields. Forces containing stationary wave patterns are increased by a temperature displacement of the ether. A negative charge increases the quantity of energy to momentum, a positive charge increases momentum to energy. They can unite to form neutral states and free photons. Organizers can absorb and liberate the energy of their own dynamic states only. Free photons are contained wave patterns moving through a configuration space with the speed of light. An increase of wave energy increases a pattern's containing forces and reduces its wavelength. A velocity pattern is a free photon captured by a stationary pattern to become the physical motion of its mass. Both retain their natural states within the wave complex. The earth's stationary state is preserved by the momentum pattern of its motion through local configuration space. The organizer of a wave pattern preserves the stationary states of matter by liberating, absorbing and organizing local wave energy. It creates a magnetic field when orbiting a center. Magnetic fields are reducible vorticular momenta. Charges evolve spin fields which can be reversed and exchanged.

4-1 Organizers of Wave Patterns.

The center of any wave structure acts as the organizer of its periodic wave pattern. In a stationary pattern it is a point at its center of inertia, interacting constantly with the forces of intruding phenomena. It is a point because its action-reaction time must be zero, its response singular, and its reactions to forces must induce a distribution which causes them to have opposite equal power. It is a point because the forces containing its integrated wave pattern are directed toward that pattern's center of inertia, thus causing its waves to become concentrated at that point and evolve a center-supported structure in reaction. It is a point because such a structure must be simple and functionally continuous in space and time.

It will be noticed that if we were to postulate the distribution of a wave pattern's central forces along a line, around slightly separated points or as originating from somewhere within a volume, the deviation from a point can be expressed in terms of a distance-time difference which become accentuated with time as a functional separation of wave periods and structural relations. In other words, the functional and structural continuity of a stationary wave pattern depends upon its integration around a point-center.

A wave pattern's inertia is its opposition to change, because forces must act upon its time-distance related dynamic processes to change their directions without changing their structural relations to the pattern's organizer. A stationary pattern must always remain stationary within its own configuration space and relative to the forces acting in its own immediate vicinity, even though it may be moving relative to the ether. Note that the point-center of a wave pattern has no inertia by itself, but acquires its inertia from interactions with its functional pattern. It reacts instantaneously to unbalancing forces with an accelerating motion or change of position that leaves it stationary, relative to all the forces in its vicinity—the forces of its pattern and of those intruding.

An organizer must have both the power and ability to interact effectively with its environment, based on its functional interactions with the forces containing its wave pattern. The wave-containing converging field forces are transmitted by the waves to their center as a compacting pressure which causes them to integrate around a point-center, thus making it possible for that center to react with a functional counter-pressure. The possible wave structures are limited, therefore, to those which are center-acting dynamic processes, continually transmitting momenta to and from the wave pattern's center. This interaction can also be defined as compacted waves contained by a static stress field.

A further restriction on a stationary wave pattern's possible structure is that its organizer must be either a potential energy state or a momentum: it cannot be both. Since the organizer is the only part of a wave pattern which can absorb or liberate energy, its ability to do so is limited to the form it takes at the center of that pattern. This restriction would be meaningless without an implementing converging field reaction, because periodic pulsations alternate between potential and kinetic states. Its compacting of a pattern's waves appears as a static stress which tends to resolve into action through the organizer in the form it takes at that point. It must be emphasized that the waves of a pattern cannot liberate energy by themselves, but exert a pressure upon their organizer which give it an action potential. An electron can liberate potential energy, and a positron a momentum, but they cannot do so unless the energy is absorbed in the form in which it is liberated.

The waves of a pattern are neutral when their local dynamic inversions alternate between equal potential and kinetic states. A neutral state has no tendencies, except those normal to all waves, such as a tendency to expand when free to do so, to integrate in containment, and to fill all available space. All wave actions in nature are, therefore, neutral; such as those of free photons, the velocity patterns of moving bodies, and the patterns of stationary wave structures. There is no tendency by a neutral wave to increase or reduce its energy by absorption or radiation; only its organizer has that tendency.

When a group of neutral waves are contained in common by the converging field, they tend to integrate their waves, but they cannot evolve an integrating organizer without a separation of their potential and kinetic states at their centers through the evolution of spherical and radial wave patterns. Spherical wave patterns absorb and integrate the potential energy of stationary states, radial waves patterns integrate the momenta of moving states. A cluster of neutral waves, such as low-energy free photons can, therefore, split up by reintegrations into electrons and positrons when conditions are favorable. They evolve because contained waves tend to integrate beyond the possibility of a neutral wave pattern, and because the containing forces are center-acting.

Note that the fundamental particles of matter are not the products of an accident or an artificial creation, but came into being because contained waves tend to escape into structure: a tendency which can also be defined by noting that organization is an energy equivalent. The efficiency with which a specific quantity of energy transmits a momentum per unit time increases with the compacting of waves associated with integration and the evolution of organizers. It will be noticed that organization is not energy, but a more efficient utilization of available energy. It can, therefore, replace energy under certain circumstances. The evolution of matter must be treated as a collapse of casually moving and distributed waves into structure, induced by the contracting ether.

My theory of organizers assumes that stationary wave patterns cannot integrate to natural quantum states without the evolution of implementing positive and negative electrostatic charges, because charges represent the ability of organizers to absorb and liberate energy in response to internal and external tendencies. This leads to the conclusion that the masses and charges of electrons and positrons are fundamental quantum states, and that protons and neutrons have been built up to their natural quantum states by evolving around a positron's charge pattern.

4-2 Static Stress Fields.

Static stress fields are functional deformations of the contracting ether's natural dynamic progression in space and time by contained wave patterns. A theoretical definition of origin postulates a free expansion momentum of the wave patterns proportional to their energies. Its interaction with the ether's local contraction mómentum, reacting in depth, results in a mutual blocking. The reflection of their momenta back upon their origins results in the appearance of a static stress field with a gradient of power in depth, decreasing with distance in inverse proportion to the ascending potential power of the reacting converging field forces. The pattern's waves are compacted by the contracting ether, and the expansion pressure of those waves displaces its natural dynamic progression in space and time.

The converging field's contraction momenta, and their displacements by contained waves, are transmitted through space with twice the speed of light. Since nothing can impede the expansion of such displacements, all local reductions of the contracting ether's natural dynamic progression will, in time, include that of the whole universe. By using its natural dynamic progression as a measure of the advance of time, we find that matter produces a local momentary reduction of its progress proportional to mass, and that it will then resume its advance as before. The containing forces of a static stress field can be defined as a tendency of the contracting ether to resume its original time schedule. Since this tendency has a gradient of descending power with distance from a mass, a static stress field can also be defined as a local deformation of space by matter—a fourth-dimension action potential of space.

The appearance of à natural balance between a wave pattern's expansion pressure and its containing converging field reactions become a continuous static equality of opposite forces, a static stress field through which the contracting ether resumes its natural progress as if no interaction has taken place. It is then ready to interact with additional energy absorbed by the pattern until a natural quantum maximum has been attained, or it may interact with any other center in the area, as if it were alone in space. Since each interaction resolves into a static stress, the converging field forces can interact with an infinite number of fundamental particles in an area without losing their ability to interact with more.

The static stress field produced by a contained wave pattern's interaction with the contracting ether would also come into being if the ether did not contract but, in that case, there would be no counter-force to prevent its continuous expansion and dispersal. The tendency of a stationary pattern's waves to expand and disperse would be inhibited by the existence of a static stress field, but nothing can prevent its dispersal with time. Although individual particles of matter are contained by static stress fields, the contracting ether determines their natural quantum states by defining the point at which dispersal exceeds integration.

The contracting ether is composed of moving particles whose casual collisions produce a mean density and a uniform increase of density over immense areas. Local wave motions increase the velocity of these ether particles in direct proportion to their energy, and the ether's local density is reduced below its areal mean in proportion. (The comparable expansion of a gas, due to a local increase of temperature, gives us the term "temperature effect" for this reaction.) Since any concentration of wave energy produces this reaction in the ether, the wave-containing forces of its contraction initiate a process which results in the observed concentrations of energy and static stress fields at the centers of the particles of matter; the temperature effect produces local expansions which become static stress fields, because the ether tends to revert to its original state by equalizing its density and particle velocities.

The concentration of energy in the fundamental particles is the product of three interacting causes. Center-acting converging field forces cause waves to integrate as center-supported dynamic actions with an energy maximum at each particle's point center. The natural gradient of converging field reactions increases the concentration by increasing the particle's energy gradient. The transitions of all center-supported dynamic actions into static stress fields leave the converging field forces free to contain additional energy at the center of a fundamental particle until a natural quantum maximum has been attained. From the charge-mass relations of electrons and protons, this last increase is equal to their second quantum energies raised to their fourth powers.

Since the temperature effect which brings the static stress field into being is greatest at the center of a wave pattern, where its energy is greatest, it follows that the static stress field is also maximum at that point, and that its force potential and its gradient of power are directly proportional to the energy it contains. Its interaction with the organizer of a wave pattern determines the pattern's reactions to intruding forces—whether it will absorb, transmit, repel or liberate energy. Their interactions produce the repulsions and attractions of similar and opposite electrostatic charges.

Gravity acts through the static stress fields as a tendency of separate masses to merge. It is a tendency of converging field forces to eliminate reducible deformations of the contracting ether's natural dynamic progression, induced by masses when separated in space. It is a feeble force in comparison with the forces producing the rest masses of matter, and it acts through the static stress fields on all waves (contained energies) regardless of shapes and functions.

The action potentials of both electrostatic and gravitational forces decrease as the inverse square of the distance between their causative centers. This gradient can be related to the static stress fields surrounding all masses by assuming that the energy of a potential action is located at the center of a particle or mass. Because this center is the only place where a stationary wave pattern can interact with its environment, its electrostatic and gravitational forces originate at that point as a static stress field with a force potential equal to the forces containing the wave pattern. The stress field is functionally stable because deviations from an equality of opposite forces are equalized in space with twice the speed of light. Since its total force—the force acting through the surface of a sphere—is the same at all distances from a wave center, it follows that its action potential in a particular direction decreases as the inverse square of the distance (like the brightness of light radiated by a point source).

4-3 Electrostatic Charges.

An electrostatic charge is the action potential of a stationary fundamental wave pattern in its natural quantum state. It acts through the organizer of a spherical or radial wave pattern by liberating or absorbing the potential energy of an electron's negative charge or the momentum of a proton's positive charge. In both types of wave patterns, attractions and repulsions are implemented by interactions between the tendencies of contained waves and their containing forces. Since interacting waves cannot attract and converging field forces cannot repel, it is evident that electrostatic repulsions are implemented by contained waves, and attractions by their containing forces. However, the interplay of these forces, with the expansion pressure of stationary waves producing converging field reactions compacting them and accentuating their tendency to expand, makes it necessary to distinguish between primary and implementing causes. The primary cause of electrostatic attractions and repulsions is a tendency of the contracting ether to reduce the local deformations of its natural dynamic progression, and their implementing causes are the action potentials of contained waves.

A stationary charge pattern's waves are electrostatically neutral beyond its point organizer. Its fundamental wave is an essential part of the organizer, but its waves beyond that are a neutral slave field whose local energies, shapes, locations and periodicities are determined by their organizer and by the momenta they must carry from center to space and back along a natural gradient, as a functional continuity of its actions in space and time. The expansion pressure produces an equalizing containing reaction which compacts the waves and causes a concentration of energy at its center. This energy can be released through its organizer as a repulsive force implementing an electrostatic attraction or repulsion in response to the converging field's tendency to reduce local static stresses by acting through the static stress fields of two interacting charge patterns. It will be noticed that the concentration of energy at a charge pattern's point-center defines its electrostatic force potential, and that the waves of its rest mass, beyond that center, can gain and lose energy only by acting through their organizer.

The organizer of a spherical wave pattern is a potential energy state—a stationary state with more energy than momentum. The waves of its rest-mass pattern can be defined as the periodic pulsations of self-contained waves when the forces of its containing field are included in their definition. It follows that when some of the wave pattern's rest-mass energy is abstracted through its organizer, the waves which come into being by this reaction take the form of stationary periodic pulsations. Since there is no incentive to produce such a transfer within the pattern itself, it must have its origin as a bias of its containing forces.

The organizer of a radial wave pattern is a kinetic energy state—a rotary motion with more momentum than energy. The combination of radial and orbital momenta which define the functional structure of its wave pattern produces deformations of the contracting ether's natural dynamic progression and the tendentious spherical shape of the static stress field. They are produced by individual waves as well as by the radial wave pattern as a whole. Energy liberated by a radial wave pattern's organizer must take the same form as its internal motions: a continuous momentum without periodic pulsations. When it is blocked by the contracting ether, a stationary radial wave pattern similar to that of its origin comes into being. It does not become a spherical wave pattern, because such a transition would leave unresolved momentum gradients. Since there is no incentive to produce a transfer of wave momenta within the pattern itself, it must have its origin in the contracting ether and the tendencies of static stress fields.

These two kinds of electrostatic charges come into being because the dynamic possibilities of center-supported periodic waves are limited to spherical and radial wave patterns. A principal condition for the evolution of such patterns is that they must be able to absorb energy from local casual waves and convert it into the form in which it appears within their functional wave structures, and that this absorption continues until they have attained their natural maximum masses. An obvious implication of this postulate is that the process is reversible; that the organizers of such masses will also liberate and transmit energy in response to external causes, and that their reactions are such as to preserve their wave structures and natural quantum states. Since the masses of electrons and positrons are normally at their natural quantum maximas, it must be assumed that energy lost by radiation is soon restored by absorptions from low-energy, casually moving ground field waves clustering about the particles, or from their velocity patterns of physical motions. In atoms, this interaction obviously produces the quantized orbits of electrons, and their radiations and absorprtions when changing orbits.

An electron's spherical wave pattern can absorb, radiate and transmit the potential energy of stationary waves only, and a positron's radial wave pattern can absorb, radiate and transmit kinetic energy (momenta) only. The difference between them can also be defined by stating that an electron is related to the energy of contained waves, and a positron to its containing forces. When the static stress fields of similar charge patterns overlap anywhere in space, their interactions are transmitted by their organizers as a directed flow with maximas opposite the point of intrusion. The converging field reacts through the static stress field with the evolution of a convection current supporting an apparent displacement of each pattern's center. Their centers will, therefore, move apart with an accelerating velocity, or exert a proportional force in that direction when a physical acceleration is not possible. Similar electrostatic charges, therefore, repel each other with a force inversely proportional to the square of the distance between their centers.

When the static stress fields of electrons and positrons overlap in space, the stationary periodic waves of the former combine with the momenta of the latter to produce a local neutral state and the neutral energy of a free photon. In such a photon the negative charge becomes its transverse periodic waves, and the positive charge its momentum pattern—a functional recurve of the contracting ether motions around and through its stationary waves, thus causing them to move with the speed of light relative to the local configuration space. The loss of energy by both organizers in the area between them produces a dynamically unbalanced state to which the converging field reacts with an acceleration recurve directed toward the center of the opposite charges, thus restoring the natural symmetry of their forces by a convergent motion. Where no accleration is possible, its force equivalent takes the form of an electrostatic attraction.

In atoms the electrostatic attraction causes electrons to circle their positive centers with quantized velocities in quantized orbits. When an electron drops from a larger to a smaller orbit, the difference in energy between the two orbits is liberated and become the energy-wavelength of a free photon. When an atom captures a free photon, such as a photon of light, the reaction is reversed and an electron jumps from a lower to a higher quantum state. In ordinary (gross) electrostatic attractions and repulsions, the energy lost or gained in a change of distance between two charges is equal to the potential energy difference between the original and terminal distance. Note that a static stress field must originate as a wave-induced deformation of the contracting ether's natural dynamic progression, and that potential energy is its product.

As long as the forces containing a fundamental wave pattern are not deforming its natural shape, its electrostatic charge remains functionally inactive. However, when that shape is deformed, its charge pattern reacts to restore it by a change of velocity or direction of motion, or both. In all such interactions, the first cause is a reducible deformation of overlapping static stress fields and the converging field forces acting in conjunction, with the action potential of each charge pattern the implementing cause of a particular response. An electrostatic charge pattern can be deformed by another charge, by a magnetic field, and by a directed force.

The compacting of an electron's rest mass wave energy at its center defines its wavelength radius, and that radius, in turn, defines the momentum it can transmit as the electron's electrostatic charge. The force of that charge decreases as the inverse square of the distance from its center. Observation shows that an electron's radius wavelength in one natural unit of length is -41.75 in basic logarithms, and its electrostatic charge at unit distance is its square root, -20.875, for a system of units in which the unit of time is the time it takes a light wave to move one natural length. An increase of this time unit increases an electron's electrostatic charge value by the difference squared. In the ultimate system of units, in which an electron's radius is the unit of length, its electrostatic charge is also unity. These figures and relations have been proved in Book One by relating them to the observed gaussian constants.

4-4 Free Photons.

A free photon is a wave pattern moving through the ether, or a configuration space, with the speed of light. It is an integrated pattern of plane-polorized transverse periodic waves with identical wavelengths, whose actions upon the contracting ether induce a containing reaction which recurves as the pattern advances, to become a directional flow defining its momentum. The photon is free in the sense that it does not contain velocity-reducing matter at its center of inertia, beyond that essential to the implementation of its motion and momentum. Its velocity is, therefore, the maximum attainable for a contained wave pattern.

In defining the relationship between a free photon's energy and momentum, it must be kept in mind that we are dealing with two absolutes. The periodic pulsations of contained and self-contained waves are functionally stationary, whereas the momenta they bring into being are transmitted through the ether with twice the speed of light. Combined in equal proportions in a free photon, their common velocity is a compromise speed—the velocity of light. That the velocity of a photon of light is less than its containing forces is an obvious conclusion, since those forces cannot surround and induce a specific structure upon the waves they contain without a velocity that is greater than that with which the pattern is moving. That a free photon is an integrated wave structure has been proved by experiments and analysis. Each photon contains a specific quantity of energy, and a wavelength inversely proportional to that energy. It can move through space for millions of light years without loss of energy, thus proving that a free photon behaves in space like a particle of matter.

Elementary logic tells us that all self-contained structures, or at least their centers of inertia, are stationary within their individual frames of reference. Since a free photon is such a structure, its center of inertia is always stationary within its own configuration of forces—its configuration space. We know from experiments with light waves that interference phenomena indicate extensions of their wave structures in space. A scientist once commented that a light photon appears to have the size of a barrel. It is to be assumed its energy decreases from center to space in all directions on its plane of vibration, and that the finite value of that energy implies a finite size; probably a tapering off to zero at infinity along a gradient which sets a practical limit to its size. My theory postulates an energy gradient decreasing with distance from the photon's center as the inverse square in all directions on the plane of its waves.

The earth's mass is composed of countless particles whose motions are supported by directional momenta which preserve their individual stationary states. The extension of those momenta into space along a descending gradient of power defines the earth's total momentum of motion and rotation, with the earth's mass stationary within its own local configuration space. When a free photon passes over its surface, these momenta are added to, or subtracted from, its own momentum. Its slight change of velocity is such as to produce the same speed of light in all directions on the earth's surface. This is my theory of local relativity, as distinguished from general relativity (a concept I reject as being unprovable and contrary to reason).

The periodic waves of a free photon are transverse, because that is the only direction in which they can expand as functionally stationary states. Its waves are plane-polarized because a rotary (magnetic) motion of its recurving converging field force interacts with a tendency of the waves to expand by concentrating their energies on a plane. This tendency is dominant, since motion displaces the converging field reactions toward its antapex; hence their recurve becomes a directional momentum acting upon the transverse waves with a force which causes them to move with the speed of light.

My theory of the contracting ether leads to the conclusion that its convergent momenta have no observable existence until they are blocked by the expansion momenta of periodic waves. The momentum of a free photon is, therefore, an equivalent of the expansion pressure exerted by its contained waves. The contracting ether acts as an inertia block at the photon's apex of motion and as an accelerating force at its antapex, with a transition from one to the other along its circumference. The photon's energy decreases in all directions on the plane of its waves, as the inverse square of the distance from its center for its total value. There is no point organizer at the center of inertia of a free photon, even though the waves at that center interact with the contracting ether momenta to produce an integrated wave structure and a wavelength inversely proportional to its energy. Its wave pattern can, therefore, be split and recombined to produce an interference pattern. Observation shows that both wavelength and energy quantum are preserved during the reaction. There are aspects of this continuity for which I have no explanation.

The relationship between a free photon's wavelength and its momentum can also be explained by starting our analysis with a free momentum in the contracting ether. Its deformation of the contracting ether's natural dynamic progression produces a containing force, a reaction which halves its velocity and reduces its active area. The transverse expansion which appears as a product of this reaction is contained by converging field forces increasing in powers with both distance and interaction time. The theoretical pulsation time of this expansion can be reduced by a subdivision of its waves to the natural wavelength of that photon. A large part of the original momentum is converted into the energy of its transverse waves, and its remaining momentum integrates with the contracting ether as the gradient of its functional recurve into a directional momentum.

Let us assume that the converging field forces containing a free photon's momentum at its apex of motion were completely removed. The high-density area defining the transition of its momentum into the ether's increasing density would disappear, and its momentum would flow on until it met a new opposition. The photon's transverse waves would collapse into its momentum and become variations of force along its axis of motion as the momentum, moving without an inhibiting inertia block at its apex, flows onward at twice the speed of light. A new point of opposition resurrects its momentum and wavelength.

When a free photon approaches an atom with potential periodicities in harmony with its own wavelength, the inertia block at its apex of motion is removed and its waves collapse into its momentum as both enter the atom at twice the speed of light. In the atom they reappear as the acceleration of an orbital electron and a quantum jump of that electron into a higher quantum orbit. This reaction is comparable to the tuning in of a radio receiver to a broadcast station's wavelength. If the electron above were to drop into its original orbit, the process would be reversed, and a free photon with the same wavelength as the one we started with would come into being.

4-5 Velocity Patterns.

A velocity pattern implements the energy-momentum of a moving "stationary" wave pattern; with the motion related to the ether in free space and to the local configuration space near matter. It can come into being in many ways through the application of force· to theoretically stationary particles of matter. Its simplest definition postulates the union of a free photon with a stationary particle, with the resulting motion a compromise in which both retain their original states. The waves of its velocity pattern will continue to induce and support a recurring directional momentum as they did in free space, and the waves of its stationary pattern will continue to act as if no motion had been induced by its union with a free photon. It can remain functionally stationary because its velocity pattern's momentum appears as its local configuration space—a directed force acting constantly on its waves, thus causing them to move to retain the stationary state.

In theoretical physics we are usually dealing with fundamental dynamic processes which make compromise states impossible, even though the union of two different wave structures appears to be such a compromise. A first conclusion assumes a functional continuity of original dynamic processes and states, as far as possible, in the union of two patterns. The center of a stationary wave pattern must always be stationary in its local configuration space, because the continuity of its wave structure and functions depends upon it. The only way it can move is by evolving or associating itself with a directional momentum pattern which leaves its center of inertia and its rest-mass waves functionally stationary, relative to the local forces of that momentum. A constant motion anticipates the continuous force of a velocity pattern's momentum, as defined for a free photon.

My theory of the ether leads to the conclusion that two momenta cannot occupy the same space without interaction. However, if these momenta are the periodical inversions of waves with different wavelengths, the statistical interaction mean is zero, and their functional continuities are as if no interaction had occurred. But if one of these momenta is a directed force with continuity in time, it acts upon other momenta and waves with an acceleration thrust if it is a separate phenomenon, and with a continuous displacement of their positions if it is a functional part of their pattern. The momentum of a moving pattern can be described, therefore, as the configuration space of its stationary waves, with the waves moving with a velocity proportional to their displacement by that space. The pattern's velocity can be defined by postulating an inertia for its stationary free photon and rest-mass waves proportional to their kinetic energies, and a force acting constantly upon that inertia to change the pattern's position in space at a proportional rate. The union of a free photon and a stationary wave pattern is a merger of their containing reaction forces, with both retaining their original states within their combined wave complex.

A momentum cannot distinguish between the waves of a complex. It acts upon all waves within an integrated pattern with a directional thrust which causes them to move as a unit. This distribution is imposed by the tendency of all stationary wave patterns to retain their natural configurations of center-acting forces by retaining the stationary state under all conditions of motion and change. It is a product of the tendency of contained waves to escape into structure which led to the evolution of matter, as it appears today.

In defining the velocity of a moving mass, it must be kept in mind that the free photon with which it is united as its velocity pattern also has a stationary energy pattern; an inertia which halves its momentum's velocity. A stationary wave pattern cannot be accelerated to the speed of light because, no matter how much energy is possessed by its velocity pattern, its opposition to motion will always keep the velocity below that of light, since the ability of a free photon to exert an accelerating force is zero at the speed of light.

The inertia of any moving mass equals the energy of its rest mass times the energy of its velocity pattern. For low velocities this last factor is negligible in comparison with that of the rest mass and can be ignored, but for velocities near that of light it becomes a significant factor. Since it is impossible to accelerate a visible mass to a velocity where the increase of mass-inertia becomes significant, the experimental proof of this increase is confined to electrons and protons. In Book One I have worked out a table of an electron's elements of motion at high velocities which includes its increase of mass. In another table, I have defined the same acceleration volts, with the electron's elements of motion being based on the assumption that no increase of mass occurs. It gives us a continuation of its observed changes at low velocities to the point where energy and momentum wavelengths are identical, at twice an electron's mass and twice the speed of light.

It will be noticed that in this theory an electron's mass is not increased by motion, as postulated by the theory of relativity. There is an apparent increase of mass because the mass-equivalent of a free photon's energy is added to its inertia when it becomes the electron's velocity pattern, but each kind of mass is related to a different quantizing structure. However, the forces containing an electron's rest-mass waves act also upon those of its velocity pattern to reduce their wavelengths. It follows that the energy waves defining an electron's energy of motion, by relating them to the wavelength of a free photon with that energy, are much longer than those defining its velocity pattern's true wavelength. The difference is greatest at low velocities and decreases with an increase, as defined by the two tables in Book One. The electron's momentum-related true wavelengths are also called its de Broglie waves, after the man who discovered and defined them.

In this book I use the term "momentum waves" for the velocity waves of a moving mass, because their wavelength is directly related to its momentum (F), as defined by mass times velocity: $F = MV$. Its wavelength (B) is obtained by dividing Planck's quantum (h) by mass times velocity: $B = h/MV$. Its energy of motion (E) is obtained by multiplying one half of its mass by its velocity squared: $E = \frac{1}{2}MV^2$.

The wavelength of a moving electron can be checked against its formal value in various ways. In the hydrogen atom it defines the circumference of a sequence of orbits by two equations. Its electrostatic attraction is equated with its centrifugal force, and the wavelength of the orbital velocity thus obtained is equated with the orbit's circumference in its lowest quantum state. For the sequence of larger quantum orbits we have two, three, four and more waves to circumference for the orbit radii four, nine and sixteen, respectively. An electron's wavelength can also be checked against its refractive index in the electron microscope. Because the wavelengths of moving electrons are much smaller than those of free photons, they can be used to observe smaller objects.

4-6 Electromagnetic Fields.

The tendency of casual waves contained in common to reduce their casual interferences by integration appears in the organizer of a charge pattern as a functional defense of its natural wave structure. This tendency to organize is constantly interacting with intrusive forces in the charge pattern's enviornment by absorbing and liberating energy in support of its wave structure, its stationary state and the natural quantum states of its mass. When the organizer is acted upon by an external force, its acceleration relative to the local configuration space causes it to absorb energy from that force and convert it into a velocity pattern. The directional momentum of this pattern is distributed through its structure in a way which restores its stationary state. By reversing this interaction, we find that a charge pattern can abstract energy from its velocity pattern and liberate it into its environment, thus losing velocity in proportion.

This intimate relationship between an electrostatic charge and its velocity pattern defines its action potentials, with the charge acting as a catalyst, and its velocity pattern as a reservoir of energy. A charge pattern can convert energy from one form to another without an observable change in its own mass and charge; it does so because the restoration of its pattern's stationary state is a functional imperative. A constant change of velocity or direction of motion produces an equally constant transfer of energy and momentum in response.

When an electrostatic charge is caused to circle a center, its constant change of direction converts its velocity pattern's momentum of motion into a magnetic rotation around that center; a rotary displacement of the ether's natural dynamic progression. A magnetic field is, therefore, produced in a coil of insulated wire (a solinoid), when a current of electrons flows through it. The momentum of this field is abstracted from the source of the current. The value of the field is such as to leave each electron in the current theoretically stationary in its local configuration field, as defined by the directional motion of its magnetic field. That this is so can be proved by inserting a paramagnetic body in the coil. This body abstracts energy and momentum from the evolving magnetic field by converting these forces into rotating fields within its own mass, thus reducing the magnetic moment within the coil. The electrons react with a transfer build-up of the magnetic field momentum until their stationary states are attained.

Magnetic fields are also produced by electrons circling an atom's positive nucleus. The simplicity of a hydrogen atom's structure gives us an elementary relationship between its two opposite charges, its electron's velocity, the wavelength of its velocity pattern, and its magnetic field. Their experimental and theoretical values are defined in Book One. My sequence formula in that book defines the magnetic field of a hydrogen electron in its smallest (K) orbit (a Bohr magneton) by dividing the electrostatic charge by four pi times the electron's rest mass wavenumber: $\mu = e/4\pi\tilde{v}$. It gives us a numerical value in accord with the conventional formula: $\mu = he/4\pi mc$.

The results of these two formulas are in accord with the figure for Planck's quantum divided by 4π in the ultimate system of units, although its apparent value of 68.5224045 electron masses is obviously out of proportion. The obvious reason is that it is, like an electron's rest mass wavelength and Planck's quantum, in electromagnetic units (emu) and, therefore, greater than values in electrostatic (esu) units by 9.75 in basic logarithms for identical energies. It reminds us that the natural unit of length is the fundamental quantizing factor, and that an electron's radius unit is an abstraction; it brings out the ideal proportions in nature for all factors related to stationary wave structures, but gives fictitious values for those related to free photons. The energy of a Bohr magneton is too large in the ultimate system of units because it is related to a free photon through an electron's rest mass wavenumber.

In the ultimate system of units an electron's mass, charge and radius wavelength all have unit values. Because the speed of light is also unity for this system, it follows that the energy of its mass unit must also be unity. Let us now assume that this electron's rest mass is converted into the wave energy of a free photon. In measuring its wavelength we find it is 861.077930 times longer than that of the electron, and we find its defined energy is also that much greater than the electron's rest mass energy, whereas reason tells us it must be the same—that it must be unity. The reason for this difference is that we are making the error of defining the free photon's energy in terms of an electron's radius length and pulse-time unit, although it takes free photon waves over 800 times longer to pass through a single pulsation cycle, thus transmitting a unit of energy from one point to another.

Planck's quantum of energy is defined as the energy of a single wave with a length equal to its system's length unit. If this definition is valid for an electron's radius wavelength as well as for the radius wavelength of a free photon with the same energy, it follows that in a conversion from one to the other we are dealing with two different systems of units. In order to make a free photon's energy-per-unit wave unity, the same as that of the electron's, we must increase both the unit of length and the unit of time by 861.077930, $\log_2$ 9.75. A Bohr magneton's energy is obtained from a system's electrostatic charge unit, divided by its rest mass wavenumber in free photon length units times two pi. Its rest mass relation means that its value is obtained by relating it to free photon dimensions. When this is done for its value in the ultimate system of units, we get the following figure in basic logarithms:

$$\mu = 6.098504/9.75 = -3.651496 = 1/4\pi.$$

A Bohr magneton in the ultimate system is, therefore, less than its electrostatic charge by four pi. This is the geometrical ratio of a sphere's surface to its unit radius; it is also the ratio of a magnet's pole strength to its flux density.

4-7 Magnetism.

A magnetic field is the rotary displacement of wave-containing converging field forces and static stress fields by orbital or revolving electrostatic charges. It is a vorticular rotation of local configuration space, with velocity gradients from center to zero with distance, and from a maximum on its equator decreasing to zero in latitude to its poles. Being charge-related, it can gain and lose energy through its interactions with the velocity patterns of the charges. Even though a magnetic field cannot exist without support from electrostatic charges, its evolution of a semi-independent vorticular momentum structure produces attractive and repulsive forces comparable to those acting between vortices in gases and liquids.

A magnet's lines of force are lines of equal velocity of rotation. They converge on its poles where their gradients, and therefore its magnetic force, are greatest. A magnet's north pole rotates clockwise and its south pole counter-clockwise. These directions are obtained by converting an electron's orbital momentum into the momentum of its magnetic field. Assuming that the earth's magnetic field is produced by its rotation, a north magnetic pole at its south pole confirms this postulated direction.

According to my theory, two continuous momenta cannot occupy the same space without an interaction which results in a merger or mutual blocking, depending on relative directions. The magnetic lines of force of overlapping fields are deformed in accordance with the theory of contained rotations and a functional continuity of motions. The tendency of parallel-moving fields to merge produces an attraction because the forces containing their rotations are reduced between their centers. When two magnetic fields are rotating in opposite directions, the mutual blocking of their momenta becomes a repulsive force between their centers. Opposite magnetic poles, therefore, attract, and similar poles repel.

When a stream of electrons (an electric current) is caused to circle the center of a solinoid, the magnetic field they bring into being is proportional to their combined momenta. The momenta of electrons moving in a straight line are maximum at the charge centers, but when they are caused to circle the center of an atom or a conducting coil, their momenta are displaced toward those centers. The magnetic field which evolves, therefore, has a functional independency, with gradients from center to space. When a ferro-magnetic substance, such as iron, is inserted in the coil, the free spin and orientation-free orbital electrons in its atoms interact with its magnetic field. An orbital momentum is abstracted from the electric current through its magnetic field by the magnetons and spin fields of the paramagnetic body. The force is expended to overcome the contracting ether's neutral orientation bias, even though the observed effect is the appearance of a magnetic field whose momentum is directly proportional to that expended by the electric current.

The contracting ether and its abstracted static stress fields react to the vorticular rotation of a magnetic field with a maximum containing force on its plane of revolution. The absence of time-related periodicities makes it impossible for a magnetic field to evolve without an implementing cause or a local rotation bias; when this cause or bias is removed, the field resolves into periodic waves, because its transformation into waves is a local reduction of the deformation of the contracting ether's natural dynamic progression through a reduction of action time.

I believe magnetic fields in the atoms are the products of three causes. The first of these is a transition of the charge momenta of orbiting electrons into vorticular rotations around their centers of inertia. These magnetic spin fields act in conjunction with the velocity waves defining the radii of the electron orbits, but their evolving structures are functionally independent quantum states. The second is a tendency of the contracting ether to reduce the rotary displacements of its natural dynamic progression, by causing counter-rotating magnetic fields to evolve around charge centers. It reduces the displacement by a primary rotation to a statistically neutral state in minimum space and time, by causing periodic interactions between opposite rotating fields, thus producing integrating periodic waves. When the interaction is between free-spin waves, the reduction takes the form of an exchange of spin directions by electrons. The third cause is a relativity effect. When two orbiting electrons pass close to each other, their velocity patterns evolve steep transition gradients to a relative zero-point velocity between them. This interaction resolves into a magnetic rotation around their centers in the same direction, thus taking the form of a magnetic repulsion between them. The functional continuity of these fields after interaction is open to question, but in my first two postulates the evolution of integrating magnetic fields to their natural quantum states has been proved.

The symmetrical shape of a magnetic momentum around its circumference reduces the tendency of its containing forces to induce a change of orientation toward a spherical symmetry to zero. But it is evident from both theory and observation that the electron producing the magnetic field responds readily to this tendency. The constant changes of its plane of revolution may prevent the evolution of a magnetic field, or its evolution may produce a compromise reaction. The electron remains on a particular plane of revolution until its reorientation bias becomes dominant. It will then jump into a new position, where it evolves a new magnetic field, while its old field disintegrates into periodic waves which unite with the electron's velocity patterns to become the momentum of its new magneton. This space-quantizing of an electron's magnetic field is brought out by superimposing an external magnetic field on radiating atoms. It is called "the Zeeman effect."

The contracting ether's opposition to the deformation of its natural dynamic progression by magnetic fields appears as a tendency to integrate the reducible effects of those fields to statistically neutral states. This is effected through an exchange of opposite spin fields and by motions and changes of orbital planes of rotation. These cyclic interactions produce periodic wave motions whose functional integrations approach the neutral state locally, and appear as a completely neutral state statistically on a relatively long time base. The magnetic fields of all substances, therefore, are normally in the neutral state beyond molecular dimensions. When a magnetic field acts upon a paramagnetic substance, its rotary momentum is absorbed by that substance as a tendentious force which causes its magnetic particles to rotate with the primary field against the neutral tendency of its containing forces. The interaction is, therefore, between opposite tendencies, although the effect is the same as if a transfer of momentum had occurred; from the orbital electron velocities of a current or in atoms, to similar motions in the evolving field. In all cases we distinguish between actual casual motions in all directions and their statistical mean motions in the particular direction, with the momentum of that mean defining a magnetic field.

When free electrons and positrons are caused to move across the poles of a magnetic field, the electrons recurve (curl) against its rotation, and the positrons with it. Their directions are changed by the magnetic field, but their velocities are not affected by it. These opposite effects can be explained by postulating a road of least resistance, or the presence of charge equivalents in the magnetic field, with their recurves appearing as an attraction between opposite charges.

The converging field's tendency to reduce its displacement by a magnetic field by inducing a counter-rotation, when acting upon a moving electron, will cause that body to recurve against momentum of the magnetic field, because that motion produces a counter-magnetic field which reduces the former's power. A positron recurves with the magnetic field because its radial organizer tends to draw the magnetic field momenta onto its own plane of motion, thus causing a contraction of the the magnetic field with an increase of the forces containing them in common. There is also a reduction of the deformation of their combined field, caused by the positron's motion. If the positron recurved in the same direction as an electron, their momenta would be acting against each other, and the positron would come to a complete stop—an impossible solution.

The vorticular motion of a magnetic field is contained by the contracting ether and its abstracted static stress field. Reducible potential energy states appear at all points where the containing forces are deflected by magnetic momenta. While an electron's potential energy tends to unite with the magnetic momenta, a positron's momentum field tends to unite with the potential energy states causing the contained momentum field to recurve. Postulating an attraction between opposite charges, we again obtain the opposite recurves of positive and negative moving charges.

4-8 Magnetons. (Spin Fields.)

A magneton is the magnetic field of a fundamental particle of matter; a vorticular rotation of local configuration space around the center of an electrostatic charge unit. It originates as a rotation bias, and it builds up to its natural quantum state by the tendency of contained waves to converge on areas of maximum expansion and thus increases the power of a rotation momentum. The symmetrical shape of a spin field's momentum causes its containing reaction forces to recurve toward its poles, thus permitting the rotation momentum to build up to its natural maximum.

The magnetic rotations produced by orbiting electrons in the atoms bring into being a counter-rotation bias, with a potential response by the organizers of their positive and negative charges. An organizer reacts with a rotation of the ground field energy which it is constantly absorbing to maintain its natural quantum mass and charge against losses by destructive intrusions. The tendency of contained waves to expand appears as a tendency to concentrate their energies on its plane of rotation, and to build it up to a natural maximum. Although the converging field provides the initial rotation bias, it does not maintain it and does not, therefore, determine its quantized energy.

The organizer of a charge pattern is also the organizer of its velocity pattern, the magnetic field of its orbital motion and its spin field. In producing these effects, it must be kept in mind that its first task is to maintain the charge pattern's natural shape and functions, and that its three secondary effects are incidental to that purpose. A charge pattern can evolve a spin field because such a field does not interfere with the natural functions of its dynamic processes. The spin field, however, is not an essential part of those functions and can, therefore, be lost or reversed by an exchange between oppositely spinning electrons.

The continuous rotation momentum of a magnetic field produces an action time of infinite duration in comparison with the pulsation periods of largely self-contained waves. The periodic waves which come into being with periodic exchanges of spin fields, therefore, represent a reduction of the forces needed to contain a given quantity of energy. The difference represents a non-electric attraction between the particles in an atom's nucleus and between its orbital electrons, and it appears as a bonding force between the atoms in a molecule. Here, as in all forms of attraction, we find containing forces are abstracted from the ether's contraction momenta by the expansion forces of contained energy; with a local force which can be defined as a reduction of the deformation of the contracting ether's natural dynamic progression and a reduction of interaction time between spin fields.

Observation shows that an electron's spin field energy is slightly greater than that of the magnetic field produced by an electron circling a proton in its smallest orbit, by about 1.0011596, and $\log_2$ 0.001672. However, its spin field momentum is only one half of its orbit's magnetic momentum. This is a geometrical ratio which defines the spin fields of the fundamental particles as half-quantum states. Opposite and similar spin fields tend to pair in atoms and molecules, thus producing zero or a full quantum spin field momenta.

A fundamental particle's spin field is built up by the action potential of its charge pattern's energy. Since the momentum of its rotation is the local configuration space of the particle's mass, its interaction with that mass reduces its value in proportion to the rotary displacement it causes. A first conclusion is that the spin field of an electron must be greater than that of a proton or a neutron by the difference in their rest masses, qualified by the observation that the mass does not revolve as a unit, and that it has a descending gradient of power to space.

Assuming that the observed difference between the energy of an electron's spin field and its orbital magnetic field is due to the differential rotation of its mass, a greater difference must be present in the far greater masses of protons and neutrons. A proton magneton is nearly three times greater, and a neutron magneton one and a half times greater than that expected by simple proportions.

The formula for a Bohr magneton is its charge wavenumber, divided by its rest mass wavenumber times four pi: $\mu = e/4\pi\tilde{v}$. The figures below are for the ideal and ultimate systems of units in Book One. The speed of light is unity for both systems, and an electron's charge is unity in the ultimate system. Its Bohr magneton is less than its charge by 4π.

Ideal system: $\mu = e/4\pi\tilde{v}$. Ultimate system: $\mu = e/4\pi\tilde{v}h$.
Ideal systems   -20.875/3.651496 × 32.0 = -56.526496 erg.
Ultimate system 0.0/3.651496 × -9.75 × 9.75 = -3.651496 erg.

Chapter 5

GRAVITY. PHOTONS. BONDING

Gravity is a relatively feeble attraction between neutral masses. The deformation of the contracting ether by a mass appears as a fourth dimension in space. Periodic changes of a gravity pattern produce periodic waves. A photon's radius is the distance from a wave center at which opposite forces are equal. It is obtained from the energy-gradient relations of a mass or quantum. Stationary wave patterns can have three photon radii: rest mass energy contained, by the contracting ether, by static stress fields, and by temperature displacements. Constants $h \times m_o = c = 1$, for systems where the speed of light is unity. The wavelength of a free photon with an electron's energy is longer by 861 electron radii. They have different action times. The energy equivalent of integration is radiated by the radial wave patterns of atomic nuclei, with organization acting as a bonding force. Periodic exchanges of energy within and between atoms determine attractions and bonding forces. Identical periodicities repel, and different periodicities attract. Atoms and molecules are defined. Quantized electron orbits become electron shells. Orientations are quantized. True motions are relative to the ether, observed motions are relative to local configuration spaces. A contained wave center is stationary in its own configuration space (its photon), even though moving relative to other spaces. Intrusive forces increase deformation of contracting ether, and the contraction reacts through the waves with an integration or repulsion. Electromagnetic induction is explained. Space relations of moving and rotating spheres are defined. All fundamental laws are qualified absolutes.

5-1 Gravitation.

Gravitation is a timeless tendency of the contracting ether to reduce the local deformations of its natural dynamic progression toward a spherical symmetry, by exerting an accelerating force on the causative masses toward their common center of inertia. It is a timeless reaction to the expansion pressures of contained waves, comparable to the tendency of a compressed spring, as contrasted with the time-related tendency of an electrostatic charge or the directed pressure of a stream of water.

Gravitation is an opposition by forces converging on the common center of inertia of separate masses against their recurves into those masses; it is a timeless tendency of local configuration spaces which, unlike an electrostatic charge, does not change the rest mass energies of its causative masses. The deformation of the contracting ether by matter is a fourth-dimension in the ordinary three-dimensional space. The center of inertia of each mass is the point on which a centripedal force, decreasing as the inverse square with distance, converges.

The gravitational attraction between two masses is, therefore, proportional to their rest masses multiplied together, with the proportion defined by the gravity constant, and inversely proportional to the square of the distance between their centers. It is a feeble force in comparison with the rest-mass energies which brings it into being and, mass for mass, it is an infinitesimal force in comparison with electrostatic and magnetic attractions and repulsions. And it differs from them by being always an attraction, since there can be no anti-gravity force to produce a repulsion—we cannot halt or reverse the contracting ether's natural dynamic progression.

An experimental determination of the force of gravity is obtained by measuring the attraction between two masses in the laboratory. The observed force is then converted into the gravitational attraction between two unit masses when their centers of inertia are one length unit apart. The gravitational attraction between any two masses can then be obtained by multiplying their masses in mass units times the gravity constant, divided by the square of their distance apart in length units.

The observed grativational attraction between two gram masses, one centimeter apart, is converted into the gravity constants of the ideal and ultimate systems by the formulas, $g = gm/c\phi^2$, and $g = gmL^2/c\phi^2$, respectively; with the latter appearing below in basic logarithms. (The symbols are defined in Book One.)

$$g = \frac{gm(L)^2}{c(\phi)^2} \qquad \frac{-23.838481X - 89.826801 \times (41.75)^2}{34.803248 \times (0.059298)^2} = -65.087126 \ dy$$

Since the electrostatic charge of the ultimate system of units is unity, its gravity constant must be the reciprocal of its electrostatic/gravity (e/g) ratio. The second conversion formula above gives us its gravity constant to a first approximation; a figure which can be checked against its e/g ratio for confirmation.

Since this first approximation must be close to the true value of the ultimate system's gravity constant, it eliminates various theoretical possibilities and serves as a guide to the selection of the most probable idealization formula. In our choice of formula we must show a proper regard for the evolution of quantized masses and the different origins and nature of electrostatic and gravitational forces.

We know that gravity is the product of a static deformation of configuration space by matter, and reason tells us that it must, therefore, be related to the statistical means of quantized rest masses contained within a natural unit of length. Electrostatic forces, on the other hand, are obviously related to the ultimate system of units because their simple functional relations are defined by that system. While gravitational forces are functionally timeless, electrostatic forces are directed resolutions of rest masses acting from their point centers through time. These differences, in conjunction with the fact that the statistical effects of gravity cannot exist in a system where wave motions are specific, once caused me to believe that no gravity constant could be defined for the ultimate system of units. Later, however, I found it possible to do so by using the wavelength of a electron's rest mass in one natural unit of length, in conjunction with factors from the ultimate system.

I obtained the gravity constant of the ultimate system to a first approximation by noting that the difference between the length units of two systems had to be cubed in order to keep the e/g ratio from changing. I also noted that a change of their time unit caused the gravity constant to change in direct proportion in the direction opposite to that of length, the same as that of the e/g ratio. Since the conversion from ideal to ultimate system units includes both a change of length and time, both of which have the same ratio value, a coincidence of values was obtained for the ultimate system by multiplying the gravity constant of the ideal system by their difference in length units squared, and by dividing its e/g ratio by their difference in time units.

The next problem was to convert this first approximation to its true, ideal proportion value, by finding a formula which would not go beyond the permissible margin of error of its experimental value. The different origins of electrostatic forces and gravity led to various probabilities, such as: the use of an electron's rest mass wavelength from the ideal system, the appearance of pi with a one-to-four ratio, and the inverse fourth power gradient of a rest mass.

A selection of probabilities based on my theory made it possible to work out the most probable ideal proportion formula for the gravity constant of the ultimate system of units. In this formula the symbol $\dot{v}$ is an electron's rest mass wavelength in one natural unit of length. The figures are in basic logarithms for easy checking, and the symbols are those used in Book One.

$$g = \frac{\dot{v}^L}{2\sqrt[4]{4/\pi}} \qquad \frac{(-32.)^3}{1 \times \sqrt[4]{2/1.6514961}} = -65.087126 \text{ dyne force in rmt.}$$

When this log number is divided by the cube of the difference between one natural length and an electron's radius, and multiplied by the same difference in action time (L^3/L^1, with L equal to 41.75), we get $\log_2$ -148.587126 dyne for the gravity constant of the ideal system of units. The ultimate system's e/g ratio times their difference in time units, gives us $\log_2$ 106.837126 as the e/g ratio of the ideal system. The gravity constant of the gaussian system is obtained by this formula: $g = gc\phi^2/mL^2$. In figures it idealized value is 6.666561×10^{-8} dynes the same as the practical value of 6.67×10^{-8} dyne obtained by experiments.

Although gravity is transmitted through the ether with twice the speed of light, its velocity is not infinite. In the solar system, the changing configurations of the planets circling its center of inertia are accompanied by dynamic changes of the system's gravity figure. The converging field reacts to these changes by causing the periodic changes of these configurations to resolve into periodic waves with orbital periods which are harmonics of the sidereal and conjunction periods of the planets. Another effect, caused by the local increase of centrifugal force relative to the force containing the planets in their orbits, appears as an expansion of the system's field at the longitude of a conjunction between two planets. There is an observable effect on the earth at the moment of conjunction and another when it passes the conjunction longitude.

These constant changes of the solar system's configuration space manifest themselves as changes of solar radiation, sunspots and changes in the shape of its corona. On earth they are related to magnetic storms and world-wide changes of temperature, accompanied or followed by earth currents, meteorological changes of wind and weather, and changes in the currents of the seas. My investigations have brought out several periodicities, most of which are reasonably above the point of casual coincidence, considering the complexity of the phenomena being investigated. An investigation of these effects by an extensive use of computers is long overdue. These effects will give us a clearer understanding of what goes on within the atoms.

5-2 Photon Radii and Gradients.

A photon's radius is defined as the distance from a wave pattern's center of inertia at which its containing and contained forces are equal. Assuming that a free photon's energy is contained by its interactions with the contracting ether, there is only one photon radius for such a pattern; however, because stationary wave patterns are contained by the contracting ether, by a static stress field abstracted from it, and by a temperature displacement of the ether at their centers, there are not less than three definitions of three different photon radii for a particular pattern. I shall call them static, quantizing and dynamic photon radii, in the sequence of increasing size.

A dynamic photon radius is postulated on the assumption that a stationary wave pattern's rest-mass energy is contained directly by the contracting ether's local converging field forces. Since a quantity of energy equal to the converging field forces raised to their fourth power is contained by a temperature displacement of the ether near the center of a stationary pattern, the quantizing photon radius is equal to one natural unit of length, and the containing forces at that distance are reduced in proportion. The convergence of these forces on the center of a wave pattern causes a concentration of energy and a proportional temperature displacement which acts as a containing force accentuating the concentration. A static photon radius is the point at which these forces and the containing forces, added together, equal the expansion pressure of the wave pattern they contain. There are two possibilities: one gives us a photon radius equal to 861 electron radii, and another equals slightly less than five electron radii.

A theory of physics must not only be based on facts, it must also give comprehensible logical reasons for the existence of those facts within the accepted frame of reference. When we go beyond facts our reasons may, or may not, be valid within the larger frame representing our totality of knowledge, and the possibility that we are making serious errors must not be overlooked. In defining the photon radii of the fundamental particles of matter we have a series of mathematical relations and ratios to go by, but beyond those there are logical implications which must also be taken into consideration, even though they range beyond immediate proof by mathematics.

In the past the fundamental particles of matter were believed to be small, solid, spherical objects, in contrast to my theory which postulates contained patterns of center-acting waves. Although the wave theory is supported by conversion phenomena and is undoubtedly true, the particle theory gives us a continuity of quantum states in nuclear concentrations and physical motions within the nuclei and the atoms which would be beyond the possibilities of a wave theory without a high concentration of energy and containing forces. The physical size of a fundamental particle's photon radius, since that size is also an information time unit, must be within limits that permit its observed interactions and motions without disintegration, or a change of mass, due to a separation of contained waves and their containing forces. Obviously, the reduction of a pattern's photon radius reduces the time it takes its waves to induce a containing reaction to their expansion momenta, and this increases its functional stability.

My theory of the evolution of local wave-containing forces by wave-induced reductions of the ether's mean density is based on the assumption that the evolution of a static stress field as the product of that reduction does not require a contracting ether momentum, but creates its local equivalents in proportion to the local concentrations of wave energy. This effect does not obviate the need for a contracting ether, because its contraction momentum and its gradient produce and sustain the evolution of local concentrations of energy around point organizers, and determine the quantum states of integrated wave patterns by defining the points where their opposite momenta have equal powers. This equality defines a wave pattern's photon radius.

A static stress field is produced by wave-induced transitions of converging field momenta into static displacements of the contracting ether's natural dynamic progression. Because its contraction is resumed through these static stresses, repeated interaction-transitions build up its wave-containing forces beyond the possibility of local contraction momenta. The energy contained and compacted by these interactions produces a temperature-related expansion displacement of the local ether, which merges with its static stress field into an inseparable synthesis of wave-containing forces, all acting in apparent independency of their primary cause—the contracting ether momenta.

My theory, that the fundamental particles of matter are contained by local forces abstracted from the contracting ether, is based on the following facts. We know that the wave structures of these particles are dynamically stable, despite motions and concentrations that might induce separations of contained and containing forces or cause close particles to merge, and we know that they have quantized masses whose values are not changed perceptibly by such motions and concentrations. It is my belief that the functional stability of fundamental particles under various conditions is made possible by local containment, and it is my contention that the three types of containment mentioned in preceding paragraphs can produce the effects noted above.

The photon radius of a wave pattern with a known energy is determined by relating its theoretical gradient of energy to a unit of length which, when multiplied or divided by the gradient's sequence of powers, gives us its anticipated value at photon radius distance. The functional relations of a unit of length to a particular configuration of forces and gradients can be deduced from its relations to other units and the natural unit of length. We convert these values into the equal opposite powers of a photon radius by postulating the same gradient of power throughout; however, the possibility that we are dealing with an assymmetrical gradient cannot be completely excluded. I can only point to my successful use of ideal proportions and gradients for the purpose of obtaining known values. The following table shows the energy which can be contained within a numerical sequence of unit distances from a wave center for different gradients of powers. The reciprocals of these numbers give us their descending powers with distance from a wave center to its photon radius and beyond.

If we were to assume that an electron's radius wavelength gives us a unit of energy per pulse time, as defined by the ultimate system of units, and if this energy decreases as the inverse fourth power of the distance in radius length units, then the local concentration of energy would make it behave like a solid particle. However, my theory of a charge pattern's rest mass does not postulate such a steep gradient, and it is assumed, therefore, that the statistical means of casual interactions and functional recurves produces the solid-particle effect without it.

According to theory, the conversion of a single spherical wave photon with Planck's energy into a single wave free photon, increases the wavelength by four. By postulating an inverse fourth power gradient of the spherical wave pattern's energy, an increase of its photon radius to that of a velocity pattern increases its energy by four raised to its fourth power. When the wavenumber equivalent to this energy is redefined for the larger radius, its value is greater by four divided by the fourth root of two. The final figure, therefore, is $\log_2 9.75 = 861.077930$ wave units. When this relationship is used to define the photon radius of an

Energy pattern. | ... | energy pattern. | Its organizer. | momentum recoil... | radial wave... |
Spherical wave. | radial wave.

— 1; High density.   --- 1; Low density.   ·····5; Magnetic plane.   ≫ Converging forces.   ⟷ Periodic waves.
— 2; Expansion.   --- 2; Contraction.   -·-·- Photon radius.   ⟩⟨ Momentum blocking.   • Organizer.

GRADIENTS OF POWERS.

The first line gives distances from a wave center in length units. The others are those figures raised to a higher power. The first lines in a power sequence are numbers and the next are those numbers in basic logarithms. Gradients are the reciprocals of these numbers. The last column defines the second quantum energy of a charge pattern in a series of ascending powers.

Linear units of length.

	2	3	4	5	6	7	8	9	10	
N 1.	2	3	4	5	6	7	8	9	10	256
L 0.	1.0	1.5849625	2.0	2.321928	2.5849625	2.807355	3.0	3.169925	3.321928	8.0

Second power (Squared).

N 1.	4.0	9.0	16.0	25.0	36.0	49.0	64.0	81.0	100.0	65536.0
L 0.	2.0	3.169925	4.0	4.643856	5.169925	5.614710	6.0	6.339850	6.643856	16.0

Third power (Cubed).

N 1.	8.0	27.0	64.0	125.0	216.0	343.0	512.0	729.0	1000.0	1.677722×10^7
L 0.	3.0	4.754887	6.0	6.965784	7.754887	8.422065	9.0	9.509775	9.965784	24.0

Fourth power.

N 1.	16.	81.0	256.0	625.0	1296.0	2401.0	4096.0	6561.0	10000.0	4.294967×10^9
L 0.	4.0	6.339850	8.0	9.287712	10.339850	11.229420	12.0	12.679700	13.287712	32.0

Fifth power.

N 1.	32.	243.0	1024.	3125.0	7776.0	16807.0	32768.	59049.0	100000.0	1.099512×10^{12}
L 0.	5.0	7.924812	10.0	11.609640	12.924812	14.036775	15.0	15.849625	16.609640	40.0

Sixth power.

N 1.	64.	729.0	4096.	15625.0	46656.0	117649.0	262144.	531441.0	1000000.0	2.814750×10^{14}
L 0.	6.0	9.509775	12.0	13.931568	15.509775	16.844130	18.0	19.019550	19.931568	48.0

electron's rest mass energy, we find that its photon radius should be equal to 861 electron radius waves, or its equivalent energy wavenumber of 256 waves Since the radius of an electron's smallest orbit in hydrogen is 18781.28 electron radii, the photon radius defined above is comparatively small. Its point of equivalence is defined as an expansion momentum decreasing as the inverse fourth power of the distance, acting against a containing force combining a temperature displacement and the static stress field abstracted from the contracting ether momenta.

When an electron's energy of 256 units is raised to its fourth power, we get the energy wavenumber of a free photon with an electron's rest mass energy in one natural unit of length. It is equal to 1.0419584 centimeters. If we assume that the electron's photon radius is to be taken as a new unit of length, with its energy retained, the result is in accord with theory. We might also state that a spherical converging field force, at the distance of one natural unit of length from its center, can contain energy equal to Planck's quantum for a free photon with that radius times 256; this figure raised to its fourth power gives us the energy of a charge pattern at its center of convergence. It follows that one natural unit of length is the photon radius defining an electron's energy wavenumber. It is therefore called the electron's quantizing photon radius.

Since a displacement of the ether from any source produces a corresponding displacement of the converging field's natural dynamic progression in space and time, a description of its mass-induced configurations in deep space must include displacements induced by the temperature effect and static stress fields. When an electron's rest-mass energy is used to define its photon radius as the distance where its expansion momentum and its containing converging field momentum are equal, its containment by abstracted static forces must be ignored. We begin the analysis by assuming that its energy is concentrated within a sphere with a radius equal to one fourth of the natural unit of length. Its spherical photon radius is equal to the fourth root of its rest-mass wavenumber divided by four, with $R = \sqrt[4]{4.2949673 \times 10^9}/4 = 64$ natural units of length; a sphere 66.685338 centimeters in radius.

The photon radius of a free photon with an electron's rest mass energy is much larger, because its energy decreases as the inverse square of the distance, and there is no ratio reduction. The square root of the rest-mass wavenumber above gives us: $R = 65536$ natural length units for its plane-polarized pattern's photon radius. It equals 68285.8 centimeters, or about 683 meters in circumference. This incredibly large figure can be checked against an electron's photon radius of 64 natural length units above, times its conversion ratio 861.07793; or rather, that figure increased by the fourth root of two, with $64 \times 1024 = 65536$ nl., the same as above. Photon radii in the visible light range are much shorter because they have less energy, but even then the theoretical sizes appears to be improbably large. Here, as in all cases in which facts appear too incredible to accept, we must withhold judgment until experiments with interference phenomena give us something specific to go by.

In defining the photon radii of the fundamental particles of matter, we must keep in mind that matter is organization, and that all organized actions originated and are supported by the organizers of positive and negative charge patterns. It is impossible for a neutral mass to evolve an integrated wave structure without a charge center and, after its evolution, it depends upon the action potentials of that center for its continued existence. The size and energy of a proton's mass are closely related to the action potentials of its charge pattern. My theory postulates an inverse cube gradient for its charge mass, and an inverse fourth power gradient for a proton's neutral mass within the photon radius defined by its charge, or within the photon radius defined by the natural unit of length. The gradient of its electrostatic charge, if this is true, gives us a larger photon radius than that of an electron, and the unsaturated areas within it become filled with neutral waves. When the photon radius of an electron's static photon radius is increased by the cube root of two, we get a positron's photon radius: $4 \times 1.587401 = 6.349604$ base units. When this figure is raised to its fourth power, we get 1625.49868 electron masses: it gives us a proton mass too small to be of any value, except as an indication of the direction a solution might take. Elsewhere I define a proton's photon radius by postulating a static photon radius smaller than that of an electron's. Since such a reduction could be produced by the compacting force of a proton's greater mass, we have another possibility which cannot be ignored, even though it contradicts my first solution. The problem is complex, and our explorations into the unknown must not be inhibited by fixations that are contrary to facts.

Because converging field forces increase as the cube of the distance, it is assumed this field's containing reactions to the expansion momenta of the waves of matter produce an energy gradient from the center of any mass equal to the reciprocal of the fourth power of the distance in natural length units. The photon radius of any mass can be obtained by reducing its rest-mass energy wavenumber to its fourth root, and redefining the result of the radius of its spherical photon in natural length units. The photon radii of planets and stars are obviously immensely large, and those of the galaxies approach that of the whole universe. There is a constant expansion-loss of energy which is liberated by the stars as radiation.

5-3 Abstracted Length-Time Units.

For any system of units in which the speed of light is unity, Planck's quantum of energy times an electron's rest-mass wavenumber equals one—unity. Since Planck's quantum defines the energy of a single wave photon with unit wavelength, and an electron's rest-mass wavenumber is that energy multiplied by the number of waves in one unit of length, the result gives us a rest-mass energy equal to unity. This relationship is obvious in the mathematical sequence used to define the constants of various systems of units in Book One. In the ultimate system, it is one of its five base units.

In that system, an electron's natural wavelength and its pulsation time gives us its length and time units, respectively. The momenta it transmits at unit distance in unit time, defining its electrostatic charge potential, is also unity. Its rest mass, defined as a single wave photon, is also unity. Let us now assume that the electron unites with a positron, and that their energies, therefore, resolve into two equal, oppositely moving, free photons, each having the energy of an electron's rest mass.

This conversion of an electron into a free photon increases its wavelength by 861.077930 electron radii. Since we are defining the transmission of this wave energy in electron radius time units, with energy increasing in direct proportion to time, the apparent energy of this photon must be the reciprocal of the increase of wavelength ($1/861$), in order to assign the same energy to this photon as to the electron; both must be unity. It follows that Planck's quantum of energy for an electron radius wave in radius time must be greater than unity by 861, in order to give us the expected unit value for a free photon wave with the longer pulsation time. In this case, energy divided by time equals unity.

A system of units with a length-time unit equal to 861 electron radii, defines Planck's quantum for a free photon with unit wavelength as unity. Since an electron's rest mass energy is defined in terms of the wavelength-energy of a free photon, its value is still unity, but the energy transmitted by an electron's fundamental wave is 861 times greater than that of a free photon with the same energy; this greater value shows up in the electron's charge pattern as an electrostatic attraction or repulsion. The ideal system of units in Book One defines an electron's rest-mass energy wavenumber as $\log_2 32$, and Planck's quantum of energy as $\log_2 -32$. When these two figures are multiplied, we get unity, as in the two preceding cases.

The speed of light through one unit of length gives us a natural unit of time. It is used, therefore, in all systems where ideal proportions are more important than practical usefulness. However, the identity of their conversion ratios may make it difficult to distinguish between length and time ratios. Let us, therefore, increase the time unit to one second and leave the length unit unchanged. While an electron's energy wavenumber is still $\log_2 32$, Planck's quantum is the reciprocal of this figure times the speed of light: $h = -32. \times 34.743950 = 2.743950 = 6.6990196$ erg of energy. It will be noticed that this figure is Planck's constant in the idealized mass system, Book One. However, it is not the reciprocal of an electron's rest-mass wavenumber, $\log_2 66.743950$, when the unit of length is made equal to the speed of light in one second. The reason, obviously, is that the speed of light is greater than unity in the ideal mass system, while the energy of Planck's constant is less than unity by the speed of light in a system in which that speed is defined as unity, by making the length unit and the unit wavelength equal to one second, about half the distance from the earth to the moon.

By making the speed of light and an electron's rest mass equal to unity for various systems, their units of length, time and mass are in simple proportions to each other and to their units of energy and momentum. When the proportions of the three base units are changed by definition, however, their energy and momentum relations become significant. When the mass of the ideal mass system is increased from that of an electron to one gram, the new system's unit of energy is greater by their difference in mass, and the value of Planck's quantum of energy for a single wave is, therefore, less in proportion. Since it takes $\log_2$ 89.826801 electrons to equal one gram, the ideal mass system's value of 2.743950, divided by this figure, gives us -87.082851 as Planck's constant for the new international system of units, as defined in Book One.

The energy of a free photon is obtained by multiplying Planck's energy quantum for a wave of unit length by the number of waves in a length unit—its wavenumber. This simple relationship can also be defined by postulating a specific invariable energy per pulse time for any wave, with the unit of time equal to the pulsation period of a wave with unit wavelength. The energy of a free photon is now that energy multiplied by the number of pulsations of its waves in one unit of time. By extending this relationship to include the periodicities of stationary wave patterns, I discovered that the energy per pulse time is the same for all types of waves, and does not change with a change of shape. Stationary waves, however, have shorter wavelengths and transmit more energy per unit time than the waves of free photons. The simplicity of this relationship is brought out by the conversion of an electron's radius wavelength, defining its electrostatic charge, to that of a free photon.

5-4 Nuclear Bonding Forces.

The atomic number of an element is defined by its positive charge in terms of the number of protons contained by its nucleus, and its isotopic number is its nuclear mass in terms of the number of protons and neutrons it contains. Elements are stable when they contain a specific proportion of protons and neutrons in their nuclei, with the number of the latter varying within a narrow range. Beyond that, the elements are unstable and tend to change into more stable elements through radioactive expulsions, absorptions, or transformation of their particles. All elements beyond atomic number 83, isotopic number 208, are unstable; as we go beyond atomic number 100, their half-lives are less than one second. There is a gradual increase of the ratio of neutrons to protons, with increasing atomic numbers, for the most stable isotopes of the elements.

According to my theory, matter evolved because contained waves escape into structure by following the road of least resistance. This tendency brought the fundamental particles of matter into being and caused them to integrate into functional wave patterns, with the bonding forces between particles defined by transitions of partial to more completely integrated structures. It is argued that integration is an energy equivalent, a more efficient utilization of available energy, and that the quantity of energy liberated defines the bonding force between the particles in an atom's nucleus, between the electrons circling it, and between the atoms in molecules.

My theory of the evolution of matter rejects the assumption that anti-matter—atoms with negative nuclei and orbital positrons—can exist in other galaxies. It is my contention that the world came into being because it is in the nature of the forces from which matter originated to become what they are today. It is assumed that matter is an escape from chaos into structure; a tendency of contained waves to integrate into functional patterns by following the road of least resistance. The different charges of electrons and protons justify the assumption that their masses are different because the structural relations of their charges makes them so. There is no rational foundation for the assumption that their mass relations can be reversed and remain stable in some other galaxy or universe. Experimenting physicists have discovered numerous particles with various masses and charges, as well as some without any charge. The latter last long enough to be recorded, but there is no proof of their existence beyond that. We accept the associations and disassociations of masses and charges under artificial conditions as momentary states, but we must not confuse them with the permanent states of nature.

Electrons are dynamically stable in free space because their spherical waves leave no marginal deformation of their containing converging field forces, but when an electron enters the nucleus of an atom it resolves into an electron equivalent of numerous spherical pulsation patterns, due to its interaction with the radial waves of that center. Positrons are unstable in free space because their deformations of converging field forces appear as a tendency to increase their neutral masses, by entering an atom's nucleus or by resolutions into free photons through an attraction merger with electrons. However, a positron becomes a stable proton when its rest mass is increased by the addition of neutral waves, because these waves fill the interspaces of its radial pattern. Neutrons are dynamically unstable in free space because their electron equivalents tend to reintegrate into electrons. Unless a neutron enters an atom's nucleus within about 18 minutes after its expulsion from another nucleus, it will resolve into a proton and a high-velocity electron.

The nucleus of an atom is dynamically stable when it contains the right percentage of neutrons to protons, up to about 200 nuclear particles (beyond this they become too numerous to be controlled by its central forces). When an element contains too few or too many neutrons, it is also unstable and tends to revert to a stable state by a radioactive reorganization of its nucleus. The sequence of about 100 elements shows that their stable isotopes relate the increase of nuclear positive charge with a percentage increase of neutrons. There appears to be a relationship between charge, mass and functional stability, comparable to that which determines the mass of a proton.

In theoretical physics there is a great difference between spherical and radial waves when the length-time unit used to define their shapes and actions is of the same magnitude as their wavelengths and periods. An increase of that unit causes a radial pattern to approach the spherical shape by a corresponding transition from a specific to a statistical mean state, until it cannot be distinguished from a true sphere. When a proton is observed from a distance, and through a time unit equal to the time it takes a light wave to move that distance, such as an atomic electron's orbit or the proton's quantizing photon radius, it appears to have a spherical shape, and its charge a spherical distribution. The quantum relations of a proton's electrostatic charge are, therefore, the same as those of an electron's, even though their action potentials are not the same when the distances separating two particles are those observed in atomic nuclei.

Note that a cluster of spherical wave patterns cannot avoid repulsive interferences, and that a cluster of radial wave patterns can do so because they have periodicities in longitude as well as radially. Also, the absence of functional deformations of converging field forces by spherical waves reduces their attraction potentials for similar charges, whereas their deformations by radial wave patterns are potentially reducible by integrations, provided that their centers are close enough to make an exchange of energy and wave functions meaningful. When two or more fundamental particles of matter are about one-electron radius apart, an exchange of wave functions will occur between similar patterns. This exchange produces an attraction, or bonding force, proportional to the marginal reduction of mass. It is opposed by the tendency of each pattern to preserve its functional structure and natural quantum states; a tendency which appears as an electrostatic repulsion.

My ether theory assumes that all wave-containing and attracting forces in nature are static stress fields abstracted from the contracting ether, and that all repulsive forces in nature are due to the tendency of all waves to expand and to evolve functional continuities in containments. All attractions in nature can, therefore, be defined by a tendency of static stress fields, acting in consonance with the tendencies of the contracting ether, to reduce the wave-induced deformations of their natural shapes—a spherical distribution around point-centers, with descending gradients from center to space. Note that all local deviations from a natural balance between the expansion pressures of contained waves and their containing static stress fields activate the converging field forces. The contracting ether's reactions resolve almost instaneously into wave-containing static stresses through which it resumes its natural dynamic progression, and a potential interaction with new deviations.

The forces binding nuclear particles together, in opposition to the positive electrostatic repulsions of their protons, are functional abstractions from the forces containing them as particles and their deformations of local space by separate existence. Because the centers of particles in an atom's nucleus are less than one-electron radius apart, their fundamental waves interact and exchange wave functions. The organizer of each particle reacts to the periodic intrusions by the waves of other particles with an integration into its own periodic wave motions, wherever that can be effected without a destruction of its own natural functions.

This exchange of energy between nuclear particles increases the functional efficiency of each, as if a part of their masses were held in common. There is a consequent reduction of the rest-mass energy of each particle in an atom's nucleus, compared with their masses when moving in free space. When a proton or neutron enters an atom's nucleus, a quantity of energy proportional to the force binding it to the nucleus is liberated. Conversely, this quantity of energy must be absorbed by the nucleus and integrated into its rest mass to remove it from the nucleus.

There is a constant contest between the tendencies of contained waves and those of their containing forces for dominance in atomic nuclei, the outcome of which determines the stability of the isotopes of the elements. The tendency of waves to expand and disperse appears as a tendency to converge on expanding axes and thus accentuates both, when they are free to do so—when they are not functional. The converging field reacts through the static stress field with a counter-force which inverts the action and causes the waves to disperse toward a physical and statistical sphericity of distribution.

If the particles in an atom's nucleus were identical, the interactions of their overlapping waves would accentuate local expansions through the evolution of harmonic pulsations which the containing reactions would not be able to convert into a statistical sphericity. The converging field would then react with the conversion of opposite expansions into a separation recurve which would cause the particles to separate. There is a mutual repulsion between identical particles when the containing reactions are limited to those of their own masses. However, when two nuclear particles have slightly different wavelengths, as in the interaction between a proton and a neutron, their interactions are cyclic, and the converging field is given time to build up a containing reaction. It causes the waves to respond to the tendencies of their containing forces with a distribution of the common field, which reduces the rest-mass energy of their separate wave patterns.

Atomic nuclei composed of similar particles, such as two protons or two neutrons, are theoretically impossible; those composed of two protons and a neutron, or one proton and two neutrons, are possible as highly unstable states. Nuclei composed of one proton, a proton and a neutron, or two protons and two neutrons, are stable. They appear in nature as the nuclei of hydrogen, deuterium and helium atoms.

Nuclear stability depends upon the interplay of various factors, all acting to reduce the local deviations from a spherical distribution toward a statistical sphericity in minimum time, with the inversion time determined by the nature of the interaction. There is an exchange of electron equivalents between neutrons and protons, an exchange and pairings of spin fields, an integration grouping of particles within the nuclei with numerous particles, and an integration of their motions within each nucleus. There is an increase of bonding with an increase of neutrons, as we go from light to heavy atoms with increasing nuclear charge. An excess of neutrons for a particular charge causes them to react as if they were in free space.

The constant exchange of information between organizers in an atom's nucleus, an essential part of their integration reduction of mass, decreases rapidly with an increase of the distance between particle centers. It may decrease as much as the inverse fifth or sixth power when the distance is in electron radii units. It follows that when a proton is caused to wander a few nuclear radii from the center of a nucleus, the forces binding it to the nucleus may become weaker than the electrostatic repulsion between them, and the proton will then be expelled from the nucleus. If the momentum of a proton approaching an atom's nucleus is great enough, as when its velocity is a temperature motion at the center of a star, it can overcome the positive repulsion of the nucleus and enter it by a spiralling recurve, thus increasing its positive charge by one unit. A neutron can enter an atom's nucleus more easily, because it has no electrostatic charge. The addition of a proton or a neutron to an atom's nucleus may increase its stability, or it may cause a stable nucleus to become unstable and revert to a stable state by a radioactive transformation.

Experiments show that the radius of an atom's nucleus is roughly its number of particles contained within a sphere, with each particle occupying a space about one-half the size of an electron. The quantizing of states within the nuclei proves that the particles are in motion within their allotted areas, and that they produce specific configurations of states by periodic (probably orbital) motions within the complex. Some nuclei have been flattened by rapid rotation.

Assuming the radial wave structure of a positron is fundamentally the same as the transverse waves of a free photon, their wavelengths should also be the same for equal energies. A positron's wavelength should, therefore, be 861.077930 times longer than that of an electron's, since they have the same energy. When the positron becomes a proton, its mass is increased to equal 1836.11810 electrons, and its wavelength is reduced by this same figure. A proton's radius is, therefore, equal to $861.07793/1836.1181 = 0.4689665$ electron radius; or slightly smaller than the half value anticipated by observation. Since a neutron's mass is equal to about 1838.6452 electrons, its radius should equal about 0.468322 electron radius units. Note that the charge centers of all particles are one-dimensional points.

My theory of matter postulated its origin in galatic clouds of low-energy casual waves through integrations into atomic particles in containment. A residue of this cloud exists everywhere in the vicinity of matter. It interacts constantly with the fundamental particles of matter to preserve their natural quantum states when casual interactions cause them to gain or lose rest-mass energy. Nuclear particles are, therefore, surrounded by an unobservable cloud of low-energy ground field waves which interact constantly with their organizers to preserve their charges and quantum masses.

These ground field clouds are particularly dense at the centers of galaxies and stars, thus making those areas the points where matter comes into being and resolve into radiation. I have already noted that the ratio of neutrons to protons increases with the increase of a nucleus positive charge. At the center of a star, where pressure and temperature strip the atoms of their orbital electrons, the tendency of neutrons to increase in proportion to protons must be greater than at its surface. It is assumed that atomic nuclei can increase their percentage of neutrons and remain non-radioactive at the star's center, while their expulsion from that point to its surface makes them highly radioactive. Heavy nuclei should, therefore, come into being at the centers of the stars, with their expulsions to the surface taking the form of a radioactive explosion, during which the nuclei release energy and resolve into stable or near-stable structures.

5-5 Atoms and Molecules.

An atom is composed of a heavy positive nucleus circled by negative electrons, and a molecule is composed of two or more atoms which are bound together by an exchange or pairing of electrons. The number of protons and neutrons in an atom's nucleus (its isotopic number) determines its atomic weight, and its number of protons determines its positive electrostatic charge quantum number and its atomic number. An equal number of negative electrons, circling the nucleus in quantized orbits, makes the atom electrostatically neutral and determines its chemical characteristics. They appear as a tendency of atoms to react to each other's presence and to their environment, according to their properties, usually by forming molecules or by exchanging electrons. Such an exchange produces charged particles called ions.

Electron orbits are quantized by a velocity which produces a natural balance between centrifugal force and electrostatic attraction, and a velocity wavelength which must equal, or be a whole fraction of, the orbit's circumference. Beginning with the smallest orbit, the possible orbit radii of 1, 4, 9, 16 and 25 are related to a corresponding quantizing sequence of velocity, momentum and wavelength fractions of the orbit's circumference: 1, 1/2, 1/3, 1/4 and 1/5. Since the velocity wavelengths of moving electrons are the reciprocals of their momenta, they increase as 1, 2, 3, 4 and 5.

The number of electrons which can move in a particular orbit increases with the relative increase of orbit radii. The saturation sequence of electrons which can exist in each shell is in the ratio: 2, 8, 18, 32 and 50. The electrons in a shell are grouped in subquantum states, with the number of possible states in a shell equal to its number of orbital waves: 1, 2, 3, 4 and 5 for the sequence. The sequence of states gives us 2, 6, 10, 14 and 18 electrons in each state. The first shell can have 2 electrons; the second, 2-6; the third, 2-6-10; the fourth, 2-6-10-14; and so on.

The smallest electron orbits are also their lowest energy states. When an atomic electron is accelerated by an absorption of energy, it will jump into a higher quantum orbit if the energy is equal to the difference between the two states. Since all electrons tend to attain the lowest potential energy state possible; this activated electron, or another electron in the atom, will drop into the vacated orbit and release energy equal to the difference as a radiation. The energy absorbed and released by these electron jumps depends also upon the difference between the energies of the sub-quantum states, spin-field couplings, couplings between orbital momenta and between the electron's spin field and its orbital momentum field. These relations are described in detail in Book One.

As we go from hydrogen, with one proton and one electron, to the heaviest elements, by adding one proton and one electron each time, the tendency of electrons to drop into their lowest quantum orbits causes the inner shells to fill up and become inactive, as the atom's normal state. The electrostatic, magnetic and electron exchange and sharing which appear as the atom's action potentials originate, therefore, in its external shells.

The atomic structures and quantum relations outlined above, and described in detail in Book One, are well known to students of theoretical physics. They give us factual relations which serve as the background for realistic analyses of the behavior of electrons contained by converging field forces in the atoms.

The organizers of electrostatic charges interact with their environment to preserve the stationary states of their fundamental charge-mass waves. Moving charges evolve velocity patterns, through which they act to produce an environment which makes the stationary states possible with a minimum expenditure of energy. This minimum is the product of a tendency to escape into structure, imposed by wave-containing converging field reactions. Since electrostatic charges extend toward infinity, decreasing as the inverse square of the distance, charges moving through free space are constantly losing energy. When caused to circle a center, they produce a magnetic field whose momentum is the charge momentum of the electric current.

The velocity patterns of moving neutral masses are also produced by their positive and negative organizers. Since the union of positive and negative charges into a statistically neutral state is the minimum deformation of local converging field forces attainable, there is no tendency toward a further reduction by the evolution of a magnetic field, and no loss of energy by motion. The tendency toward an electro-dynamically neutral state is the principal cause of attraction in the atom, and between atoms in molecules. It is also the reason for the normally neutral states of matter in our environment.

The magnetic field produced by an electron's organizer as it circles the positive center of its atom's nucleus is directly comparable to that produced by an electric current. In the atom, however, the positive electrostatic charge which binds the electron to its orbit reduces the reducible energy potential of its negative charge toward zero, with increasing distance from its center. There is a consequent reduction of the electron's action potential with distance, and a tendency of the forces containing it in its orbit to reduce it still further, by causing it to change the plane of its orbit and its eccentricity, thus approaching a statistical spherical distribution of its charge in minimum time, and a mean distribution in depth within the dynamic limits imposed by its quantized velocity. The theory of wave mechanics defines this statistical distribution in terms of a charge cloud when the electron is in an s sub-quantum state.

The behavior of electrons in an atom is the product of their tendencies as wave patterns with reducible charge-related action potentials and those of their containing forces, with the containing static stress fields abstracted from the local contraction of the ether by the charge patterns and their related velocity waves and magnetic fields. The tendencies of these abstracted forces are normally dominant. Contained waves tend to evolve a maximum integration with minimum energy and maximum wavelengths, while their containing reactions tend to induce a spherical distribution of that energy, in space wherever possible, and/or statistically in minimum time. Note that casual interference deformations of contained waves reduce their wavelengths and increase their energy. The containing reactions to this abnormal state appears as the reintegration of a pattern's functional periodic waves and an expulsion of the excess energy, thus reverting to its original or another natural quantum state within the atom.

The wavelength of an electron's velocity pattern in an atom must equal the circumference of its mean orbit, or be a whole fraction of that circumference. This relationship defines the sequence of quantized electron orbits as noted at the beginning of this section. The converging field's tendency to induce a spherical distribution of wave energy causes the electron to approach a statistical sphericity in minimum time. In atoms with more than one electron, the electrons interact to produce this effect, and the combinations which do this most effectively produce the strongest attractions. Observation shows that eight electrons in the largest orbit produce the strongest bonding forces within the atoms, and that atoms with fewer electrons tend to combine with other atoms to produce this combination.

In defining the repulsive forces between electrons, I noted that identical wavelengths permit a free absorption transmission of one pattern's energy through another to become the acceleration apex of a divergent motion, implementing a converging field recurve which becomes their velocity patterns of motion. A difference of wavelength will, however, cause their interaction to run through a cycle to which the converging field reacts as to a periodic wave, and the repulsive force between them is reduced in proportion. Note that the steady pressure of an expanding axis (a center-supported directional force) causes the converging field reactions to recurve around it as they approach its central cause, while a cyclic pressure lets the containing reactions flow into the axis at the moment of minimum expansion.

When this relationship is applied to the interactions of orbital electrons in the atoms, it is evident that if there is a difference between their elements of motion which reduces the repulsive forces between them to a cyclic interaction, the forces binding them to their orbits are increased. Observation shows that their orbits are composed of four principal elements, called n, l, m and s states. They symbolize the principal (orbital) quantum number, the sub-quantum (eccentricity) number, the magnetic (orientation) quantum, and the half-quantum spin field (+ or -), respectively. These states are described in Book One. It has been proved that no two electrons in an atom can have the same four quantum numbers; at least one of them must be different.

The reason, obviously, is that electrons with identical quantum numbers are dynamically unstable, because energy can flow freely between them. A slight difference in their environments will, therefore, cause one to lose a quantum of energy to the other, thus leaving it in a lower quantum state. The converging field initiates the reaction, because a slight difference in wavelength becomes a cyclic interaction which appears as an approach to a spherical distribution of energy.

In wave dynamics all repulsions are implemented by a tendency of contained waves to expand. This tendency causes free and semi-free waves to converge on expansion axes, as when a quantity of energy is radiated by an atom as a free photon. All attractions are products of the tendency of wave-containing converging field forces to reduce the deformation of the natural dynamic progression of the contracting ether in space and time. Electrostatic forces are abnormal states of local converging field forces, reducible by the transition of overlapping opposite charges to a dynamically neutral state. The fundamental characteristic of the neutral state is that it has no organizer and no built-up static stress field.

The converging field tends to reduce all waves contained in common to a spherical symmetry in space and time: in space, where possible, and as a statistical mean in minimum time, or the nearest approach to both where a physical sphericity is not possible. An orbiting electron approaches a spherical symmetry in minimum time by changing its plane of rotation. The interactions of two or more electrons become interference cycles which resolve into periodic waves that integrate as quantized harmonics of their primaries. The functional approach by the electrons and their waves to a spherical symmetry in minimum time determine the forces binding them to their orbits.

Because electrons are contained wave bundles, they behave like waves in their reactions to the forces binding them to their atoms. It will be noticed that the forces containing them in their orbits on a particular plane are reactions to their expansion pressures on that plane, and that the wave-containing reactions build up through a time-related increase with the expansion of wave momenta in depth. An electron will tend to move on a plane where its containing forces are minimum. It may change the plane of its orbit gradually, as its containing forces increase, or it may remain on that plane for a time and then change its orbit abruptly to a new plane. The gradual changes occur where there are only one or two electrons in an orbit, and the abrupt changes occur where the interactions between multiple electrons makes graduation impossible. They occur, also, where an external magnetic field causes the electrons to change orbits by quantized orientations relative to its plane. Electrons tend to set their orbits and spin fields with or against a magnetic field.

The tendency of periodic waves to expand by converging on a plane increases with a reduction of their functional relations and an increase of their numbers and energy. Since electrons are localized waves, their behavior in the atoms should be comparable to those of contained waves. In elements with few electrons in a shell, the tendency of converging field forces toward a spherical distribution predominate. As the number of electrons in a shell increases, there is an increasing tendency to concentrate their energies on a plane, and to expand their orbits by moving in the same direction on that plane. This tendency is greatest in iron, whose atoms behave like small magnets.

The deformation of converging field forces by the expansion pressure of an electron's contained spin field on its plane of rotation cannot be reduced by functional changes of that plane, because its continuous momentum has a symmetrical distribution. It can be changed by an external magnetic field, in which case the spin sets itself with or against that field. Two half-quantum spin fields can unite to form a full quantum or zero-spin value. It must be assumed the choice is related to the relative dominance of contained and containing tendencies. A periodic exchange of spin fields is accompanied by a periodic wave motion whose functional inversions and motions reduce their deformations of the contracting ether to a minimum in comparison with their effects as separate spin fields.

The forces binding two atoms together are caused by a reduction of the deformation of converging field forces by a functional integration of wave structures beyond their possibilities as separate bodies. Observation shows that two and eight electrons produce the most effective integrations of wave structures. An atom with too many electrons may unite with one having too few. A transfer of electrons increases the internal integrations of both, even though the consequent appearance of opposite electrostatic charges is an increase of the contracting ether's charge-related deformation. This is called an electrostatic bonding. When the atoms of such a molecule are caused to separate, they retain their charges. They are, therefore, called positive and negative ions. An integration can also be effected by the interactions of their spin fields, magnetons and wave functions, without an exchange of electrons. See Book One for a detailed description of molecular bonding.

The subject of atomic structure and molecular bonding covers an immense field, far beyond the purpose of this book. My purpose is to show that the theory of contained waves can explain the most commonly known phenomena of physics by logical extensions of basic premises, without ignoring pertinent facts. If I have succeeded in this task it must be assumed, by implication, that the laws, postulates and principles defined and described in this book can be applied with equal effectiveness to phenomena beyond its scope.

5-6 True and Apparent Motions.

A definition of true and apparent motion depends upon the phenomena we wish to describe and the relationship we want to emphasize. Fundamentally, all motions are relative to a stationary, contracting ether, with its local stationary state defined by its transmission of momenta in all directions with twice the speed of light. However, since all momenta originating at wave centers are contained in depth by contracting ether momenta, the distance they can travel as free momenta is limited to one natural unit of length or less. The only way they can travel through space to indefinite distances is as the momenta of contained wave patterns moving with the speed of light. Although that speed is defined in theory by its velocity through the ether, its observable velocity is relative to the forces containing it locally—its local configuration space. Our definition of a free photon's true velocity in a specific direction depends on which one of these two relations we choose to use.

Since all motions through the ether are as contained wave patterns, the statement that a free photon moving through the ether with the speed of light is stationary in its own configuration space is obviously true. It is also true for the motion of any stationary wave pattern, regardless of its motion relative to the ether. By letting a large moving mass, such as the earth, define the stationary state of local space, in the sense that any relatively small mass or free photon moving through that space is acted upon by its directional forces in direct proportion to its speed, it becomes impossible to distinguish between a configuration space and the stationary ether.

The wave centers of electrons, protons and neutrons are functionally stationary. They must surround themselves with configurations of forces that make their fundamental waves stationary in space relative to the local configuration of forces acting in that space, because the preservation of their natural shapes and periodicities depends upon it. Their organizers are, therefore, also the organizers of their neutral masses, magnetic fields and velocity patterns. They act constantly through these fields and patterns to preserve the stationary states of their fundamental waves. Since there can be no such thing as a neutral stationary organizer, it is evident that all the properties and functions of matter are brought into being by the organizers of positive and negative charges.

The velocity pattern of a functionally stationary wave pattern implement its motion. The particle's inertia is an opposition by its rest-mass momenta and its containing momenta to changes imposed by external forces to increase or reduce its velocity or direction of motion, because the momentary effect is always a destructive interference with functionally integrated dynamic actions accompanied by an increased deformation of its containing forces in space and time. The converging field reacts with a reduction of the deformations to their lowest terms, by integrating them into the velocity pattern of an increased velocity, and by a liberation of energy when the velocity is reduced.

The deformation of converging field forces by contained waves has attained a natural balance in electrostatically neutral wave patterns. A moving neutral mass, therefore, does not tend to reduce its velocity pattern, or interact with a charge or magnetic field beyond the minor effect it has on the total area defining its pattern's configuration space. The momentum of a moving mass appears as a velocity pattern whose directional force on the waves of the mass leave them functionally stationary, even though they are moving relative to the configuration space beyond the mass. When two such masses, moving in opposite directions, pass one another, each mass has a theoretically stationary state, relative to which the other is moving, and both may be moving relative to the earth. Even though this explanation resembles that used to describe the general theory of relativity, it is not the same, since it has limitations which makes it differ vitally from that theory.

Forces intruding into an integrated stationary wave pattern are always destructive before converging field reactions cause either their expulsion or their integration into the pattern's structure. It will be noticed that all reductions of interactions between physical phenomena are initiated by the contracting ether, and are implemented by the organizers of stationary wave patterns as an integration of contained waves which reduces the functional displacement of converging field forces in space and time. Where there are no potential reductions of static stresses in the contracting ether, there can be no observable interaction. It follows that a neutron does not react to a changing magnetic field, because its containing forces have already attained maximum integration. However, electrons and positrons do react, because a physical acceleration, deceleration or recurve reduces the deformation of the converging field forces held in common. Since electrons circling a center produce a magnetic field, it follows that a free electron moving across such a field will recurve against it, because that motion reduces its local force. A proton recurves with the magnetic field because its functional momenta integrate with those of the field.

The positive atomic nuclei and their semi-bound negative electrons of an electrical conductor recurve in opposite directions in a changing magnetic field. The current opposing change can be defined as being due to the relatively greater inertia of a positive mass. All atoms evolve velocity patterns in a magnetic field, on the plane of that field, which leave them stationary, except for the rate at which the magnetic field is changing. The excess force of an increasing magnetic field and the excess force of the atoms' velocity patterns in a decreasing field appear as an acceleration pressure on their orbital electrons in the opposite direction of the changing field forces. If the electrons are firmly bound to their atoms, nothing will happen, because the opposite thrusts of positive and negative charges are equalized. However, the semi-free electrons of a conductor (electrons free to move from atom to atom within a molecular complex and yet unable to leave it) will accelerate against the magnetic field changes, in response to the repulsive forces acting between opposite charges within the atoms. Since the electrons accelerate against a changing magnetic field to preserve its immediately preceding state, they induce a counter-magnetic field in an increasing field and appear as a current in support of a decreasing field. In both cases, the current is proportional to the rate of change of the magnetic field.

An induction current can be defined by postulating an apparent motion of atoms in a magnetic field. Local changes of the field accelerate or decelerate their apparent velocities, thus causing the atoms to react with a tendency to separate their positive and negative charges and cause the latter to move against the changes. The question now is whether this tendency to separate charges must be restricted to a magnetic field, or can be brought into being by other changes of apparent velocity due to wave dynamics and gravity, and by the changes associated with overlapping configuration spaces.

This problem can be solved by an analysis of the effects of wave dynamics in the solar system on various phenomena. The waves are produced by the changing configuration of planetary gravities and their overlapping configuration spaces. My own investigations into these relations have brought out some interesting coincidences. They relate planetary periods and their conjunction periods with such phenomena as: sunspots, solar prominences, variations of solar radiation, earthquakes, magnetic storms, temperature changes, cyclic changes of climate, tornados, wind and weather.

The countless stationary states which make up the masses of all visible bodies cause them to be surrounded by stationary configuration spaces in the immediate vicinity of each mass, and by a gradient of that state to the configuration spaces beyond. A free photon moving across the earth's surface is moving, therefore, relative to the earth's configuration space, and not relative to the stationary ether. However, if it passes the earth at some distance from its surface, its velocity is a compromise relation between that of the earth and the configuration space through which the earth is moving. It will be noticed that the earth's momentum is defined by a velocity pattern which, in turn, defines the gradient of its configuration space. While it accounts for the relativity effects on the earth's surface, its gradient is a rejection of the relativity theory which postulates a relativity of all motions regardless of distance.

The velocities of bodies moving across the earth's surface are so small, relative to the speed of light, that the interaction of the configuration spaces of two masses passing each other is infinitesimal. Being electrostatically neutral, their velocity patterns can overlap without interaction. When a light ray is passed through a rapidly flowing liquid there is a reaction. A high velocity lead bullet will pass through a steel plate, but this interaction is not reversible because the bullet's velocity pattern relative to the earth's configuration space is the cause of penetration.

The velocity pattern surrounding a body moving in a straight line with a constant velocity has a simple gradient in all directions. The value of this gradient is not known. When a charge pattern interacts with a magnetic field, the action potential of its velocity pattern is concentrated on the plane of magnetic rotation. When a mass is caused to circle a center by electrostatic or gravitational attraction, the forces producing its recurve also displace its velocity pattern toward the common center of inertia. The velocity pattern of a rotating sphere is concentrated on its plane of rotation, with a maximum on its equator.

When we analyze the velocity gradient of a large revolving sphere, such as the sun or the earth, it will be noticed that the gradient of a theoretically solid rotation is approximately true at the surface, and that it graduates into an ideal vorticular rotation with distance. The tendency to evolve into an ideal vorticular rotation is transmitted to the mass as a physical rotation bias, with the equator tending to rotate faster than the poles, and the surface of the mass faster than its deeper layers, because the inhibiting forces of common rotation increases with depth toward a spherical symmetry at the center. While a gaseous star should approach an ideal vortex beyond its central area, a semi-gaseous star like the sun should rotate more rapidly on its equator than at its poles. On earth the effect should appear in the motions of high clouds and charged particles in the ionosphere. The question now is what effect the interaction of spherical and vorticular rotation bias has on the evolution of a magnetic field and earth currents.

5-7 Laws of Action.

There are several laws of ether physics that can be expressed in the form of an imperative. Some of these are idealizations that cannot exist in real space, but nevertheless make phenomena that can be observed or defined meaningful by abstraction. The first of these, the continuity of momenta, is idealized by using the term "free" to designate the absence of those intrusive forces and gradients that are constantly acting on momenta in our universe. A momentum originates as an ether motion which resolves into a transmission of that motion through space with twice the velocity of light. The fundamental postulate of my theory is that all physical phenomena are momenta and potential momenta in the form of ether motions and density differences.

A. All free momenta have theoretical continuities of transmission through the ether in straight lines with twice the speed of light and unchanging power to infinity.

B. Two momenta cannot occupy the same space without interaction. Momenta moving in opposite directions cannot pass through each other without a momentary transition into a local increase of ether density—a potential momentum state which resolves at once into a continuity of the ogirinal momenta.

C. Static stresses are impossible in an ether with the properties of a perfect gas. In all interactions between momenta, ether motions and density differences resolve into each other in such a way that the single and/or periodic wave motions which appear produce no lasting deviations from the local mean ether at any point.

D. Energy is idealized as the stationary alternating momentum and potential momentum states of periodic waves. The mean of each complete wave's opposite momenta and opposite densities in space and time must equal zero.

E. A theoretical equality of opposite momenta is preserved by reducing the greater momentum's force and inverting an equal part of the lesser momentum, thus preserving the theoretical continuity of both in space. A great difference causes an apparently complete reflection of the lesser momentum.

F. An increasing density at the center of a spherical wave with an immensely long period causes static stresses of equally long duration to appear where it interacts with the momenta of periodic waves in that area.

G. The convergent momentum of a contracting ether interacts in depth with the expansion momenta of periodic waves. These interactions can be interpreted as a containment of the waves, and as the continuity of their momenta into space as a reduction-displacement of the whole universe.

H. Stationary periodic waves react to spherically convergent momenta with the evolution of center-supported structures and equalizing spherical expansion momenta, implemented by spherical and radial (statistically spherical) waves.

I. In theory, momenta can pass through matter as easily as through empty space, because matter is composed of periodic waves. In practice, there is an interaction because the stationary states of matter evolve apparent motions in a moving field. The combined motion of many such states becomes the configuration space of matter. If matter absorbs the momentum as motion, it becomes its velocity pattern and configuration space.

Chapter 6

EVOLUTIONARY PROGRESSION.

The universe is a contracting spherical wave. Matter appeared in its central area of increasing density several billion years ago. It began as galaxies of contained periodic waves which integrated into clouds of hydrogen gases. These gases consolidated into stars, with matter integrating at their centers. The stars grew, divided and became star clusters. Compacting pressure caused heavy elements to appear at their centers. Violent changes occurred six billion years ago. The solar system began its evolution from the condensations of a rotating hydrogen star. Its contraction produced an excess of energy whose expulsion became an incandescent ring of matter. The ring consolidated into a planet which receded slowly from the sun. A sequence of nine rings became planets. The earth began as an incandescent mass circling the sun. High solar tides made its rotation and orbit periods identical. Receding, the liquid earth's orbit period became longer than its rotation. Granite accumulated and solidified in its anti-sun tidal bulge. Its whole surface solidified, and the solar tides prevented its rotation. Later, rotation was induced by its liquid core. After day one, the anti-sun continent split and its parts drifted to their present positions. Life was made possible by a tendency of molecules to reproduce, and by energy from the sun. It began as a variety of competing forms. Twenty-three amino acids became the building blocks of life, acting in conjunction with DNR organizers. Cell division was perfected and evolved through amitosis to mitosis. Sex makes integrations of properties and characteristics possible. Marginal destruction and death are essential to evolution.

6-1 Evolution of the Universe.

My theory of the universe as a spherical pulsation pattern in its contracting stages, with an area of increasing density at and near its center, was outlined in Chapter one, Section four. This is a continuation of that section, with emphasis on the probable evolution of galaxies and stars from their origin, through the present to their eventual disintegration. It is a difficult abstract subject with questionable marginal proof. It is possible, therefore, that I have made serious errors.

At the beginning of our universe, near Stage one, it contained no matter, but immense clouds of periodic waves moved and pulsated in casual confusion. As we begin our advance toward its maximum contraction at Stage two, the clouds of casual waves contracted and evolved galatic centers of maximum concentrations. Integrations of wave energy into electrons and protons at these centers brought into being immense clouds of hydrogen gases. A continuation of original motions, acting in conjunction with gravitational accentuations of local concentrations, produced stellar concentrations of moving hydrogen clouds. Low-density hydrogen stars came into being. The forces which caused the fundamental particles of matter to divide into electrons and protons, acted upon and between the galaxies to convert them into spherical and spiral structures, with the latter containing the greatest energy and masses.

It is assumed that the areas of maximum concentrations of energy are also the points where casual waves are contained and converted into matter, and where matter disintegrates into energy. It is assumed, therefore, that matter comes into being at the centers of the stars in proportion to their masses, and that its rate of increase is greatest at the centers of the galaxies, where the concentration of matter is greatest. This is so because the forces containing matter also act as a containing and compacting force on the casual waves from which matter evolved. It seems logically probable that the increase of matter also caused elements heavier than hydrogen to evolve at the centers of the stars.

It is my belief that the stars were radiating away a part of their masses from the moment of their first appearance, even though the increase of mass exceeded their radiation losses between Stages one and two. The immense pressures at the center of a star cause destructive interferences of local atomic and molecular structures. The constant rebuilding of these structures is accompanied by an equally constant absorption and liberation of energy. The original concentration of casual waves, although reduced by conversions into matter, must be present at the centers of the stars as a high temperature which also takes the form of quantized radiations and physical motions of stripped nuclei, atoms and molecules. The tendency to integrate, causing a constant increase of matter at that time, must also have acted upon colliding atomic nuclei to induce reintegrations into more complex structures, thus converting hydrogen into heavier elements.

The constant increase of wave-containing forces between Stages one and two was accompanied by a compacting of the hydrogen stars and an increasing density of their nuclei, with the percentage of heavy elements increasing constantly with time. The tendency of the stars to increase their masses until they become unstable and divide in two, must have been far greater at that time than at present, because the residue of casual waves was greater. It is assumed numerous star clusters in our galaxy came into being at that time by repeated growth-divisions.

We do not know what causes a star to divide in two, but there are several possibilities. The fundamental reason may be that the wave-containing forces abstracted by a galaxy from the whole universe have a natural upper limit, defined by the galaxy's photon radius and a theoretical expansion of its energy beyond that radius through the area of increasing density toward infinity in space. As a galaxy approaches its maximum mass, the percentage of energy liberated to implement the expansion of its mass-related static stress fields increases toward an equality between its increase of mass and its loss of mass by radiation. The energy radiated by its stars increases, and they become more unstable. Its largest stars with the greatest masses, being the most unstable, will divide to regain stability. It is also possible that the increasing instability of a large star sets a natural limit to its mass by causing it to divide when the growth of its mass reaches that maximum, regardless of its galaxy's reactions to its environment.

When the stability of neutrons in atomic nuclei is compared with their instability in free space, a similar relationship can be postulated for their behavior in nuclei near the centers of stars and on their surfaces. It is assumed that radioactive isotopes, with an excess of neutrons on the surface of a star, may be stable near the star's center because the close proximity of other nuclear particles increases the percentage of neutrons in that area.

In a star with no internal perturbations, the percentage of potentially radioactive atoms may increase to explosive proportions, while stars with convection currents are stable because they are constantly bringing such atoms to their surfaces. Let us assume that a normally stable star with a potentially explosive nucleus is perturbed in some way, perhaps by a passing star, and that some of its radioactive elements are brought to its surface where their explosion initiates an increasingly violent perturbation of its center, until the whole star explodes and becomes a nova.

Our universe's contraction momentum increased from zero to maximum between Stages one and two. The transition was accompanied by a contraction of casual waves as they integrated into matter, and a contraction of gaseous clouds into stars with definable sizes. The galaxies contracted and converged on the center of our universe between Stages one and two. Velocities of moving matter increased to a maximum at Stage two. The temperatures of the stars and their motion and rotations increased with contraction. The rotations of spiral galaxies increased also. The quantity of matter in our universe was greatest at Stage two.

The rate at which casual waves were converted into matter increased as we approached Stage two. But before reaching that stage a decline occurred, because the reservoir of free (convertible) energy had decreased toward the absolute minimum. The loss of matter by radiation increased also toward Stage two and beyond. Before Stage two, integrations exceeded radiation losses, but after that stage radiation losses exceeded integrations. At potential Stage three, all matter will have disintegrated into radiation.

The maximum contraction of our universe at Stage two represents a threshold, defined by a maximum rate of transition from an increase to a decrease of matter in our universe. The question is whether this change is to be defined as gradual or abrupt. In the first case there may not be any specific phenomenon which can be dated relative to the present; however, the second may give us several phenomena from which it can be dated. Many astronomers appear to be of the opinion that something happened about six billion years ago. If that is so, our crossing of the second-stage threshold at that time seems to be the most logical answer.

After Stage two, the forces containing matter began to decrease, with a constant decrease of the ether's contraction momentum. It caused the quantity of matter in our universe to decrease by causing energy losses by radiation and expansion to exceed integrations into matter. A decreasing force of gravity caused an expansion and slowing down of orbital motions. The motions of the stars were slowed by an expansion of the galaxies, and the galaxies began to move apart.

This motion may be the observed expansion of the universe, but there are reasons to believe it is an apparent motion. The difference in the rate of increasing density between the center of the universe and those at various distances from it may cause a difference of energy between comparable quantum states. The dynamic changes associated with advancing time may be the cause, because we observe the radiations of distance galaxies as they occurred when the universe was younger. However, it seems that such radiations should be more energetic. Another possibility is the loss of energy by free photons as they move through space.

6-2 The Solar System.

We know from observations that stars are constantly agitated from within. Some explode once, suddenly and violently, and others periodically; some pulsate with regular, and others with irregular, periodicities; many stars, like our sun, keep radiating with a quiet constancy that appears to cover their whole life span. The sun's surface is constantly being agitated by temperature motions, like boiling, and sometimes by explosive outbursts that may eject gases for thousands of miles into its chromosphere.

The solar system is composed of the sun, nine planets, numerous asteroids and comets, and countless meteors. The planets circle the sun on nearly the same plane in the same direction, with the sun's plane of rotation inclined about six degrees to this dynamic plane. The sequence of planets from the sun are: Mercury, Venus, Earth, Mars, Jupiter, Saturn, Uranus, Neptune and Pluto. The first four are minor planets and the next four major planets, with Jupiter the largest and Saturn next. Pluto is a minor planet about the same size as the earth, farthest from the sun. All the planets from the earth to Neptune have satellites, with the systems of the two giant planets in many ways comparable to the solar system. Saturn is circled by a ring of countless particles, moving in the same direction as its rotation on the plane of its equator.

It is my belief that the planets originated from a series of incandescent rings thrown up by the sun at various times during periods of exceptional activity; Saturn's ring shows the possibility of such an evolution. It is also indicated by the rotations of the sun and Jupiter. The sun's revolution has a period of about 28 days on its equator and 34 days at its poles. The equator of Jupiter also rotates faster than its poles. The earth has a liquid core which appears to rotate slowly relative to its surface. According to my theory, the natural velocity gradients of a rotating sphere transit into the vorticular gradients of an ideal vortex with distance; with the latter tending to convert its rotation into a differential rotation, as observed on the sun and Jupiter. By postulating a time when the sun's surface rotated rapidly enough on its equator to expel incandescent gases into its chromosphere with enough rotation momentum for a reasonable percentage to remain there, we obtain a ring comparable to that of Saturn's. As it cools, the ring becomes liquids and solids which casual collisions and gravity would cause to consolidate into a single orbiting mass.

To induce this planet to recede to its present orbit we must postulate an accelerating force emanating from the sun. It is assumed the sun's rapid rotation on its equator produces a configuration space which rotates faster than the planet, and that the planet reacts with an acceleration-recession. The physical relationship between the sun and the configuration field produced by its rotation, with the sun tending to rotate as a whole and its field as a pure vortex, can be outlined by noting the cyclic changes which causes sunspots.

The sunspot cycle of about 22.25 years is an alternating acceleration and deceleration of the configuration space produced by the sun's rotation, with these half periods of 11.125 years apparently caused by an alternating expansion and contraction of its field in space. The momentum of a rotating field appears as an opposition to change. The change of rotation, therefore, appears first at the poles where its opposition is zero, and then moves toward the equator as a contracting rotation shell of diminishing size, until it disappears at the equator at the end of a half-cycle. The motion of an acceleration or deceleration shell across the sun's surface causes eruptive prominences to rotate in the areas of maximum change. These become sunspots, which appear and disappear as the shell drifts across the sun's surface. The spots are magnetized by electric currents produced by the changing field.

In the light of facts, the current belief that the sunspot period is caused by a pulsation of the sun itself is, in my opinion, untenable. We accept the exchange of magnetic fields between atoms, and I can see no reason to reject the existence of comparable effects in the dynamics of stellar evolution. My theory of a contracting ether, and the displacement of its natural dynamic progression by matter, postulates a tendency to eliminate reducible stresses by a gravitational approach and an exchange of momenta and wave functions between galaxies, between the stars and star clusters in a galaxy, and between the sun and its planets in the solar system. On this larger canvas the forces are gravitational and not electrostatic. However, their observable powers are great because they are associated with great masses and act through times which range from a few days to millions of years.

It is evident that changes in the gravity figure of orbiting planets and satellites is acted upon by the contracting ether in much the same way as it acts upon the particles in an atom. Since changes of gravity are not transmitted with infinite velocity, but with twice the speed of light, it is evident that pulsations and waves with periods of planetary dimensions will appear in the solar system in response to its changing gravity figure. I have traced some of these waves through their effects on various phenomena on the sun and the earth. The tendency to integrate the motions of planets and satellites through functional exchanges of momenta over immense periods of time, implies an organization beyond the possibility of conventional theory. This organization has been noted by Moulton and other prominent astronomers.

My theory of the evolution of the solar system begins with a hydrogen star of immense size and low density. For some unknown reason it had acquired a rotation which caused its distant gases to take the form of a vorticular disk. Widening toward the center, its shape transited into the sphere of an ordinary star in its central area. This transition is the product of an interaction between gravity and rotation. Rotating gases cannot be retained by a star if their velocities exceed its local force of gravity, but they deform its natural spherical shape, and that deformation is greatest where gravity is weak and gas density relatively low. Rotation increases with gravitational attraction as we approach the central area of the sun, but at some distance from its center both attain a maximum and then decrease to zero at its center. (A hollow center would have reversed gravity.) There is a dominance of gravitational attraction between the masses in the central area which produces the spherical shape postulated for that area, and with this dominance there is a tendency of the central sphere to revolve as a unit.

With the passage of time, the sun's central area enlarged, and the density of its mass increased with the evolution of elements heavier than hydrogen. There was a consequent increase of its tendency to revolve as a single body, accompanied by the ejection of masses with excess velocities to its surface on the equator as an increase of its equator's velocity relative to its poles. At the same time, its rotating cloud of gases was contracting and accelerating in response to the increasing gravitational attraction of an increasing central mass. Since a contraction is accompanied by an increase of rotational momentum, a critical state appears when its rotational motion passes the point near the sun's surface where the sun's gravitational attraction is equal to its centrifigal force, and a dominance of the latter within that point which increases with time. We have, therefore, an orbiting cloud of hydrogen gases accelerating the sun's rotation on its equator, with its central areas ejecting gases composed of different elements into the cloud with orbital velocities which cause a large percentage to remain there.

The question now is whether the ejected gases can consolidate into liquids and incandescent solids during ejection, immediately afterwards, or gradually over a period of time. If these postulates are rejected by science as improbable or impossible, my theory of an incandescent ring of solid particles, such as Saturn's, must be modified or rejected. It assumes that an incandescent ring was formed from matter ejected by the sun during a period of exceptional activity, and that this ring consolidated, first into larger bodies, and then into a single mass by casual collisions and gravitational attraction. An accelerating force acting constantly on this new planet from the sun caused it to recede gradually, first rapidly and then slowly, to its present distance. The repulsive interaction between sun and planet produced an increasing inclination of the planet's orbit to the sun's equator.

When a large mass comes too close to the sun it is torn to pieces by tidal forces. The minimum distance, called "Roche's limit," is about a million kilometers above the sun's surface, for a liquid mass with the same density as the sun. It is closer for a solid mass and for a mass with greater density. For the distance above, a planet's orbital velocity is 140 km. per second, and it completes a period in about 10.5 hours. Comets are known to have been within Roche's limit without being destroyed. Stars circled by rings of incandescent gases have been observed.

However, the anticipated presence of liquid and solid particles in a proto-planet ring is still in question. Assuming their presence, it is further assumed that the forces which brought it into being are accelerating its particles until they are beyond Roche's limit. In the meantime, collisions and gravitational attractions by the largest masses increases their sizes until a single mass comes into being. An alternate theory assumes a violent explosion within the sun which ejects an immense cloud of heavy elements into a rapidly rotating hydrogen cloud. Their interaction displaces the cloud, now cooling condensing and liquifying, into an eccentric orbit around the sun. Meanwhile, the gravitational forces within the cloud causes it to evolve a heavy nucleus and the spherical shape of a planet.

I am not too satisfied by the solutions offered above, but they serve my purpose and my belief that the solar system did not come into being by accident, but by evolution. It is assumed that each planet came into being from matter ejected by the sun during a period of violent agitation. Each appeared in an orbit beyond Roche's limit, and then receded gradually to its present orbit. The energy for this recession was abstracted from the rotation momentum on the sun's equator. It produced a rotating configuration field, relative to which the orbiting planet had an apparent counter-motion, (though moving with the field). To reduce this motion the planet accelerated in its orbit. This transfer of momentum produced a hiatus in the sun's expulsion of matter. Several million years later, however, the sun began a new cycle of agitation, and another planet came into being and began to recede. This process continued until all nine planets had come into being, and the sun's rotation momentum had been reduced to its natural value. The system is apparently dynamically stable at the present time.

6-3 The Earth's Evolution.

In developing a theory of the evolution of the galaxies, the solar system and the earth billions of years ago, it must be kept in mind that we have very little to go by, and that my conception of the most probable sequence of events may not be true or even close to the truth. It does, however, give the reader a new approach to these problems, and this is my justification for suggesting the following theory of the origin and evolution of the earth.

The earth came into being from matter ejected by the sun; either as a ring of incandescent matter, or in the form of a cloud of heavy gases, large enough to produce a gravitational cohesion long enough to prevent its dispersal, before a radiation loss of temperature and a concentration of heavy elements at its center brought a dense gaseous or liquid core into existence. This core became the center of a constantly growing and cooling mass.

This theory, therefore, begins with a gaseous, incandescent mass with a heavy core circling the sun, beyond Roche's limit, with an orbital period of about ten hours. It is orbiting a sun whose atmosphere extends far beyond its orbit, and its motion through it is accompanied by a capture of heavy gases and the escape of light gases from its envelope. We know that heavy gases are expelled periodically by the sun, and that some stars are circled by rings of gases, comparable to the rings of Saturn. But we do not know if such a ring can also contain lumps of matter in liquid or solid form. Assuming their presence in a ring near the Earth's orbit, an infall of meteoric matter would produce a constant increase of its mass until this source was exhausted. If the moon was formed in such a ring and solidified before the infall had ended, we have a possible origin of its craters.

The sun's tidal force kept the earth's mass from revolving relative to the sun. Its period of axial rotation was, therefore, the same as that of its orbital period. The excess of orbital solar energy which brought the earth into being was also acting upon it to increase its distance from the sun. We are dealing here with an exchange of momenta which gives results contrary to the irreplaceable losses usually expected. Since the forces containing electrons and protons in the atoms are the same as those containing stars and galaxies, the action potentials observed in the atom must also be present in the solar system, including an exchange of momenta to reduce the deformation of the contracting ether.

It is possible the moon came into being at the same time as the earth; either by a separation of its mass from that of the earth by the solar tide, or as a separate mass which was subsequently captured by the earth. It might have come into being some millions of years after the earth's evolution, moving in an independent orbit until it was captured by it several million years later. The evolution-recession of a planet inhibits the sun's activity for a time, and it is assumed that the moon came into being as the product of its renewed activity. A comparison with the asteroids and Mars, following the evolution of Jupiter, leads to the conclusion that the inhibiting forces of a preceding mass cause the one immediately following to be smaller, as if the sun's rotation momentum had been reduced and was slowly rebuilding.

As the earth receded toward its present orbit, its axial rotations retained its original period, even though its orbital period was increasing. Its recession was accompanied, therefore, by a constantly increasing eastward rotation of its gaseous and liquid mass. A short time after its formation, the earth's temperature dropped to the point where its gases became liquid, with heavy elements gravitating to its center and light elements and molecules floating to the top. It produced the present density gradient and stratification of the rocks. As the earth left the gaseous envelope it held in common with the sun, its high temperature gases escaped, and it was left without an atmosphere.

At this stage of the earth's evolution, we find it a liquid body of stratified rock molecules without an atmosphere, revolving slowly as it circles the sun in an orbit of less than one day. It revolves through an elliptic shape caused by solar and anti-sun tides. It carries with it liquid granite, which tends to accumulate in the two tidal bulges. One of these is heated by the sun, and the other is cooled by radiation and escaping gases.

Before continuing, a few facts will give us a background for reference and comparison. Because the earth's composition is about the same as the sun's, it is assumed that it originated from matter expelled by the sun. That the earth was once a molten mass is proved by the composition of its oldest surface rocks and by the density gradient and stratification of its mass from center to surface. It is also proved by the increase of temperature with depth, and the existence of a liquid core about 3,740 kilometers in radius, which is believed to be composed of nickel and iron. At the present time, this core is believed to be rotating slowly relative to the surface.

The earth's radius is 6,378 kilometers. Its average density is 5.5 times that of water, increasing in depth from 2.75 at the surface to about 12 at its center. Earthquakes show discontinuities at depths of 35, 150, 400 and 700 kilometers below the surface. Its crustal layer of sediment and granite composing the continents and continental shelves, has mean depth of 11 km. and a mean density of 2.65. Its actual distribution is in continental blocks with an average depth of about 60 km. The continents are floating on basalt which covers the whole earth, with an average thickness of 24 km. and a density of 2.87. This basalt floats on a layer of diorite and dunite, which has an average thickness of 35 km. At a depth of about 60 km., solid rocks will flow in response to a constant pressure. Liquid magmas can contain a large percentage of gases and water vapors in solution. When they solidify, the gases and vapors are expelled. It is generally assumed that the earth did not have an atmosphere at its beginning because the temperature of its gases exceeded the velocity of escape. Its present atmosphere and oceans came into being following the solidification of its mantle by gases and vapors expelled during volcanic eruptions.

We know that the continents float higher than the ocean floors because they are composed of lighter matter, but science has no explanation for the concentration of granite in continental masses on the earth's surface. It has been suggested that convection currents might have caused it, or that an infall of granite planetesimals of continental dimensions during the earth's formation might have produced the continents. Another theory assumes that solar tides on the earth, at a time when the earth was closer to the sun, caused granite to become concentrated in two tidal bulges, one of which subsequently became detached and converted into a satellite of the earth. The moon's escape left a scar which became the Pacific ocean. It also left us with a single continental mass and a potential drift.

Wegener's theory of a continental drift starts with a single continental mass which he called Pangea. Other scientists have found proof confirming his postulate. It will be noticed that if the two Americas were moved into contact with Europe and Africa, their coast lines fit together with only slight alterations. The other continents can also be brought into accord with the assumption that all the continents originated as one land mass, and that they migrated to their present positions through millions of years. A migration of the continents has been proved by an agreement between geological features, and immense deposits of sediments which could only have come from the rivers of a large continental mass. Glaciers on the four southern continents and India during the Permian period indicate a common mass near the south pole. An identity of the fauna and flora, on continents now separated by thousands of miles of sea, indicates a land connection during the early carboniferous period. The Devonian period began about 300 million years ago; the carboniferous, 50 million years later. The earliest known plants and animals appear in the Cambrian period, which began nearly 500 million years ago. The earth's age is estimated at about 3500 million years from radioactive analyses of its oldest rocks.

We will now continue the earth's evolution from the time it was a liquid non-rotating mass, deformed by two immense tidal bulges; a solar and an anti-sun tide caused by its orbital motion near the sun. The earth's central mass, now known as its liquid core, was only slightly deformed, because it has a relatively high density; but as we approach its surface, the sequence of layers are increasingly deformed. The relatively low density of liquid basalt and granite appeared as thick deposits in the two tidal bulges. As the earth receded from the sun, its mass began a slow rotation that increased with time. Its equator, like those of the sun and Jupiter, rotated faster than its poles on the surface. Its motion through the centers of the two tidal bulges undercut them in their thickets areas and divided each into two rotating masses. It also carried matter from one bulge to the other. The heating effect of the sun kept the surface granite liquid on the sunward side, while the cooling effect of heat escaping into space caused the granite on the anti-sun side to solidify as soon as the earth had cooled enough for that to occur.

Observation shows there was only one continental mass. It is assumed, therefore, that the temperature difference between the two tidal bulges caused the liquid granite to move with the equatorial current to become a part of the anti-sun mass. As the earth receded from the sun, the bulges began to expand in width and decrease in height with the decreasing power of the solar tide. However, this is a highly questionable postulate which suggests an alternate solution. It is assumed that most of the silicates, the last to crystallize in a melt, accumulated on the anti-sun side during the earth's formation. Granite is lighter than basalt because it contains about 73 per cent silicates to 48 per cent in basalt.

It has been estimated that it took the earth about a hundred thousand years to develop a hard crust from the liquid state. The first part to solidify was the granite in its anti-sun bulge; the last was probably the part heated by the sun. At first a thin crust would form, break up, sink in its melt, and then remelt. As the earth cooled, the crust increased in thickness, and the size of the sinking blocks increased. Next we have a solid surface with long rifts through which liquid magma ascends, spreads and solidifies. The rifts become less frequent, and volcanos appear where the magma has melted through the solid crust. The solidifying rocks liberate gases and water vapors, and an atmosphere comes into being. It begins to rain, and the rain becomes an incessant torrent. Immense rivers come into being, eroding the rocks and carrying the sediments to low-lying areas, filling geosynclines, while the water becomes the sea.

The sun's attraction for the tidal bulge kept the earth's surface from rotating relative to the sun (comparable to the moon's motion relative to the earth). The equatorial drift current ceased, but the underlying liquid mass continued a slow rotation relative to the crust which built up a static stress against it in the form of a tendency to rotate. On the equator, where the drift current had reduced the thickness of the granite crust at its center, a down-warping appeared which became the Tethys ocean separating two continental masses. Its present location is through the Mediterranean and the Himalayas. It is assumed that the high points on the two continents became covered by glaciers at that time.

As the earth's orbit increased, the sun's tidal-making force decreased until the point was reached where the friction between the surface and the revolving core became greater than its opposition, and the earth began to revolve relative to the sun. Its rate of revolution must have increased rapidly at first, as the stresses which had caused it decreased to a minimum. Those forces which had deformed it by acting directly on the tidal bulge as a deviation from isostacy reversed direction and matter began to flow westward. After day one, the sun's tidal-making force became a periodic deformation of the earth's mass, and the high points on the two continents began to flatten out. The glaciers melted and increased the sea level, thus flooding low areas. The earth's south pole of rotation was near longitude 30 E., and latitude 45 S., and its north pole 150 W., and 45 N: the first, south of Africa and the other, south of Alaska. This location of the south pole is in good agreement with the glaciers which covered parts of four southern continents and India, and the location of the Tethys ocean is in accord with my postulate of a down-warping on the equator. Note that Alaska was far from its present location at that time.

Day one is obviously an important date in the earth's evolution. Reason tells me that the continents should have begun to migrate some time after that date, but I have no conception of how long it took a drift of underlying magma to tear the continents apart and cause them to drift toward their present locations. As a pure guess, I would say between a hundred thousand and a million years; but my ignorance on this point is such that if a scientist extended it to a hundred million years or longer, and proved it by facts and figures, I would accept it with qualifications. My first guess is that the earth's rotation relative to the sun began at the beginning of the Cambrian age, 500 million years ago, and that it caused the destruction of numerous life forms and made it possible for those remaining to evolve toward their present forms. This postulate, however, leaves a hiatus of 300 million years before the Permian age, when the continental drift apparently began. A second guess is that it began at the beginning of the carboniferous age, 250 million years ago, and 50 million years before the Permian age. However, this postulate leaves us with four ages, the Cambrian, Ordovician, Silurian and Devonian, unaccounted for.

We have indications that gravity adjustments in the magmas deep below the surface are extremely slow. Earthquakes have occurred at depths up to 800 kilometers below the surface. The magmas in those areas must have the cohesive properties of a solid to produce tearing stresses where they fail to adjust to a liquid flow. Experiments shows that a solid will flow under the pressure existing at those depths. Recent observations of the orbital motions of earth satellites shows that the earth, in addition to the flattening at its poles due to rotation, has a slightly pear-shaped form. If this is the remains of its original deformation, it shows that it takes an immensely long time for sub-crustal motions to adjust to the changes which followed Day one. If that is so, the time lapse of 300 million years after Day one may not be impossibly long. However, in this case, the relatively rapid motions of the continents, after the original continent had split apart, needs explaining. Although it averages only about ten centimeters a year, with the greatest motions occurring immediately after separation, the problem at the moment is one of proportion.

It will be noticed that the continental masses, on the whole, moved as unified blocks of granite after separation. They were compressed into mountain chains in areas where great depressions, called geosynclines, had accumulated immense quantities of sediment from the rivers which flowed into them. However, the cases in which the continental block expanded and split into divergent segments, repeating the original process, seems feeble in comparison with their compression and drifting apart. The first reason which comes to mind is that a gravity slope with a decreasing gradient causes the rear part of a continent to move faster than its front. We start with a single continent expanding along its edges and producing geosynclines in the process, because the cohesive forces of the principal mass opposed the expansion. As it split into continents, the rear part of each moved faster than its front, causing the sedimented depressions to become uplifted into mountains.

There appear to be forces besides the gravity slopes, which kept the continents from subdividing, and it is assumed that they acted also on the original continent as an opposition to its subdivision until underlying divergent motions of subcrustal magmas tore it apart. After separation, the containing forces no longer acted as a restraining influence on the motions of the continents. The gravity anomaly produced by a mass of continental dimensions, being such a force, is one of the possible causes of cohesion.

The continents are in isostatic balance with their denser underlying magmas, by floating on it, like ice on water. Ocean floors are lower than the continents because the matter below them is denser, and the force of gravity is, therefore, greater. Because all masses produce a gravitational force, the mass of a continent above the isostatic balance at sea level deflect the earth's force of gravity in proportion to its mass, the distribution of that mass, and its height above the point of isostatic balance. The gravity recurve, acting against the tendency of the original anti-sun tidal bulge to disperse, must have been a strong force before the flattening of the bulge reduced its containing power.

In describing the earth's evolution, I have ignored factors which cannot be assigned to a specific time, which are local phenomena or phenomena which are not vital to its evolutionary progression. Among these is the time of the moon's capture and the condition under which it took place. We do not know if the moon was close to the earth and receding toward its present orbit near Day one, or whether it was already in that orbit at the time. Was it a factor in causing the earth to revolve, and did it have any influence on its plane of revolution and the changes of that plane?

The blanketing effect of a continental mass causes the temperatures under it to increase far above those under the seas. A significant factor in this increase is the presence of radioactive atoms in continental masses, as contrasted with their absence in the body of the earth. These factors might have increased the rate at which the continents moved. Among the factors which produced the present contours of the continents is the eruptive outflow of basalt. It occurs because liquid basalt is lighter than solid granite. It passes through granite by melting and following breaks and weak spots, thus causing granite masses to sink in its melt.

The liquid basalt may overflow large areas and produce thick layers which solidify and cause the underlying granite to sink and melt. The molten granite, now lighter than molten basalt, flows outward and causes an uplift of adjacent granite and sedimentary masses, while the sinking solid basalt forms a bay, a lake or a sea. Such a sea may take the form of a geosyncline, which in time becomes filled with sediment, followed by its uplift into a chain of mountains.

Sceptical scientists may contend that my theory of a momentum exchange between orbiting and rotating masses in the solar system is an *ad-hoc* device to avoid the difficulties which accompany the invariable momenta normally expected. However, those who have read my theory of the atom, should be able to perceive the fundamental identity between atomic and planetary exchange phenomena. I started out by postulating a rotating liquid earth, followed by a solid nonrotating earth which eventually began to rotate in response to its rotating liquid center. An obvious first conclusion is that its liquid core retained enough of its original rotation momentum to produce the 24-hour axial rotation of today. An orbital period of a few days, at the time of day one, might make this postulate acceptable, but such a short orbit is obviously impossible. Since it is equally impossible to accept a rapid rotation of the core in a non-rotating surface shell, it is assumed the core lost rotation momentum before Day one and gained momentum after that date. It was probably abstracted, either from the rotation momentum of the sun or the orbit momentum of the moon.

6-4 The Evolution of Life.

Before the cells of a living body can divide by mitosis, each active cell passes through a cycle of change before it divides into two cells; with each gene in its chromosomes going through a process of growth, reproduction and division which takes us back to the beginning of the life process and its first cause. The wide variety of molecules which pass through this process shows that the tendency of a molecule to extend its organization through its immediate enviornment is a general one, provided the local conditions are favorable. It is a tendency of all atoms and molecules to extend their organizations into the environment, thus eliminating reducible interferences with their functional waves. The philosophy of logical continuity supports the postulate of identity above by noting that: "The forces and tendencies which now support evolution and the fundamental processes of cell division are the same as those which brought them into being." Life would be impossible if molecules did not tend to reproduce their kind.

The fundamental properties and processes of life are the properties and tendencies of atoms and molecules in that larger sphere of activity. An atom can exist indefinitely because its organizer acts constantly in support of its existing structure, through functional interactions with its environment; it tends to extend its organization by an exchange-integration of intruding forces and the expulsion-repulsion of those which cannot be integrated. Its primary effect is the formation of molecules; its secondary effect is an action, through the specific wave functions of particular molecules, to extend those functions by causing environmental matter to integrate, where possible, into similar molecules. The tendency to integrate is the first law of both living and non-living matter. In life, it takes the form of growth and reproduction.

Scientists have succeeded in reproducing numerous living processes by imitating the conditions under which they occur in nature. A crystal dropped into a solution may, by inductive crystallization, cause the appearance of crystals on its own pattern. Fragments of crystals will grow into perfect crystals in the solution. Some crystals are so small that they can float in the air. Snow crystals can take on an almost infinite variety of forms, even though they are all composed of the same (H_2O) molecules.

The products of the experiments above are not living or proto-life, because a single reaction exhausted their possibilities; but the reactions which brought them into being are significant since they show what molecules tend to do under favorable conditions. The logical implication of the first experiment is that molecular structures with reproductive tendencies can, and do, appear in nature in countless forms. Among them there will be some with those additional tendencies, properties and potentials that make them the nuclei of evolving life forms. These are proto-viruses; the stepping stones between living and non-living matter. However, if a scientist accidentally came across such molecules, he probably would have no inkling of their potential as proto-life, because the variety of conditions under which they evolved in nature cannot be reproduced in a laboratory.

From the very beginning of life on earth, it appeared in a variety of competing forms, with each form of elementary life having properties and potentialities which determine its ability to survive in a hostile nature, in competition with other life forms. At first, the most successful life forms (genus) were those which survived the longest and reproduced at the greatest rate because they used elements which were in greatest abundance. As competition for growth material increased between the species, and between the individual mutant members of a species, survival became a handicap because it inhibited the appearance of those mutations which determine the rate at which a species evolves. It will be noticed that, in the economy of nature, the survival of a species is important to life, whereas its individual members need survive only long enough to give it meaning and purpose. Because the destruction of individuals with undesirable characteristics releases growth material, it increased the rate at which its species adopted itself to a changing environment. Those species which depended upon evolution for survival evolved functional weaknesses which made their destruction more probable, and with time it became death, by age, of all its members.

However, as a species evolves more complex properties, it also evolves a more complex structure and growth sequences of structure, which reduced its rate of reproduction. The ability to survive by rapid reproduction came into conflict with survival through the evolution of favorable properties, some forms of life taking one road, and others another. The difference, during the early stages of evolution, was determined by different molecular potentials and environmental conditions, and later by the compulsive necessity of complex life forms to continue their evolution of specific survival potentials or perish.

The argument by some scientists that life came into being by an accidental combination of favorable properties is acceptable only in the sense that everything pertaining to life is a combination of fixed processes and relations accompanied by a continuous succession of accidents. However, if they mean to imply that life could not come into being without the sudden appearance of all the basic characteristics of life, they are talking nonsense. The essence of life is the growth of identical forms, with all its other properties derived from it by accentuation, inhibition and variations from the norm. Some scientists believe that life appeared first in the form of a protoplasm; others argue that it must have been a virus. It is my belief that both forms appeared at the same time, since the only real difference is that one type of proto-life molecule would adhere, forming a protoplasm, while another would not, becoming a virus. A small difference between two molecules could produce both. It seems probable that free viruses would enter a protoplasm and either become functional within it or take the form of a destructive disease. It is my belief that life first appeared in multitude of forms, and that the change from inanimate to animate matter was so slow and gradual that it is impossible to define the moment of transition.

A living body requires energy to support its growth and reproduction. This energy is stored by the body in the form of potential chemical reactions which are released under controlled conditions to produce specific effects. Energy can be obtained from the elements in a body's environment and by photo-synthesis. The former, at the time when no organic molecules existed, was at best a series of simple chemical reactions with comparatively few possibilities and little energy. The latter is the absorption of radiated energy by a body's molecules, and the storage of that energy in the form of potential chemical reactions. The photo-synthesis of sunlight not only provided an abundance of energy, it also made it possible for a body to use the same elements and chemicals over and over again, releasing only those most easily obtained from its environment.

In postulating the evolution of first life from simple molecules, it should be noted that a primary condition is the ability to grow and divide; the second is an abundance of growth material and usable energy; and the third its dispersal in space. It is assumed, therefore, that first life began as simple, naked, growing and dividing molecules, which either originated in the sea or entered it at an early date. With time, their simple chemical processes became increasingly complex as they began to use sunlight for energy and evolved protective envelopes, which also served as containers and selective membranes for their chemicals. Some of these molecules were amino acids which combined in various ways to form proteins. The versatility of amino acids are so great that they became, with time, the building blocks of all life. The 23 known amino acids are comparatively simple molecules whose different properties and potentialities became, in various combinations, the countless complex kinds of proteins of which all organic matter above the simplest forms of life are composed.

The fundamental unit around which all life evolved is a single complex molecule called DNA (deoxyribonucleic acid). It is shaped like a ladder, with its rungs composed of two pairs of molecules (adenine-thymine and gaunine-cystosine). It divides by splitting the rungs and reforming the two parts into identical molecules by the addition of new base units. The activation of specific units within a DNA molecule produce the specific organs and processes of all living things from viruses to man. The subject is complex and beyond the purpose of this book.

At first, reproduction was simple. The organic molecules within a protective envelope grew, divided and enlarged the envelope until the waves of the sea tore them apart. With time, the pressure of survival in a hostile environment speeded up the process of division by evolving an internal incentive which became, ultimately, organic reproduction. To produce an equal division of essential molecules, the cells passed through a cycle of change which, at first, was a simple device to insure division when the cells had reached a specific size or age. Some types of cells had adhesive propensities and formed a protoplasm; others separated at once and became single-cell life forms. As time went by, the former evolved an organization in which each cell became subordinated to the whole, and all the cells were changed to serve as the functional processes of an integrated body. The countless types of structures which evolved from the integration of cells became the plant and animal life of today. In contrast, the limited possibilities of solitary cells, in terms of size and function, were compensated for by rapid reproduction and dispersal. This made possible a rapid adaptation to new or changing environments, and many of these simple types of organisms became parasites on multi-cell bodies.

As the organic processes become more complex, changes during cell division became more specific and complex. The simple cell division noted above became division by amitosis. Before division, the molecules (genes) carrying specific properties become concentrated in a nucleus which split into equal parts. Their separation was followed by a division of the cell. But this type of cell division did not satisfy the more exacting requirements of the increasingly complex properties and functions of evolving life, and amitosis became mitosis. With the evolution of sex, mitosis developed a sex-determination process called meiosis. Mitosis is a complex process of cell division which ensures that the traits of two parents, present in each cell, are properly mixed through an exchange of genes, and then divided by an equal division of the gene-carrying chromosomes in the two new cells. The cells of plants and animals all divide by mitosis, with a slight difference which is believed to indicate that the process had been nearly completed at the time when the two forms of life took separate evolutionary paths.

The evolution of the species is based on accidental changes (mutations) in the sex cells, and a testing of their value by the bodies which result from the fertilization of an egg cell by a sperm cell, as each individual struggles for survival in a hostile environment. If we define the mutations of sexless reproduction as vertical lines that do not cross, sex is a horizontal process that causes them to combine in various proportions. It makes each body in a species different from all others and, therefore, a unique experiment in evolution. Since most of the mutations have already been tested for survival by other bodies, the deviation of each individual from the norm is a search for maximum integration of characteristics. Most surviving mutations are marginal within a species, because great changes are usually lethal or an insurmountable handicap in the struggle for existence. Sex makes it possible for a species to evolve gradually through numerous marginal deviations from the norm, accompanied by the elimination of its unfit members. The statistical probability that the fit will survive makes it possible for a species to become adapted to a changing environment. In comparison, evolution by sexless reproduction, although possible, is so slow and wasteful that it rarely occurs in nature; as in the most primitive forms of life and by alternating with sexual reproduction.

Investigations of mutations indicate that 99 percent of those which occur are detrimental to the survival of a species. Sex was invented by nature to exploit the possibilities of the remaining one per cent to the outmost. However, for maximum effectiveness, the numerous deterimental traits which appear in a species must be eliminated as soon as possible. Since death before reproduction is nature's only weapon, it follows that those species closest to the brink of destruction have the greatest evolution potentials, provided their new members are numerous enough to equate their loss of those that are unfit. Since there is no way to equate the two, the course of evolution is a repeated destruction of species which become dominant for a time and, in the ease of multiplication, acquired aberrant mutations that doomed them, with increasing competition and a changing environment. In nature, the term "unfit" can mean many things; some of these are difficult to discover because they may be hidden potentialities and limitations of dividing cells, or they may be inversions of normal expectations. Since evolution is based on mutations, we may overlook the fact that they can also destroy when the unfit are protected and permitted to produce their kind. Human life on earth may eventually be destroyed by those who are most intent upon preserving it.

In the evolution of life, some factors are natural processes and others are invented by nature for special purposes; in all cases, however, the latter cannot come into being without implementing natural causes, since any other conclusion would introduce the supernatural by implication. Among the natural processes is the reproduction of molecules, while mitosis and sex are inventions. Since an invention must have a casual beginning, sex must have started as a casual union and mixing of primitive cell protoplasm, followed by division. The advantages of sex converted this casual relationship into a functional process. Its increasing importance in the evolution of protoplasm, as a way to create a series of uniform products with numerous marginal variations, which made adaptation to a changing environment possible made sex the dominant factor in reproduction. The union of two cells initiated a growth-division which resulted in its separation from the parent body to become an independent unit.

Let us note that bodies came into being to protect their sex cells until reproduction, and that they still serve that purpose. Since nature acts blindly without purpose, the means of protection became increasingly elaborate and abstract. The first bodies to protect a sex cell were spherical masses of protoplasm. With time, their shapes became functional and developed properties appropriate to those shapes in the local environment, as the cells began to differentiate.

The evolution of life on earth is a continuous process of reproduction, with the members of each species fanning out from its main stem into a multitude of marginal variations. A few of these may branch out into a new species, while the others or their descendants die out and leave the main stem to repeat the process. At some early stage of life on earth, plants and animals took separate paths. The subject of actual evolution is outside the purpose of this book, but I shall outline some of its stages by noting the changes that a developing embryo passes through.

A fertilized human cell passes through a sequence of changes which recapitulates, in part, the stages of Man's evolution. It begins by dividing and redividing until it is a cluster of cells, called a morula. A cavity appears, due to water osmosis, and it is now a blastula. This is followed by a differentiation between the cells, with those on the exterior called ectoderm, and those within called endoderm; the whole body is called a gastrula. A third type of cells, called mesoderm, is found in all animal forms. The body now begins to take shape, as differentiations appear and develop when specific genes in its local cells are activated according to a set plan, within the cells and in response to chemicals liberated by other cells within the body. About three weeks after conception, the human embryo passes through a fish and reptile stage, with gill clefts and tail easily recognizable. All responsible scientists agree that this and other evidence, such as the similarity of characteristics in related species, their evolution through the ages and by selective breeding, prove that Man's early ancestors were once fishes in the sea, then amphibians, reptiles, mammals, primates and, finally, man.

In the development of an embryo, organs which were once functional, although now useless to the final organism, must be reduced to those fragments which are essential to the functional continuity of change toward its final integration of organs. This means the elimination of genes, or mutative changes of their functions, or the addition of genes which act upon them to change their functions as the embryo grows. Since a simple cell structure and sequence is more stable than a complex one, it is assumed that there is a natural tendency toward simplification by mutating elimination of all non-essentials. Unused organs, therefore, tend to disappear, gradually, or by abrupt transitions. The human appendix is one such organ. If it were to disappear by a mutation, its loss would be beneficial, provided it is not an essential part of the evolutionary ladder.

It is possible to outline the requirements for a vigorous life and a maximum rate of evolution. The stage must be large and varied. There must be an abundance of energy, easily accessible and constantly available. There must be a wide variety of essential elements available for the storage of that energy, and for those molecular structures which carry the life processes forward. A means of easy transportation should be available during the early stages of evolution. The forces of nature must vary to produce a varying experience which conditions the life forms to long-lasting changes, but they must not go beyond the range of adaptive changes; the struggle against nature must not convert the competition between life forms into a marginal process. The over-all processes of advancing life must be able to effect an integration which increases the potentialities of all its forms. Life must have an existence potential over immensely long periods of time to effect this integration.

It should be noted that if we were able to compare life on two planets, and find that it advances twice as fast on one as on the other in a unit of time, the difference does not increase in proportion to time, but as time squared. When we check the possibility of life on earth against the conditions above, its rate of evolution must be near the attainable maximum. Evolution was slow at the beginning because conditions were unfavorable. After cells and cell division had come into being, control of growth and shapes was at a minimum until the process of amitosis, and later mitosis, had appeared and evolved toward its present state. Proto-life probably began as soon as conditions on earth were favorable, two or three billion years ago. It might have transited into life, perhaps, a billion years later. The term "life" is used to define the origin of known organic processes, such as cell division, energy from the sun, amino acids and their conversions into proteins, etc.

If my theory of the earth's evolution is true, first life probably appeared and evolved for billions of years, while one side of the earth was constantly facing the sun and the other in permanent darkness. Between the two tidal bulges a shallow sea probably circled the earth in the twilight zone. Life probably evolved in this sea until that day when the earth began to revolve relative to the sun. On Day one, most of the animals and plants living on its equator must have perished, while those near its poles became adapted to the alternation between day and night, heat and cold, and moved into the vacated areas. If the Cambrian age began shortly after Day one, the absence of preceding life can be explained by migrations from the polar areas.

In developing my theories, I have been striving for consistency in bringing facts and their logical implications into accord with my conception of total knowledge. While this consistency makes it possible for the reader to evaluate and criticize, it also obligates you not to ignore the facts. But, then, what is a fact, except something a person believes true for reasons which, to him, appear both reasonable and sufficient.

Chapter 7

C O M M E N T S   A N D   C R I T I C I S M.

In the preceding chapters I was exploring virgin soil, and my theories were developed without references to the work of others; such references are confined to this chapter. Some are comments by scientists implying a support of my theories; some define functional relationships which can be reinterpreted in their support; while the majority of references are opinions and observations in support of the theories and practices of modern science and its philosophy. These are followed by comments in which I criticise modern science for drifting away from the realities of this world, and evolving a philosophy which has more in common with a religion than science.

7-1 Introduction to Comments on Physics.

In Book One I idealized the fundamental constants of physics, by proving their origins as simple mathematical proportions in nature; in Book Two I give logical reasons for those proportions. My proof is probably more specific, complete and comprehensible than anything ever offered in support of the theories now accepted by modern science; but experience tells me that physicists will try to ignore this proof because it is a radical departure from the rules of research which they accept for themselves, since its acceptance as valid brings their competenance as research scientists into question. By postulating a sea of ignorance as normal and unavoidable, they use the commonly held belief that ignorance is no crime as a valid reason for the acceptance of irrational theories and the avoidance of unpleasant truths, by ignoring their implications. This negative approach to the problems of physics has worked so well in the past that it has become the philosophy of modern science; a belief that its theories need not be comprehensibly logical, and that the fantastic ideas proposed in the name of modern science are acceptable because they cannot be disproved.

The following sections will give the reader an opportunity to compare the positivist philosophy of modern science (a belief that the rules of theoretical science can be legislated) with my belief that logical explorations of the implications of physical phenomena in depth open the door to understanding, and that comprehension is the final criterion of all sciences. The opinions of prominent scientists are condensations and quotations from articles and books.

They outline the philosophical musings of scientists on the implications of relativity physics, preceded and followed by my comments.

The references in the text to books listed on page 133, have been simplified as follows. The first letter of the symbol, Psm 129, is from the author's name, the next two are from the title of his book, and the number is the page from which the text was obtained.

7-2 Reluctance in Acceptance of New Ideas.

It might be assumed that, even though modern science approaches the problems of theoretical physics from a direction different from mine, a mutual regard for facts and their implications would serve as a means of communication. However, when I state that real waves must be waving in something real, a believer in modern science will state that waves are creations of the mind, and we remain as far apart as ever. This last belief is new only in the sense that it was forced upon the physicists by their acceptance of the preeminence of mathematics in relativity physics, the growth of which can be traced through the centuries to its present-day climax. It is my contention that the gulf between modern physics and the realities of everyday experience came into being because physicists have always shown a preference for mathematics and a reluctance to explore the logical implications of facts.

This reluctance has many roots, all of which can be traced to the fact that scientists are human beings who respond to the forces and prejudices in their environment, as we all do. The following comments by Galileo, Ford and Burtt, give us some of the reasons why scientists sometimes fail to perceive the obvious.

In 1609 Galileo made the first telescope. He invited the philosophers at the university of Padua to look through it at Jupiter and the moon and, by doing so, confirm the Copernican theory, but they refused. In a letter to Kepler he wrote: "They believe that the truth will be discovered, as they themselves assert, through the composition of texts rather than through the study of the world of nature. They try to argue the planets out of existence."

G. Garrett quotes Henry Ford: "We have most unfortunately found it necessary to get rid of a man as soon as he thinks himself an expert. The moment one gets into the expert's state of mind a great number of things become impossible." (Gww 47.)

E. A. Burtt comments on modern physics: "When in the interest of clearing the field for exact mathematical analysis, men sweep out of the temporal and spatial realm all non-mathematical characteristics, concentrate them in a lobe of the brain, and pronounce them the semi-real effects of atomic motions outside, they have performed a rather radical piece of cosmic surgery which deserves to be carefully examined. . . . Is it not a plausible hypothesis to suppose that wishful thinking underlay this extreme doctrine of modern physics—that because it was easier to get ahead in the reduction of nature to a system of mathematical equations by supposing that nothing existed outside of the human mind that was not reducible, naturalists proceeded at once to make the convenient assumption?

And there is a certain peremptory logic in this." (Bms 305.)

The opposition of an educated person to something new, as noted by Galileo and Ford, is a logical product of that education; because he cannot distinguish between facts and fiction, between the things he knows and the things he belives he knows. The comments by Burtt bring out another aspect of education. Facts are integrated with hypotheses, and the synthesis is accepted as true, with the various aspects of that synthesis explored without questioning the physical reality of its base. We are told not to question realitivity, even though some of its implications leads to absurd conclusions.

7-3 Physical Reality of First Cause Postulated.

Before the turn of the century, all scientists believed that the phenomena revealed by experiments were physically real and acting logically within the framework of simple mechanics, and they expressed that conviction in various ways. However, when the implications of their proof went beyond permissible limits, as defined by elementary logic, measurements and mathematics, they hedged, qualified and ignored them. Their indifference to logical implications and their demand for mathematical proof was substantially the same as that of modern science, though qualified by an expectation that the logic of physical reality would eventually be revealed with the growth of knowledge.

Since my theories are based on the classical concepts of physical reality, the following quotations support my postulates. James Jeans quotes Huygens: "The causes of natural phenomena are conceived in mechanical terms. Unless we do this we must give up all hope of ever understanding anything in physics." (Jpp 38.) According to J. Sullivan, Kelvin said he could understand nothing of which he could not make a working model (Sls 39). In comments on Euclidean geometry, Lindsay and Margenau observe that Kant asserted that the axioms and postulates of Euclid are a necessary condition for knowledge, since man cannot hope to describe experience without it (Lfp 63). It is conceivable that nature does not disprove the mechanistic postulate; it is legitimate to uphold it as beyond immediate refutation (Lfp 189). In the writings of von Helmholt he postulates that all forces in nature are resolvable into central forces acting between all pairs of point masses (Lfp 188). According to A. d'Abro; Bergson is "contending that mathematicians, not being trained in philosophy, are severely handicapped when they attempt to interpret their equations, and are incapable of distinguishing mathematical fiction from physical reality." (Aes 215.) In the opinion of Olive Lodge: "A dynamic theory is at once necessary and sufficient."

Despite these beliefs in a physically real word, there are three principal reasons why classical science failed to develop the theories outlined in this book. From the beginning of science the world of matter was believed to be made up of indivisible particles with different properties, called virtues. This particle-with-virtue theory has persisted to the present day in various disguises, despite conversion phenomena which clearly disprove it. (A recent theory of the two kinds of electrostatic charges postulate particles, like those of a disease, located on the surfaces of electrons and protons.) This failure of scientists to follow through on their postulates also gives us a reason why the classical ether theory appears to be a failure. Classical science postulated an ether, to give waves something to wave in, but this ether theory was a gratuitous addition to the matter-particle theory without meaning and purpose beyond that single function. The third reason was, therefore, their failure to develop a theory of wave-containing forces based on the ether theory. Descartes' attempt to develop an integrated theory of matter failed because he did not recognize this need.

7-4 Comments on Science Theories.

Most scientists are under the illusion that the theories they accept were forced upon them by the facts of physics, even though reason should tell them that more than one interpretation of those facts are possible. If there is more than one explanation of the phenomena which led to the rejection of the classical principles of mechanics, logic and causality by modern science, the question is whether such radical surgery is justified, or leading us astray. From the comments by prominent scientists below it will be seen that my reinterpretations of those phenomena are in accord with the rules of research and theoretical explorations they outline.

According to de Broglie, the history of science shows its advance is hampered by the influence of conceptions which came to be considered dogmas (Brp 237). He comments that some physicists are reluctant to abandon a rigorous determinism. "They have gone to the length of saying that a non-deterministic science is inconceivable." (Brp 216.) Poincare comments: "It is by logic that we prove, but by intuition that we discover. Criticism is good but creation is better. Do you possess the art of selecting among all the possible combinations." (Pfs 129.) D'Abro comments on the changes of the scientific viewpoint with the discovery of new facts: "A requirement demanded of any physical theory, is that it form a consistent whole." It must be free of *ad hoc* hypotheses. "A coherent theory . . . must inevitably collapse, owing to its very coherence, when any one of its anticipations is proved incorrect by experiment." (Aes 409.) According to Lindsay and Margenau: "The energy concept has meaning for electricity only to the extent to which electrical theory can be developed along mechanical lines." (Lfp 127.) They comment that: "The condition that causality shall have meaning is the same as that for the existence of science." (Lfp 524.) According to Whitehead: "The anti-rationalism of the moderns has checked any attempt to harmonize the ultimate concepts of science with ideas drawn from a more concrete survey of the whole of reality." (Waw 141.)

Note that Poincare's comments on logic and intuition are in full accord with my own. The anti-rationalism of modern physics, noted by Whitehead would have made my theories impossible if I had accepted the restrictive rules which it tries to impose. The assumption that a knowledge of causes and consequences is essential to science, have not prevented physicists from rejecting causality where it appears in conflict with their concept of permissible conclusions.

7-5 Postulates of a Scientific Theory.

A fundamental principle of science is to question all things, and accept only those which can be proved true. However, in practice the question, "What is proof?" is usually answered with a combination of indisputable facts and questionable interpretations of their implications, because we cannot even be sure a fact is beyond dispute until it has been related to other facts through meaningful associations. This is why it is necessary to develop theories that tell us when the elements of a physical event are not singular occurrences or mental hallucinations, and thus tell us what their implied relations may be, so we can test them and come to conclusions regarding their significance.

The search for fundamental causes in physics was answered by Hume with this comment: "No philosopher who is rational and modest has ever pretended to assign the ultimate cause of any natural operation." A prominent physicist once voiced the opinion that: "No scientist can mislead his fellow scientists for longer than it takes to check his observations or verify his conclusions and their consequences." In 1947 Franck, during a lecture at Gottingen, Germany, stated: "It is a custom in science—and perhaps a principle—to select from the infinite reservior of unsolved problems only those simple ones the solution of which seems possible in terms of available knowledge and skill. We are trained to subject our results to the most severe criticism. Adherence to these principles results in our knowing very little, but on the other hand being very certain we know this little." Quoted by R. Young (Ybs 34.) In a lecture at Cambridge, England, in 1933, Einstein said: "A theory ought to form a bridge between experienceable facts and bring these into as many-sided a connection as possible. It ought to be built upon the simplest possible premises." Russell comments that when there is more than one hypothesis compatible with the facts, "the scientist adopts the simplest as a working hypothesis, and only reverts to more complicated hypotheses if new facts show that the simplest hypothesis is inadequate." (Rso 68.) According to d'Abro, an accumulation of disconnected facts does not constitute a science (Aes 402). On the next page he comments that in the integration of these facts, simplicity of coordination decides the orientation of science. Elsewhere in his book he notes that "there is nothing in the nature of an explanation in a scientific theory. Phenomena are not explained; they are merely interconnected, or described in terms of their mutual relations." This failure to explain is caused by the limitations of the human mind itself (Aes 397). Lindsay and Margenau state that physics has nothing to say about a possible real world behind experience (Lfp 2).

Modesty is commendable, but a modest person is not apt to solve those problems in physics where it is necessary to go contrary to accepted beliefs. It is probably the principal reason why traditional beliefs and practices are retained by science long after they have been disproved by facts. There are numerous cases in the past where scientists have succeeded in misleading their fellow scientists—usually through arbitrary limitations on the implications of the proof they were presenting, thus isolating that proof and keeping it separated from the realities of physics. Timid people prefer to advance physics by small steps, and indifference to the implications of their postulates beyond permissible limits makes that possible. I take issue with Franck on his belief that a small step is a sure step, because, small or large, it is a functional part of an inseparable whole, and there is no certainty until we know that whole. Note that the comments by Einstein, Russell and d'Abro, on what a theory ought to be, are in accord with my own. The inability of modern science to explain the relations and proportions it discovers means that it lacks one essential ingredient, because the ability to perceive reality—to distinguish between what is real and unreal—is the essence of a true theory.

7-6 The Basis of Theoretical Physics.

In this section the arguments in support of modern physics are contrasted with those of classical science. To me there is something fantastically weird about an approach to theoretical physics that repudiates the various aspects of reality as we perceive it in our daily lives, a repudiation that includes its dictionary definition.

In a lecture by Einstein he notes that: "The axiomatic basis of theoretical physics cannot be an inference from experience, but must be free invention." See the substance of this comment in Ees 15. On the next page he observes that in Newton's time the concepts and postulates of physics were deduced from experience by logical abstraction. They were not free inventions of the human mind. Einstein hoped, according to Barnett, that the statistical method of quantum physics was a temporary expedient. He repudiated the positivist doctrine and believed that man might yet attain knowledge of physical reality (Bue 36). Lindsay and Margenau comments that, to physicists at the time of Lorentz, Maxwell and Hertz, waves without a medium for its propagation were unthinkable (Lfp 328). They note that atomic physics is in a state of flux, and indications are its postulates and theories are becoming more abstract. They wonder if physics is drawing away from experience and becoming metaphysical (Lfp 24). According to Sullivan, light is not to be explained in mechanical terms (Sls 50). According to Barnett: "The whole march of science toward the unification of concepts—the reduction of matter to elements and then to a few types of particles, the reduction of 'forces' to the single concept 'energy,' and then to a single basic quantity—leads still to the unknown." (Bue 65.)

When a scientist applies the term "free invention" to a law of nature, instead of the classical term "discovery," he means that it is one possibility among several, and that it is not necessarily true. The invention of relativity, the fourth dimension and quantum states, led to the belief among scientists that the fundamental relations in nature are not comprehensible, and that it is futile to search for universal laws by logical abstractions from experiments. The only thing we are sure of is the mathematical relations and proportions obtained by experiments. Modern science started out as a philosophy of despair, but is now one of negations; we are forbidden to look for comprehensible logical relations in physics because modern theoretical physics is a monolithic structure of irrational concepts which cannot permit the intrusion of rational solutions of its problems.

Einstein once said: "No amount of experimentation can prove me right, a single experiment may prove me wrong." To him the word "free invention" meant just what it says, but to those who accept his theory it is a flexible intellectual shield hiding an inflexible truth of nature—a discovery. Their rationalizations of this belief are making the theories of modern science increasingly abstract and bringing them closer to metaphysics. Note that the comment by Barnett is in accord with my approach to the problems of physics.

7-7 The Ether and the Quantum of Action.

Scientists are in the habit of isolating their problems by asking simple questions and expecting simple answers. To test the ether theory they postulated an ether wind across the earth's surface. Since experiments gave negative answers they had the choice of questioning this postulate or rejecting the ether theory, and decided in favor of the latter, even though their acceptance of electromagnetic waves implied a transmitting medium. The discovery of quantum states was used as proof that, since the classical ether theory cannot account for those states, the ether theory had to be abandoned because nature is apparently illogical in its fundamental processes. They decided to accept the irrationalities of modern science, rather than attempt to work out explanations that go beyond permissible limits.

This categorical rejection of the ether by most scientists is not shared by Einstein: "To deny the existence of the ether means, in the last analysis, denying all physical properties to empty space. But such a view is inconsistent with the fundamental facts of mechanics." (Ees 106.) According to d'Abro, Lorentz believed absolute motion through the ether could be detected, were it not for compensating physical effects (Aes 426). Elsewhere in his book he comments: "There is every reason to suspect that the atomicity of matter is itself a quantum manifestation." (Aes 353.) He notes that Heinsenberg and Bohr have suggested that nature may be irrational in its microscopic processes (Aes xiii). According to d'Abro, Planck's constant h represents an entity of action. "We must assume that there exist atoms of action in nature, just as there exist atoms of matter." (Aes 352.) He notes that the function of action L may be within our grasp. It would be a momentous discovery, since it would enable us to derive all the laws of the physical world (Aes 325).

Most of the comments above can be interpreted as supporting my theories. Lorentz's belief gives implied support to my theory of stationary states. d'Abro's comments on matter and Planck's quantum of action anticipate my theory of the electron and my definition of the natural unit of length. Einstein is of two minds about the ether, because some facts support it and others appear to reject it.

7-8 Is Nature Rational or Irrational?

In all observable physical events, the interaction between causes and consequences makes it possible to anticipate the future by postulating laws and rules of probability from repetitious occurrences in the past. If causality could not be established for some events, their occurrence would appear to be casual and, therefore, unpredictable. Since science is based on anticipation, it would be impossible without causality.

This relationship is noted by Lindsay and Margenau: "Causality is an empty phrase unless the universe is periodic. . . . The condition that causality shall have meaning is the same as that for the existence of science." (Lfp 524.) According to Eddington: "A rather serious consequence of dropping causality in the external world is that it leaves us with no clear distinction between the natural and the supernatural." (Enw 309.) Having thus done away with science, he comments that the world must not be thought of as being singular, since there is an infinite number of possible worlds, all equally true. A man can create his own imaginary world and be as right as anyone else. de'Sitter laments: "What used to be the most fundamental concepts of physical science, determinism and causality, are called into doubt, the foundation of science appears to be shaking, and it seems as if the whole building were tottering." (Sko 100.) d'Abro quotes Weyl: "There has been unloosed a cataclysm which has swept away space, time and matter, hitherto regarded as the firmest pillars of natural science." (Aes 401.) Reichenbach comments: "We have abandoned Euclidean geometry and the principle of causality, and now we must give up a principle of logic." (Rpp 8.) (The positivist philosophy states that what cannot be observed and measured is outside the scope of science and is to be treated as non-existent.) In "Endeavor," July 1950, Schrodinger comments on the nature of electrons: "Positivist philosophy is invoked to tell us that we must not distinguish between the knowledge we can obtain of a physical object and its natural state. The two are one."

The doubts assailing scientists contemplating the philosophical implications of modern physics are expressed in various ways in this section. Eddington's postulate, that there can be an infinite number of equally true worlds, is questioned by Einstein when he said that: "Out of all conceivable constructions, a single one has always proved itself absolutely superior to all the rest." (Ees 4.) It appears to me that logic, causality, determinism and Euclidean geometry, are too important aspects of natural phenomena to be abandoned to a conception of physics that does not even pretend to be true beyond a narrow compass. The slim pretext, that nature may not be comprehensible, is converted by modern science from a vague belief into an ultimate truth that no scientist in his right mind dare question. It seems that modern science is willing to consider all possibilities, even the most outrageous mathematical postulates, except the assumption that nature is comprehensibly logical. Some scientists tell us that they are not interested in the philosophy of reality, and then use the positivist philosophy to justify a negation, as if measurements and mathematics are everything and reality nothing.

7-9 Is Nature a Product of Mind?

Theoretical physicists must also be mathematicians, logicians and philosophers, because their proof cannot be validated without these disciplines. A scientist starts out with experimental mathematical proportions which, though true, mean nothing to theoretical physics until their logical relations have been established and fitted into a generalized theory based on a philosophy of universal causes and repetitious phenomena, with the significance of these causes and phenomena outlined by laws and rules that appear valid or permissible to other scientists. In this section scientists try to justify their acceptance of relativity, the fourth dimension, and their preference for mathematics in the interpretations of phenomena; with logic and philosophy gratuitous rationalizations of that preference.

According to Einstein: "Physics really began with the invention of mass, force and an inertial system. These concepts are free inventions, they lead to the formulation of the mechanical point of view." He continues by noting that science combines facts and laws with freely invented ideas and concepts—creations of the human mind. (The substance of these comments appears in Ees 15.) d'Abro observes that, to scientific philosophy, absolute reality is a myth (Aes 99). In another comment on this subject he says that a majority of scientists would assert that "it reduces in the last analysis to a mere mental construct, the product of a synthesis of the mind." (Aes 165.) Again: "Whether or not this objective universe can be identified with the real world of the metaphysician is a subject ... of no interest to science." (Aes 388.) He quotes this comment by Lamor: "Laws of matter are, after all, but laws of mind." And Poincare: "Are the laws of nature, when considered as existing outside of the human mind that creates or observes them, intrinsically invariable? Not only is the question insoluble; it is also meaningless." ... "The Bergsonian world has no laws." However, d'Abro observes that the physicists are "compelled to operate and reason as though they believe in the real existence of a real absolute objective universe." (Aes 375.) According to Russell, reality is a product of mind. This view states "that the relation of knower and known is fundamental, and that nothing can exist unless it either knows or is known." (Rkw 16.)

It is my contention that inferences from experience are our only safe guide. Nobody "invented" the sun and moon, light and heat, or the specific properties by which we identify objects and phenomena. We invented the terms by which a mass and its properties are known; but we did not invent that mass and those properties, and to say that we did it is nonsense. In questioning the mental origin of matter, it would be enlightening to consult an expert on the evolution of the mind, and a psychiatrist. The first would tell us that mind is a physical-chemical-electrical process originating in the potentialities of matter, and the second might comment on its incredible capacity for self-deception.

7-10 The Nature of Waves.

The difference between material and immaterial things is that the former have a constancy of properties that can interact with those of other material objects, while the latter have no properties apart from the mind perceiving them and cannot, therefore, produce observable effects on matter by itself. By definition, electromagnetic waves are as real as any of the material objects we see and handle every day. However, relativity physics expects matter and waves to behave in a way that is physically impossible in a real world, and to justify its choice it postulates immaterial waves.

According to Sullivan, we cannot conceive electromagnetic waves to be physical disturbances in the ether. "They are, it appears, completely immaterial waves. They are as immaterial as the waves of depression, loyalty, suicide, and so on, that sweep over a country." (Sls 68.) Eddington wonders whether Rutherford found or made the atomic nucleus he showed us. "It will not affect our achievement either way—only we should rather like to know what he did." . . . It is a matter of expression, like whether a spectroscope finds or makes the green color it shows us (Esp 109). Jeans rejected the ether as the transmitter of waves with the comment: "They are waves of knowledge." In one of his books he observes that waves are not a part of nature, but are brought into being by our efforts to understand nature. There can be no waves in the absence of human knowledge, because they are created by those observing them. Following up this line of thought, he wonders what happens to waves when there is no human knowledge to bring them into existence.

In reading the mind-over-matter postulate of modern science above, I wonder whether we are dealing with the apostles of a new religion, or scientists in need of psychiatric treatment. We see them ignoring obvious facts and their implications by creating barriers where none exist in nature, rejecting those laws and rules of research that used to guide science in its search for truth, and doing so on the basis of facts which can be interpreted in various ways. To those of us who believe physical phenomena are real by definition, the opinions above appear to be the nonsense of immature minds—the opinions of opinionated people who lack the flexibility of mind to explore alternate, more realistic solutions to their problems, and do not have the wisdom to perceive the enormity of their transgression.

7-11 Relative motions.

My theory of matter postulates its origin as contained waves, functionally stationary in their own configuration fields, as defined by their motions and the local momenta of other fields, even though they may be moving through the ether. Because all motions are relative to local directional ether momenta and not to the stationary ether transmitting those momenta, phenomena on the earth's surface move relative to its functionally stationary mass, in accordance with Einstein's relativity postulate: "No experiment, regardless of its nature, whether mechanical, optical or electromagnetic, can enable us to detect our absolute velocity through the ether." This postulate must be qualified by noting that, according to my theory, all momenta have a descending gradient of power with distance which is, theoretically, definable and observable. This gradient invalidates his second postulate, that all motions have the same relativity values regardless of distance—an assumption which provides the logical basis for modern science's mind-over-matter philosophy, as defined in the preceding section. This implication of Einsteinian relativity is the principal reason for the rejection of causality, logic, determinism and other classical postulates by modern science.

Russell defines Einsteinian relativity motions by comparing the difference between objects moving at ordinary velocities and when they are moving with the speed of light. His comments are, in substance, as follows: You are going along a road at 4 miles per hour when two cars pass you going in opposite directions at 40 miles per hour. After one hour they will, therefore, be 36 and 44 miles from you and 80 miles apart. But if they had been passing you with the speed of light, they would also be passing each other and the point of passage with that speed. After one hour they are, therefore, one light hour from you, one light hour apart and one light hour from the point of passage (Rar 30).

According to Sullivan: "We can start with any set of axioms we please, provided they are consistent with one another, and on the basis of these construct a geometry which is, logically, as impeccable as Euclid's." (Sls 18.) Classical science, according to d'Abro, "assumed that a distance in space, a duration in time and a simultaneity between distant events were absolute concepts." But in relativity they vary with the observer's motion (Aes 101). Rotational motion presents a problem because, if all motions are relative regardless of mass, it appears to be absolute as before relativity (Aes xviii). Mack and Neuman tried to eliminate this contradiction by suggesting a theory of absolute relative rotation (Aes 110). Russell defined it by noting that "all motion is relative, and there is no difference between the two statements: 'the earth rotates once a day' and 'the heavens revolve about the earth once a day.' " However, according to d'Abro (Aes 111) and Lindsay and Margenau (Lfp 330), the centrifugal effect produced by Newton's rotating bucket, the bursting of a rotating flywheel and other rotations, cannot be produced by a rotation of the stars about a stationary object as postulated above. Eddington ignored these problems when he commented that a comparison between the four-dimensional continuum and the practical Euclidean world makes the latter seem like a dream (Esg 48).

Sullivan's comment, that any logically consistent group of axioms are as acceptable as those of Euclid, does not make sense to me, because a realistic approach to the problems of physics anticipates axioms that are in accord with the facts of physics and their logical implications. To those who believe in a physical reality, the specific information obtained by experiment and observation serve as a guide to those axioms which appear to be most probable in the light of facts, while the world of modern science is, apparently, anything a mathematician can conceive, regardless of facts. Obviously, the relativity effects described by Russell are not possible in a real world, but must be the creation of conceiving minds, as postulated by the philosophers exploring the implications of modern science. A mind-created world may be acceptable to a religious person, but not to a scientist who is guided by the implications of facts alone.

7-12 Doubts About Relativity.

In the preceding section the difference between the ordinary Euclidean world and the world of relativity was defined. In terms of a philosophy, it is as great as the difference between the philosophy of an atheist and that a religious fanatic, and there is, therefore, no hope of a graceful retreat by either side. Below are listed some additional failures of the relativity theory; but the very abundance of reasons for abandoning that theory, most of which are known to those accepting its postulates, become a reason for its retention, because any step backward leads to a precipice which cannot be descended by short steps. Einstein once said: "No amount of experimentation can prove me right, a single experiment may prove me wrong." It is my contention that that experiment had already been made and was known, though not understood and appreciated, before his theories were proposed. All I can do is to point it out and hope there will be scientists who are more interested in reality than in mathematics.

According to d'Abro, Einstein's general theory does not establish the complete relativity of motion, because we cannot subscribe to the kinematic principle that a complete relativity of motion would necessitate (Aes xix). He observes that a complete relativity of motion would demand that all frames should be identical. However, if that was so, the law of inertia would express nothing at all, because we could make the motion of a body appear to be anything we want it to be by selecting a suitable frame (Aes 108). According to Eddington, the precession of the Foucault pendulum on the surface of a revolving planet, and the centrifugal force of its rotation, cannot be explained by the theory of relativity. Heyl comments that these effects cannot be explained by the masses of fixed stars, and that they prove relativity to be a hollow mathematical shell (Hnf 40). According to Lindsay and Margenau, the theory of relativity is not complete, because it fails to take account of electromagnetic properties and the quantum theory in the atomic domain (Lfp 376). d'Abro observes that relativity cannot account for the electron, proton and neutron, the two kinds of electrostatic charge and the fact that electrons and protons do not explode under the repulsive forces of their internal charges. It seems that a counter-balancing pressure is needed. He says that attempts by Mie, Hilbert, Weyl, Einstein and others to explain it have failed.

We might assume that the failures noted above and elsewhere, in conjunction with the violations of the classical laws and axioms by modern science and its resort to mind-creation to justify them, would lead to the rejection of Einstein's theory of relativity. The comment by Heyl, that this theory is a hollow mathematical shell, is one of those unpleasant truths which modern science tries to hide in a dark corner with its other failures. d'Abro's comment about the need for a counter-balancing force is in full accord with my theory of a wave-containing force.

7-13 Mathematics and Reality.

When an engineer builds a bridge, he will try to learn as much as he can about his material and the type of construction that will give it maximum strength. When a scientist tells us we must limit our investigations in theoretical physics to the possibilities of mathematics, and that we are not to explore the logical implications of physical reality, he is asking us to build an imaginary bridge with imaginary material that cannot possibly become a useful structure in a real world, because mathematics is nothing more than a useful tool. The limitations imposed by modern science on logical explorations of physical facts in depth, must not be allowed to become a barrier which prevents us from arriving at conclusions that are in reasonable accord with the nature of physical reality—the final criterion of all physical sciences. Note that the preference by modern science for mathematics, as outlined below, leads to problems that are beyond solution within the limitations of that medium.

According to Weyl: "Our intuitive perception of space and time can have no place in a world constructed by mathematical physics." Tolman, in commenting on the paradox that each of two clocks must be behind the other if one of them has moved, observes that, since it is consistent with the mathematics and assumptions of relativity, the paradox must be accepted as reality (Brr 57). (It will be noted that Russell's description of relativity in section 7-11 gives us other paradoxes which must be accepted with that theory.) d'Abro notes that scientific philosophy considers absolute reality a myth (Aes 99). Lindsay and Margenau comment: "Whether or not this objective universe can be identified with the real world . . . is of no interest to science." (Lfp 388.) They reject logical implications with this comment: "There is no law of connection between cause and effect known to science; these concepts are foreign to physical analysis." (Lfp 517.) They observe that in mathematics it is not possible to distinguish between causes and consequences (Lfp 19). According to d'Abro: "The mathematician is not primarily interested in knowing whether his abstract speculations have any counterpart in the real objective world." (Aes 381.) He says that a rational coordination of facts have their most perfect prototype in mathematics. However, mathematical equations are nothing but relations from which other relations can be deduced (Aes 371).

The preference by modern science for mathematics goes far beyond its merit as a tool of research. Its treatment of mathematics is more like a cult than a science, because it is at one moment used to prove the unacceptable, and at another it is used to reject the obvious. And to give these decisions meaning, mathematics is at one moment assumed to be identical with the realities of nature, and at the next moment it is assumed to be a provisional substitute for those realities, with its limitations defining also the limitations of the human mind. My first objection to the comments above is that reality is what the dictionary says it is, and all theories of physics must begin by accepting its definition. My second is that, in a conflict between observed realities of nature and their interpretations by mathematics, the latter must yield to the former. If it does not do so, physical research will cease to be a search for the truths of nature and become nothing more than a mathematician's plaything.

7-14 Time and Relativity.

Time has no meaning without mechanical actions to define it. It is the interval associated with a motion from here to there and the periodic repetitions of configurations. A time interval is defined by postulating a distance between active points and a limitation of the speed with which an action can be transmitted between those points. The flow of time is not reversible on the basis of this definition, and it cannot be treated as an independent dimension. However, that is not the opinion of modern scientists.

Minkowski's theory of space-time led to his famous remark: "From now on space in itself and time in itself dissolve into shadows and only a kind of union of the two retains an individuality." (Lfp 346). According to Dingle, Minkowski's four-dimensional continuum is essentially metaphorical. When our standard of rest is changed by a rotation of axes, we are leaving prose for poetry (Brr 59). According to Lindsay and Margenau, the question of the real nature of time does not enter (Lfp 340). Jeans comments: "The fundamental laws of nature give no reason why time flows on; it can be standing still or flowing backwards." (Jmu 100.) Gamow once described the reversal of time by noting that in such a case an adult chicken would grow to babyhood and then become an egg. This is possible because the mathematics of modern science does not distinguish between causes and consequences. He noted at another time that a reversal of time is not possible because nothing can go faster than the speed of light (Goi 105).

The fantastic notions that the possibilities and limitations of mathematics are also those of nature, and that time can be manipulated by disregarding its true nature, lead to some peculiar conclusions by the theorists of modern science. The possibility that the variations of time postulated by modern science are symbolic of physical changes is invalidated by the theoretical reversals of time because mathematical formulas are reversible. It gives us an insight into the mental attitude of those accepting the theories of modern science, telling us that if we accept these concepts our explorations in theoretical physics will repeatedly bring us into contact with mental barriers, and that they would make the logical integrations of facts by deductive reasonings impossible.

7-15 Gravity Postulates.

In my theory, the difference between electrostatic and gravitational forces is the difference between the potentials of specific and statistical wave actions.

Gravity is a potentially reducible deformation of the contracting ether, produced by the waves of matter. It is assumed that this deformation is also the fourth dimension postulated by Einstein. However, his theory of gravity is based on two negations. Einstein postulated an identity of gravity and acceleration because it cannot be proved they are different, and he postulated a difference in the advance of time at different points because it cannot be proved they are identical.

According to d'Abro, Einstein noted an identity of the forces of gravitational and inertial masses, and there is no prior reason why this should be so. It appears to be a miraculous coincidence (Aes 236). Russell comments: "The whole conception of 'force' is a mistake. The sun does not exert any force on the planets; in Einstein's law of gravitation, the planet only pays attention to what it finds in its own neighborhood." (Rar 14.) According to Bridgman: "There must be an energy flow in the gravitational field through empty space across from one body to the other." (Bnt 91.) d'Abro observes that in an enclosed space there can be no difference between a force generated by acceleration or by gravitation (Aes 240). He comments that science has no explanation of gravitation, and that "those who seek explanations will find no comfort in science. They must turn to metaphysics." (Aes 398). According to Sullivan, the force of gravity is not affected by physical or chemical conditions. Faraday showed that light and electrical and magnetic forces are propagated through space with the speed of light, while gravitation appears to act instantaneously as a force which cannot be screened (Sls 58).

My postulate, that the forces containing the energies of waves also produces gravitation, gives us a comprehensible reason why the inertia of a mass changes in the same ratio as its gravitational attraction. Since gravity is transmitted with twice the speed of light and nothing can screen it, it is difficult to set up an experiment to measure that velocity. However, being a finite velocity, it is theoretically possible to observe its effects in the solar system, due to the constantly changing gravity figure. My theory supports Einstein's gravity postulate and rejects that of Bridgman, qualified by the effects of the changing configuration just noted. d'Abro's comment, that science never tries to explain, is the fundamental reason why I have been plowing virgin soil.

7-16 Is Space Relative or Absolute?

A philosopher may clarify the question above by rewording it: "Is space physically real or a product of mind?" while a scientist may change it to: "Is relativity a product of facts or an atmosphere?" My answer to the first question is that we have no choice but to postulate a physically real world as a working hypothesis, because we live in such a world by definition and have no cause to question the dictionary. Since all our experiments, observations and measurements are conducted in a physically real world, our theoretical explorations into the unknown must begin and end with its rules, laws and axioms and their logical implications, unless there are compelling reasons for going beyond those limits. My answer to the second question is that there is more than one way to interpret the observed relativity effects, and that the choice of a particular interpretation is biased by the atmosphere prevailing in science: a combination of habitual beliefs and practices and human traits, such as vanity, fear, wishful thinking, greed, etc. The comments by scientists in this section show that the theory of relativity is incomplete.

D'Abro notes that even in Einstein's theory, the centrifugal force of rotation will make an observer realize he does not stand in a Galilean frame (Aes 266). Bergson comments that light is a propagation, and that it is only natural it should be an invariant. He continues: "Why should it be affected by a certain too human way of perceiving and conceiving things?" (Aes 375.) According to D'Abro, the problem of matter is far from solved. It is highly probable a new departure will have to be considered, since we are faced with something we do not understand (Aes 339). He wonders about the nature of the metric field. Is it a structure of space caused by matter? But space, being a void, is not amenable to structure. Is it a direct emanation from matter, or is it a matter-molded, ether-filled space (Aes 58)? Lindsay and Margenau note that boundary conditions, such as the reflection boundary of waves, impose restrictions on the type of activities possible for a system; the spatial boundaries of a wave field modify its whole pattern (Lfp 53). They comment that quantum mechanics "was initially founded with the purpose of connecting more closely the facts of experiments with theory, has actually severed this bond and drifted away into a formalism that belies its initial promise." (Lfp 397.) They note that "if the photons (of light) were to possess any rest mass . . . their actual mass would be infinite (according to the theory of relativity." (Lfp 383.) According to Barnett, Einstein's principle of the equivalence of mass and energy makes it possible to imagine the congealing of diffused radiation into the particles of matter (Bue 102).

The problems above are due, primarily, to the restrictions on permissible conclusions imposed on theoretical physics by modern science. Most of them are solved by my theory of a contracting ether; with the consequent appearance of wave-containing forces and relative motion effects. The only function of a light photon's rest mass is to make the motion of its momentum through space possible. When it unites with a particle of matter, the two types of rest masses retain their original roles—their masses are added but do not combine.

7-17 Problems of Modern Physics.

The early philosophers described matter in terms of virtues. An object could have the virtue of wetness, fire, heat, light, etc. Being an obvious description of properties without implications beyond the terms used, the postulate has been applied to various physical phenomena through the centuries to the present. A recent model of the electron is that of a revolving body, with particles having the virtue of a positive or negative electrostatic charge imbedded in the surface of its mass. It is my contention that particles with specific properties, such as quantized masses, charges, magnetic and gravitational fields, cannot exist in the form of solid particles, because a solid body cannot develop natural quantum states with functional extensions into space along descending gradients to zero at infinity. However, my theory shows that the deformation of a transmitting medium can take the form of quantum states with functional gradients.

In 1928 Dirac suggested this theory of electrostatic charges. The universe is packed with negative energy electrons in its ground state. When an electron jumps out of that state it becomes an ordinary negative electron, while the hole it leaves behind becomes a positron. (Lfp 512). (Some years later he suggested that the ground state might be reversed elsewhere in space, and that in such areas there are anti-matter galaxies in which the charges of electrons and protons are reversed.) However, Lindsay and Margenau note that the negative energy states anticipated by Dirac's theory are apparently false (Lfp 511). Jeans comments: "A hard sphere takes up a very definite amount of room; an electron—well, it is probably as meaningless to discuss how much room an electron takes up as it is to discuss how much room a fear, an anxiety, or an uncertainty takes up." (Bue 28.) However, de Broglie is of a different opinion when he comments that physics has an urgent need to be able to introduce a radius for the electron. It is hindered "by the exclusive use of the statistical Ψ wave to describe the particles, for it prohibits the use of any structural image for these particles." (Brp 236.) According to Sullivan, the determination of an electron's mass-charge ratio showed that its whole mass was due to its electric charge (Sls 33). He finds Bohr's particle conception of electrons inadequate, because they have properties peculiar to waves. An electron's nature is outside pictorial imagination (Sls 38). Goudsmit suggested that an electron's spin (magnetic) field is a rotation of its electrostatic charges. However, Dirac once questioned this postulate; he argued that the theories of modern physics permit a separation of the smallest magnets into polar units.

Dirac's theory of the electron is one of those postulates, so often proposed by scientists, which explains a small part of the truth and ignores the rest. If my theories are correct, his postulate of anti-matter is impossible; they also confirm my rejection of his negative energy states. Jean's comment that waves take up no room is not true for contained waves, because compacting and integration make them behave like particles. The comment by de Broglie on the need for an electron radius is satisfied by my theories. They also confirm Goudsmit's postulate of a magnetic rotation and reject Dirac's suggestion that magnetic poles can be separated. That suggestion was made possible by modern science's rejection of structural images, because it left a structureless particle theory as its only alternative in the light of facts.

7-18 The Universe, Stars and Planets.
The cautious approach to the solution of problems by small steps, and the critical evaluations of those solutions by numerous scientists, as outlined by

Franck and others in section 7-5, did not prevent the theories of modern science from becoming fantastically weird. Many theories have been proposed with limited objectives and scant regard for facts, origins and implications beyond a narrow range, arbitrarily selected to fit the purpose of those objectives. The fact that time is nothing by itself did not prevent Mack from postulating a theory of the universe's origin, in which time suddenly comes into being and increases to its present value, as defined by the speed of light in one second. It is apparently an extension of Lemaitre's assumptions below.

According to d'Abro, Lemaitre postulated a primordal atom about eight times larger than the sun and incredibly dense. It exploded into radioactive fragments which scattered and swelled the volume of space (Aes 317). D'Abro observes that, according to Newton's law of gravitation, interacting material bodies should be packed densely at their centers and then thin out with distance (Aes 299). Elsewhere he notes that there must exist a definite limit to the size of a star with a given density (Aes 287). Sullivan notes that, according to the law of entropy, the energy of the universe is constantly being dissipated in space. This process of disorganization implies a time when a perfect state of organization existed, and we are to assume this state represents the moment when a perfectly organized universe sprang suddenly into being (Sls 24). Moulton observes that the orbits of the planets are nearly circular. Since orbits can have any eccentricity, this is as remarkable as if the trees in a natural forest were arranged in straight lines (Mda 152). According to Lowell, the organization of the planets and their satellites tells us of an evolution. They speak of the manner of its work by specifying the mode of action, but we do not understand their language (Lew 141).

It will be noticed that Lemaitre's theory is, primarily, an attempt to explain the expanding universe. However, besides the arbitrary postulate regarding the beginning of our universe, the theory fails to account for such facts of physics as quantum states, the fourth dimension and relative motions. Sullivan's assumption, that entropy implies a time when the universe was perfectly organized, is one of those idealizations that so often cause scientists to go astray. Even if my theory of contained waves did not qualify our acceptance of entropy, there is still no reason to accept his conclusion that the organization of the universe was once perfect; while there is a good reason to assume that what once was can reappear—that there was a time when a tendency to organize brought the universe into being by reversing entropy.

7-19 Concluding Comments.

After modern physics has collected all known physical phenomena, and competent scientists have analyzed, evaluated, criticized, interpreted and integrated all this data into a unified whole, the question upon which the direction of all research in theoretical physics depends has not been answered, and cannot be answered without the combined effects of a stationary ether and a relativity configuration space. Less than a hundred years ago this problem, whether natural phenomena are physically real or products of mind, did not arise, because all responsible scientists rejected the second solution with all other supernatural events. However, Einstein's theory of relativity makes it the most important problem in theoretical physics, because his postulates would have no rational foundation without the origin of relative motions in the minds of those observing them. It is the refusal of physicists to accept my compromise solution by postulating relative motions on the surfaces of large masses and a descending gradient of this relativity effect with distance, that makes the problem of mind-creation or physical reality of paramount importance.

The reasons why classical science rejected supernatural events are also the reasons why I now reject Einsteinian relativity. They rejected the supernatural because the products of mind, like astrology, ghosts, and the supernatural events postulated by religion, have irrational origins and give results which cannot be integrated into the general body of physical laws, axioms and relations. Scientific proof of a supernatural event is not enough, because its irrational associations make it impossible to predict a reoccurrence with scientific precision, and the assurance that rules which were valid in the past do not change for no predictable reason. Science is not opposed to religion, but rejects anything which, by definition or implication, does not show that permanence of powers, relations and proportions needed for the checking and re-evaluation of postulated phenomena within the framework of scientific verifications.

By equating the theories of modern science with a religion, I reject its postulates for the same reasons: its fundamental assumptions were accepted on faith because they are beyond experimental proof; the rationales through which they are related to observable phenomena do not give the only possible solutions; while explorations in depth of their implications lead to increasingly weird and irrational premises and conclusions, when measured by the rules of elementary mechanics, as defined by everyday experience.

To justify their approach to the problems of modern science, theoretical physicists have passed a series of prohibitions which, if accepted, would make criticism of their premises and conclusions impossible. They tell us that science is not interested in the nature of physical reality or its philosophy, even though the experiments through which it verifies its postulates are real by definition. It might be assumed that this relationship between theory and reality would make scientists interested in the meaning of that which serves as the foundation for their abstract flights of fancy. Many scientists, however, support the positivist philosophy; not because it brings them closer to the truths of nature, but to justify their indifference to the problems of physical reality by substituting the logical implications of known phenomena by the limitations and possibilities of mathematics. The use of mathematics for this purpose is justified by modern science as a pragmatic necessity—an artifice used as a provisional substitute for reality. We might assume that physicists would hesitate to accept its conclusions on this slender foundation, but we find these scientists repeatedly asserting or implying that the possibilities and limitations of mathematics are also those of natural phenomena, and that the prohibition against pure logic and structural images are due to the limitations of the human mind.

It is my contention that the physical realities of experience and the dictionary are real by definition, and that to assert that we do not know if there is such a thing as a reality is nonsense. To equate that reality with mathematics, and to prohibit exploratory excursions in the unknown by other means, is to my mind also nonsense. Experience tells us a mass cannot be in two places at the same time, that its velocity relative to absolute space cannot be changed by a mental construction; that time, being nothing by itself, does not progress at different rates at different points in nature, or become reversible, just because it is a mathematical possibility and serves the purpose of modern science.

I want to emphasize that my rejection of the theories and practices of modern science is not, primarily, based on the development of a successful alternative. I reject it because I consider its postulates, its arguments, its restrictions on permissible conclusions, an insult to my intelligence. Its mental-construct postulate has this in common with the supernatural: because it is incomprehensibly irrational apart from mathematics, its critics cannot produce convincing arguments against the proof it presents, because they deny that which a believer accepts without question. While a realist must base his arguments on experience, logic and the mechanical limitations of the facts of physics, a believer in modern science can, in the words of Eddington, create his own world and be as right as anyone else.

Although I have spent most of my time since 1938 on the development of the theories and proof presented in my two books, they still present significant problems. It seems that a problem does not become clear in the mind until it has been written down as a proposition in logic. This book, therefore, is the latest in a long series of manuscripts, each of which was discarded because my constantly increasing understanding of causes and consequences showed it to contain errors of judgment in my interpretation of facts and logical possibilities within the accepted frame of reference. But my time is running out, and what problems are left I leave for others to solve. If you have a helpful criticism, suggestion or opinion on the subjects of my two books, please write the author at the address below.

January, 1970

Eigil Rasmussen
P.O. Box 57007
Los Angeles, Cal.
90057.

REFERENCES

The books from which the numerous references in Chapter 7 were obtained are identified by 3 letters and a number. The first letter is the author's initial and the next two are from the title of his book, and the number is the page. If the book is a paperback (pb) reprint, its trade name is followed by the name of the publisher owning the copyrights ©.

Aes d'Abro, A., *The Evolution of Scientific Thought*. Dover, pb., 1950. ©, Dover Publications, New York.

Bms Burtt, E. A., *The Metaphysical Foundations of Modern Science*. Anchor, pb., 1954. ©, The Humanities Press, Inc., New York.

Bnt Bridgman, P. W., *The Nature of Physical Theory*. Dover, 1936. ©, Dover Publications, New York.

Brp deBroglie, L., *The Revolution in Physics*. Noonday, pb., 1956, The Noonday Press. ©, Farrar, Strauss & Giroux, Inc., New York.

Brr Barter, E. G., *Relativity and Reality*. ©, The Philosophical Library, Inc., New York, 1953.

Bue Barnett, L., *The Universe and Dr. Einstein*. Mentor, pb., 1948. ©, William Sloane Associates, Inc., New York.

Dst Dingle, H., *The Special Theory of Relativity*. Menthuen, 1950. ©, Menthuen Publications, New York.

Ees Einstein, A., *Essays in Science*. ©, The Philosophical Library, Inc., New York, pb., 1934.

Enw Eddington, A. S., *The Nature of the Physical World*. Macmillan, 1928. ©, Macmillan Company, New York.

Eps Eddington, A. S., *The Philosophy of Physical Science*. Macmillan, 1939. ©, The Macmillan Company, New York.

Esg Eddington, A. S., *Space, Time and Gravitation*. ©, Cambridge University Press, New York, 1921.

Fst Fowle, F. E., *Smithsonian Physical Tables*. The Smithsonian Institution, Washington D. C., 1934.

Goi Gamow, G., *One, Two Three . . . Infinity*. Mentor, pb., 1957. ©, The Viking Press, New York.

Gww Garrett, G., *The Wild Wheel*. Pantheon, 1952. ©, Random House, Inc., New York.

Hnf Heyl, P. R., *New Frontiers of Physics*. ©, The Williams & Wilkins Company, Baltimore, 1926.

Jmu Jeans, J. H., *The Mysterious Universe* Macmillan, 1933. ©, The Macmillan Company, New York.

Jpp Jeans, J. H., *Physics and Philosophy*. ©, Cambridge University Press, New York, 1943.

Lew Lowell, P., *The Evolution of Worlds*. Macmillan, 1909. ©, The Macmillan Company, New York.

Lfp Lindsay, R., & Margenau, H., *Foundations of Physics*. Dover, pb., 1957. ©, Dover Publications, New York.

Mda Moulton, F. R., *Descriptive Astronomy*. Macmillan, 1931. ©, The Macmillan Company, New York.

Pfs Poincare, H., *The Foundations of Science*. ©, The Science Press, New York, 1913.

Rar Russell, B., *The ABC of Relativity*. Mentor, pb., 1958. ©, Harper & Row, Publishers, 1925.

Rkw Russell, B., *Our Knowledge of the External World*. Mentor, pb., 1960. ©, W. W. Norton & Company, Inc., New York.

Rmg Rasmussen, E., *Matter and Gravity*. Exposition Press, 1958. ©, By the Author.

Rpp Reichenbach, H., *Philosophy of Physics*. ©, University of California Press, 1948.

Rso Russell, B., *The Scientific Outlook*. ©, W. W. Norton & Company, New York, 1931.

Sko deSitter, W., *Kosmos*. ©, Harvard University Press, New York, 1932.

Sls Sullivan, J. W., *The Limitations of Science*. Mentor, pb., 1957. ©, The Viking Press, Inc., New York.

Wsw Whitehead, A. N., *Science and the Modern World*. Mentor, pb., 1958. ©, The Macmillan Company, New York.

Ybs Young, R., *Brighter Than a Thousand Suns*. ©, Harcourt-Brace & World, Inc., New York, 1956.